Vector Geometry

JAMES A. HUMMEL
University of Maryland

ADDISON-WESLEY PUBLISHING COMPANY, INC.
READING, MASSACHUSETTS · PALO ALTO · LONDON · DALLAS · ATLANTA

This book is in the

ADDISON-WESLEY SERIES IN INTRODUCTORY MATHEMATICS

Richard S. Pieters and Gail S. Young
Consulting Editors

Printed in the United States of America

Library of Congress Catalog Card No. 65-13609

Preface

This text has been written for use in a one-semester precalculus course for students who have had a good preparation in high school mathematics. Most high schools now give courses which cover all of the topics needed to begin calculus, and many high schools even offer an introduction to the calculus. However, only the very best students obtain from their high school courses the mathematical sophistication necessary to begin a college calculus course in which the emphasis is on the concepts as well as the techniques. The great majority of the students must be started in a calculus course which begins very slowly, or they must be given a precalculus course which helps develop their mathematical insight. The total amount of time required to reach the end of the basic calculus sequence is about the same in either case. However, the second method offers some extra advantages, since the students can at the same time learn something new which they may find useful.

There is a basic problem in the design of any first-year college course in mathematics. This is the great variation in the mathematical training offered in the different high schools. Some students have had a complete set of modern courses, such as those represented by the SMSG sample textbooks. Others have had a few such courses. But many are still graduating from high school with three or three and a half units of strictly traditional material.

No single course can cover this entire range. Each textbook must make some assumptions about what the student already knows and what type of training he has had. In this text, we assume that the student has some knowledge of trigonometry and elementary analytic geometry. Furthermore, we assume that the student has been exposed to at least one course with the modern point of view. To bridge the wide gap that still remains, the first two chapters of this text have been included, which offer a review of the material which the student is assumed to have seen already.

The instructor must decide how rapidly the material in these first two chapters can be covered. It should be noted that this material is presented in too brief a fashion to be suitable for the student who has never seen these topics before. To learn this material from the start would require an entire semester for most students. On the other hand, a very well-prepared student could skim over these two chapters in two or three weeks. The average amount of time which might be spent on these two chapters with a normal class would be about four weeks.

It is recommended that this review material be included in the course, even for rather well-prepared students. There are several reasons for this. First, these chapters cover all of the topics needed to proceed with the rest of the book; they contain the definitions of our terminology and tell us what we can assume to be known in our proofs. The inclusion of this material makes the entire text (essentially) complete in its mathematical development. Secondly, the student who has taken mostly traditional courses will learn here some of the modern mathematical terminology and will be introduced to some aspects of this point of view. Finally, if a student has had a number of the more modern courses, the contents of these chapters will offer him a fast review and should also show him how we can be precise when necessary and relax our precision when it is unimportant. In many cases, such a student will find that the development given here differs from what he has seen before. This may help him understand that there is no single "correct" way of developing mathematics.

Chapter 3 starts the "new" material in this text. This chapter introduces the mathematical study of vectors. As mentioned above, the main purpose of this text is to prepare students for the study of the calculus and other future courses. Many topics could be chosen which would be useful for this purpose. We have chosen to study vectors, because they are useful to engineers and physicists and because they can be used to prepare the student for the study of vector spaces, linear algebra, functions of several variables, and functional analysis.

Because of this effort to build for the future, some of the material studied may seem rather strange. Obvious things are sometimes looked at in what may appear to be an unnecessarily abstract point of view. When this happens, it is done with good reason. An attempt is being made to introduce the student to the proper point of view in order to facilitate his future studies. On the other hand, there are also places where a more abstract point of view could have been taken, and yet was not. The emphasis throughout the chapters on vectors is on the geometric picture. Excessive abstraction cannot be allowed to interfere with geometric understanding. In fact, we make use of geometric intuition to motivate the abstract mathematical development. Many students will see here for the first time an abstract mathematical system developed to fit a specific intuitive picture.

In Chapter 5, we discuss the conic sections. Many students will already be familiar with a more standard development of the conic sections. If so, we hope that they will find this approach new and interesting. The student who knows nothing about the conic sections will have to work hard here, since the discussion is rather rigorous and somewhat brief. While the vector methods developed in earlier chapters are used wherever convenient, we avoid using these for their own sake when other methods might be more efficient or more revealing.

The last chapter discusses the rotation of coordinates and ends with two sections in which the quadric surfaces and polar coordinates are discussed in as concise a manner as possible. These topics are useful in a calculus course and are included for this reason. Unfortunately, there would not be time left in a one-semester course to expand on these topics beyond what is given here.

The last comment may also help to explain why other material was not included. Each topic added to a one-semester course would require the deletion of something else. The topics included here were chosen to serve the basic purposes of the course in what seemed to be the best way. Other choices could also have been made, but it would require a great deal of revision to make more than very minor changes.

This text has been used for several semesters in a preliminary edition. The results of these trials were quite satisfactory. The students found the material difficult, of course, but they acquired the desired knowledge and point of view. Both the students and the instructors seemed to find the text interesting. Their many helpful comments and suggestions were taken into account in preparing the final version of the text.

I wish to express my appreciation to all of my colleagues for the many discussions which helped to mold this text into its present form. In particular, I wish to thank Professor Stanley Jackson for his help in reading the manuscript in its several versions and for his many thoughtful suggestions.

College Park, Maryland
December 1964

J.A.H.

Contents

Chapter 6 THE CONIC SECTIONS

Chapter 7 QUADRATIC CURVES AND SURFACES

1

The Real Number System

1-1 MATHEMATICAL REASONING

In this book an attempt is made to introduce the student to the "mathematical way of thinking." This is not to imply that there is some essential difference between this and any other (logical) way of thinking; the main point of mathematical reasoning is common to all disciplines: *precision.* There are, however, some special features, peculiar to mathematics, which require study.

The student is expected, and required, to learn how to operate the mathematical "tools" and—this is of equal importance—he must learn to judge when these tools may (and when they may not) be applied. For these purposes, he must learn to distinguish between what is known and what is assumed, between the "actual world" and the "mathematical model" of it, and between a plausible argument and a proof. Few students will be required to be able to provide proofs for mathematical facts after leaving school, but many will find it essential that they be able to understand such proofs. In particular, they must know on what assumptions the particular results are based.

As we study the various topics in this text, we will see how basic assumptions (axioms) are used to derive results. At this point, however, let us discuss something else which must be understood: *mathematical definitions.*

In a dictionary a definition is supposed to explain the meaning and the use of a word. Of course, the definitions of one word are given in terms of other words. For example, we might find that the word *cord* would have "a string or small rope" as one of its meanings. This means that wherever applicable this phrase could be substituted in the place of the word "cord" without changing the meaning of the sentence in question. Suppose however, that one knew no English at all. What good would the English dictionary be? Imagine that you had a Russian dictionary with both the words and the definitions in Russian, and that you did not know any Russian. Every word of the language is there, and each word is defined. Yet this dictionary would be of no use to you if you wished to read something written in Russian.

In compiling a dictionary, the editors must assume that the users already know something about the language. If a definition is given for every word, then some circular definitions *must* be present. For example, in the same dictionary which defined a cord as "a string or small rope" we find a *string* defined as "a small cord or slender strip of leather," and a *rope* defined as "a large stout cord made of strands of fiber or wire twisted or braided together."

One way of explaining the mathematical point of view is to describe the way in which a mathematician would write a dictionary. First, there would be given a list of "primitive words" which would be left undefined. Next, there would be a list of words whose definitions used only the primitive words. Finally, there would be the remaining words so arranged that the definition of each made use only of primitive words or words which had been already defined.

A mathematical definition differs from a dictionary definition in another way. A good dictionary will attempt to *explain* the meaning and the use of a word and to distinguish it from other words with a similar, but not identical, meaning. A definition in mathematics will merely give an equivalent to the term being defined. Explanations of the meaning and the usage of the term must be given separately. This is true even for the terms which are taken as undefined. An essential characteristic of most works in mathematics is the precise use of terms. The exact meanings of these terms must be known.

Let us give an example of what we mean by discussing the mathematical use of the word *set*. We assume that the student has been introduced to this concept already, but even if he hasn't, the basic idea is simple enough to grasp. We are treating the concept of a set as an undefined term, but this does not prevent us from explaining carefully what we mean when we use the term.

A *set* is a collection of things which are called the *elements* of the set. In our use of this term, there are only two things which need to be kept in mind. First, an element either is in a set or it is not. If a set is specified by listing its elements, an element which is listed more than once is still in the set only once.

Secondly, the elements in a set have no order. Listing the elements of a set puts them in some order, but this order is not part of the structure of the set. In loose, but picturesque, terms this idea can be expressed by saying that a set is a "bag full of elements."

One of the sources of the power of mathematics is in the use of symbols. Thus elementary algebra has as its basic idea the introduction of letters to symbolize real numbers. In the same way, it is useful to introduce symbols, single letters, to represent sets. Capital italic letters are used for this purpose in this text. Unfortunately, the same letters are used for other purposes also, but in every case the meaning of the symbol used should be clear from the context.

If A is a set and x is an element of that set, we write

$$x \in A,$$

which can be read, "x is in A" or "x is an element of A."

When a set is specified by listing all of its elements, it is customary to indicate the set itself by enclosing the list in braces. Thus the set whose elements are the three integers 1, 2, and 3 is written as

$$\{1, 2, 3\}.$$

When a set is specified by giving some rule which allows us to determine whether or not a given element is in the set, another notation is used. For example,

$$\{x \mid x \text{ is an integer, } x > 1\}$$

is read: "The set of all x such that x is an integer and $x > 1$." The braces indicate that we are defining a set. The x before the vertical bar is the symbol indicating the general form of the elements of the set we are talking about. It is a "dummy variable," meaning that any other symbol can be used in its place, just as we can use x, y, or any other letter to indicate some unknown number in an algebraic problem. The rule for determining whether or not an element is in the set is given after the vertical bar. It is to be noted that the vertical bar does not mean "such that"; it is merely a symbol which divides the "dummy variable" from the rule and, in this context, can be read as "such that."

Usually the type of element under consideration is understood and no explicit statement of its nature need be made inside the symbol for the set. That is, if it were understood that we were considering only the integers, the above set could be written $\{x \mid x > 1\}$. However, this will usually be done only when the elements under consideration are the real numbers, or doubles, or triples of real numbers. In any case, it will always be evident which elements are to be considered as possible candidates for inclusion in the set.

If A and B are two sets such that every element of A is also an element of B, then A is called a *subset* of B, and we write $A \subset B$. Thus, for example, the set $\{x \mid 1 < x < 2\}$ (x being allowed to be any real number) is a subset of the set of all real numbers. It is also a subset of the set of all positive numbers, $\{x \mid x > 0\}$.

There is one peculiar type of set which frequently causes confusion, the *empty set*, which is also called the *null set* or *void set*. It is defined to be the set which contains no elements. The symbol commonly used for the empty set is $\emptyset$. The empty set occupies the same position in discussions of sets as the number *zero* occupies in the discussion of integers, and is often objected to by the beginning student for the same reason that the number zero was objected to when it was first introduced. Since it represents nothing, why do we need a symbol for it? If the student can answer this question for the number zero, then he should be able to answer it also for the empty set.

As the student goes through this text, in addition to learning the material, he should spend time considering why the definitions are given as they are, and why the proofs of theorems are given in the form that they are. The student is not expected to be very familiar with mathematical proofs when he starts this course. Therefore, when proofs are given in the text, comments about their logic will be made. It is hoped that by the end of the course, the student will know a good deal more about how theorems in mathematics can be proved.

PROBLEMS

1. Each of the following sets is to be a subset of the set of all real numbers. Some are equal; some are subsets of others. Find all the relations between the sets. (*Note:* equality is always used in the sense of identity.)

$A = \{x \mid 0 \leq x < 1\}$ $\quad B = \{x \mid x^2 \leq 4\}$

$C = \{y \mid y^2 \leq 1\}$ $\quad D = \{z \mid z^2 < 1 \text{ and } z \geq 0\}$

$E = \{w \mid -2 \leq w \leq 2\}$ $\quad F = \{t \mid t \geq 0\}$

2. Write in set notation:
   (a) The set of all real numbers whose squares are less than 2
   (b) The set of all pairs, (x, y), of real numbers for which the first member of the pair is smaller than the second
   (c) The set of all even integers
   (d) The set of all integer multiples of 5
   (e) The set of all positive real numbers whose squares are less than 2

3. Write each of the following sets of real numbers in a simpler form such as $\{x \mid a < x < b\}$.

   (a) $\{x \mid x^2 - x < 0\}$ $\quad$ (b) $\{x \mid x^2 + x + 1 < 0\}$
   (c) $\{x \mid x^2 + x - 2 \leq 0\}$ $\quad$ (d) $\{x \mid x^2 + 3x + 4 \geq 0\}$

4. According to the definition of a subset, is a set a subset of itself? Explain.

5. According to the definition of a subset, if B is some set, is $\emptyset \subset B$? Explain.

6. Two sets A and B are equal, $A = B$, if and only if they consist of exactly the same elements. To show that two sets are equal, you must show that every element in one is in the other, and vice versa. Identify each of the following statements as either true or false. Explain your statement. (Note that in order to disprove a statement, it is only necessary to give a single example in which the statement does not hold.)
   (a) If $A \subset B$ and $B \subset A$, then $A = B$.
   (b) If $A \subset B$, $C \subset D$, and $A = C$, then $B = D$.
   (c) If $A \subset B$ and $C \subset B$, then $A = C$.
   (d) If $A \subset B$ and $B \subset C$, then $A \subset C$.

7. (a) Let A_1 be a set containing exactly one element. How many subsets does A_1 have?
   (b) Let A_2 be a set containing exactly two elements. How many subsets does A_2 have?
   (c) Let A_3 be a set containing exactly three elements. How many subsets does A_3 have?
   (d) How many subsets are there of a set which has exactly n elements?

8. Using a dictionary of "collegiate" size or larger, find a circle of definitions. That is, look up some noun. Choose a noun in the definition which is crucial to at least one part of the definition. Look up this noun and continue in this way until you arrive at a noun already in the chosen list.

9. Using a good dictionary, try to find the exact difference between the following pairs of words.
   (a) enclose and inclose
   (b) further and farther
   (c) whence and whither
   (d) should and would
   (e) as and like
   (f) imply and infer
   (g) affect and effect
   (h) that and which

1–2 THE REAL NUMBER FIELD

The student probably feels that he has a good working knowledge of the real numbers. After all, he has been studying them for years. In this section, and the next few sections, we wish to review the basic properties of the real numbers. The student may recognize the particular properties which we single out as being the rules of elementary algebra, but he is warned that the attitude adopted toward them here is different. We discuss these properties in terms of the axioms which define them; and the particular axioms we choose to discuss will be the important thing.

No attempt will be made to define the real number system here. Instead, we shall merely list the properties which distinguish the real number system from other more or less similar mathematical systems (such as the integers). As will be seen, the particular properties that will be discussed are fundamental. Some of them will appear again as properties of entirely different systems. Some of them will prove to be false in other mathematical systems, but all of them should be known by the student in order to help him gain an understanding of what underlies the mathematics he is to learn.

Let us start by making a precise statement of our assumptions about the real number system:

The real number system is a set of elements on which two binary operations, called addition and multiplication, and a binary relation, called order, are defined.

We shall not define the terms binary operation or binary relation in general at this point, but only explain them in the given context.

The *binary operation of addition* on the real numbers associates to every pair of real numbers, a and b, a *unique* real number c, called the *sum* of a and b. We write $c = a + b$ to represent this sum. The *binary operation of multiplication* on the real numbers similarly associates to every pair of real numbers, a and b, a *unique* real number d, called the product of a and b. We write $d = ab$, or $d = a \cdot b$, to represent this product.

These statements explain what we mean by the binary operations of addition and multiplication. They do not, however, explain what the operations *are*, or how they behave. (The binary relation of order will be studied in the next section, so we shall not discuss it here.)

In order to try to explain what addition and multiplication are, we list some of the properties of these operations. These properties are nothing more than the basic laws of algebraic manipulation and will be well known to any student who is familiar with elementary algebra. The particular set of properties we choose to write down may appear to be rather brief from this point of view, but it so happens that one can prove the computational properties of the real numbers, assuming nothing more than these. These properties are therefore the *axioms* which determine the elementary properties of the real numbers.

Before listing these axioms, we should say a word about equality of real numbers, or about equality in general. In this text, the equality sign, $=$, is used to mean actual identity of the elements separated by it. That is, we write $a = b$, if and only if a and b are actually the same. This can also be explained by saying that a and b are two names for the same thing. Actually, what we are doing is using the equality sign in its meaning as applied to the elements of a set (the set of real numbers in this case).

The axioms we now introduce are called the field axioms, since they constitute the axioms for a special mathematical structure known as a field. The student will encounter the concept of fields again if he takes a course in abstract algebra.

The Field Axioms for the Real Numbers

1. ***The Commutative Law for Addition.*** For any real numbers a and b,

$$a + b = b + a.$$

2. ***The Commutative Law for Multiplication.*** For any real numbers a and b,

$$ab = ba.$$

3. ***The Associative Law for Addition.*** For any real numbers a, b, and c,

$$a + (b + c) = (a + b) + c.$$

4. ***The Associative Law for Multiplication.*** For any real numbers a, b, and c,

$$a(bc) = (ab)c.$$

5. ***The Existence of the Identity for Addition.*** There exists a real number 0 such that if a is any real number,

$$a + 0 = 0 + a = a.$$

6. ***The Existence of the Identity for Multiplication.*** There exists a real number $1 \neq 0$ such that if a is any real number,

$$a \cdot 1 = 1 \cdot a = a.$$

7. ***The Existence of Inverses for Addition.*** For any real number a, there exists a corresponding real number $-a$ such that

$$a + (-a) = 0.$$

8. ***The Existence of Inverses for Multiplication.*** For any real number $a \neq 0$, there exists a corresponding real number a^{-1} such that

$$a \cdot a^{-1} = 1.$$

9. ***The Distributive Law.*** For any real numbers a, b, and c,

$$a(b + c) = ab + ac.$$

A few comments about these nine axioms are called for at this point.

First, many mathematicians would add to this set two further axioms, the *closure axioms*. These state that if a and b are real numbers, then $a + b$ and ab are also real numbers. The uniqueness of $a + b$ and ab is usually included in these same axioms. We prefer to think of these properties as being implied by the assumption that the binary operations of addition and multiplication are defined on the set of real numbers, and that the result of these binary operations is in every case a unique real number. These properties would become important if we wished to discuss the operations of addition and multiplication on subsets of the real numbers or if we were to discuss similar operations in other mathematical contexts. We also need to quote the closure and uniqueness properties as the reason for some steps in proofs (as we will see below).

Definition 1–1. Let R be a given set and let a binary operation be defined on R; that is, for every pair of elements a, b in R, there exists a unique element c in R which we write as $c = a \oplus b$. Let S be a subset of R. Then we say that the set S is *closed* with respect to the operation $\oplus$ if and only if for every a and b in S, $a \oplus b$ is also in S.

This formal definition should help make clear exactly what is meant by the closure property. We shall not give a formal definition of the uniqueness property, since we understand this to be an integral part of the concept of a binary operation.

The student should observe the names attached to the various axioms. The properties described by these axioms are fundamental and will be found over and over again in different mathematical contexts. If, therefore, the student does not already know these properties by name, he is advised to learn them; these names are an essential part of the language of mathematics.

Finally, observe closely the wording of these axioms. The order in which the phrases occur is most important. Here the content is familiar, and it is easy to slide over the full significance of the various phrases.

Look, for example, at the fifth axiom. It says that there exists a real number zero and that this number exists once and forever, without any regard to the real number a that it is being added to. In the seventh axiom, however, the order of the phrases is reversed. This statement asserts the existence of the negative of a number, *once we are given the number.* No implication is made that there is a single, universal number $-a$. Look at the various statements and observe the logic of their construction. Try to see how the assertions made would be altered if the statements appeared in a different order.

From these nine axioms all of the purely arithmetic properties of the real number system could be proved. For example, the obvious extensions (which could be formally proved) of the first four of these axioms permit us to write sums or products in any order without having to worry about introducing parentheses to specify which operations should be done first.

While we do not wish to spend much time on the development of the algebraic properties of the real number system from these axioms at this point, two particular results which show how this development could proceed might be of interest. We will sketch their proofs.

Theorem 1–1. If a and b are two real numbers, then there exists a unique real number x such that

$$a + x = b.$$

Proof: We first note that the real number

$$(-a) + b,$$

whose existence is guaranteed by Axiom 7, does indeed satisfy the requirement for x. This is proved by successive applications of Axioms 3, 7, and 5.

To see that the solution, x, is unique, suppose that $a + x = b$ and $a + y = b$. Then from the identity of the numbers involved, $a + x = a + y$. We then merely need to add $(-a)$ to this number in its two representations to conclude (after using Axioms 3, 7, and 5) that $x = y$.

Theorem 1–2. If a is any real number, then

$$a \cdot 0 = 0.$$

Proof: We have that

$$1 + 0 = 1,$$

and hence that

$$\begin{aligned} a(1 + 0) &= a \cdot 1 \\ &= a. \end{aligned}$$

But then, from the distributive law

$$a \cdot 1 + a \cdot 0 = a$$

or

$$a + a \cdot 0 = a.$$

However, we know that $a + 0 = a$, and hence from Theorem 1–1 we conclude that $a \cdot 0 = 0$.

The proofs of the above theorems have been written in the typical informal style used in mathematical works these days. They could also have been given in a formal style, with each step being given a full justification.

For example, the formal proof of Theorem 1–2 would look like this:

	Statement	Reason
(1)	$1 + 0 = 1$	Existence of the identities for addition and multiplication
(2)	$a(1 + 0) = a \cdot 1$	Uniqueness of multiplication
(3)	$a \cdot 1 = a$	Identity for multiplication
(4)	$a(1 + 0) = a$	Equality of numbers in (2) and (3)
(5)	$a(1 + 0) = a \cdot 1 + a \cdot 0$	Distributive law
(6)	$a(1 + 0) = a + a \cdot 0$	Equality of numbers in (3) and (5)
(7)	$a + a \cdot 0 = a$	Equality of numbers in (4) and (6)
(8)	$a + 0 = a$	Existence of identity for addition
(9)	$a \cdot 0 = 0$	Theorem 1–1 applied to (7) and (8)

If the student writes out the complete formal proofs of a few theorems, he will see how we can say that these results can be derived from the axioms alone. However, these formal proofs are usually too long and too detailed for ordinary use. The fragmentation of the steps makes it difficult to see exactly what the main point of the proof is. Informal proofs need to give only enough detail to be convincing. Correctly done, the informal proof should give the reader enough information to enable him to write out the complete proof in a formal fashion if required.

The proof of Theorem 1–1 contains two distinct parts. In the first part, it is shown that a solution of the given equation does indeed exist. This is done directly, by exhibiting a number whose existence is proved from the axioms and which satisfies the equation. The second part of the proof shows that this solution is unique. This is proved by showing that any two numbers which satisfy the equation must in fact be the same. Note that proving this part alone does not prove the entire theorem. It might well be possible to prove that any two solutions of a given equation would be equal when there were in fact no solutions at all. Another way of saying this is to observe that the first part of the proof of Theorem 1–1 shows that there is *at least one* solution while the second part shows that there is *at most one.*

PROBLEMS

1. Show that the set of all integers, with the usual operations of addition and multiplication, does not satisfy all of the field axioms.

2. The *rational numbers* can be represented in the form p/q where p and q are integers, with $q \neq 0$. Two pairs of integers, r/s and p/q, represent the same

rational number if and only if $rq = ps$. Addition and multiplication of rational numbers is defined by

$$r/s + p/q = (rq + ps)/(sq),$$
$$(r/s)(p/q) = (rp)/(sq).$$

The set of all rational numbers satisfies the field axioms. Prove that Axioms 7, 8, and 9 are satisfied, assuming that the first six have already been proved.

3. Show that the set consisting of the two elements 1 and 0 satisfies the field axioms if we suppose that

$$0 + 0 = 0, \qquad 0 \cdot 0 = 0,$$
$$0 + 1 = 1 + 0 = 1, \qquad 0 \cdot 1 = 1 \cdot 0 = 0,$$
$$1 + 1 = 0, \qquad 1 \cdot 1 = 1.$$

4. Prove from the field axioms that if $a \cdot b = 0$, then either a or b is zero. [*Hint:* suppose one of them, say b, is not zero. Use Axiom 8 to prove that a must then be zero.]

5. Let V be the set of all possible pairs of real numbers, (a, b). Two elements of V are equal if and only if both consist of the same pair of numbers in the same order. Define the sum and product in V by

$$(a, b) + (c, d) = (a + c, b + d),$$
$$(a, b) \cdot (c, d) = (ac, bd).$$

Which of the field axioms hold in V? Give an example showing the failure of any of the axioms which are not true. Give an example showing the failure of the property of Problem 4.

6. With the same set V as Problem 5, define sums and products by

$$(a, b) + (c, d) = (a + c, b + d),$$
$$(a, b) \cdot (c, d) = (ac - bd, ad + bc).$$

Which of the field axioms hold in this case?

7. Let m be any positive rational number which is not the square of a rational number. Show that the set of all numbers of the form $a + b\sqrt{m}$, where a and b are rational, satisfies the field axioms.

8. Write out a full formal proof of Theorem 1–1.

9. Prove that if $a \cdot a = a$, then either $a = 0$ or $a = 1$.

10. Which of the field axioms are satisfied by the set of positive real numbers?

11. Prove that for any a, $-a = (-1)a$. [*Hint:* $1 + (-1) = 0$. Multiply both sides by a.]

12. Prove that for any a, $-(-a) = a$.

13. Each of the following binary operations is defined on the set of real numbers. Check each operation as to whether or not it is commutative or associative. If there is an identity for the operation, state what it is. If there is none, show why not. If an identity for the operation does exist, do inverses exist?

    (a) $a * b = \frac{1}{2}(a + b)$
    (b) $a \triangle b =$ the larger of a and b
    (c) $a \circ b = a + 2b$

14. For each of the following subsets of the reals, check whether the subset is closed under the three operations defined in Problem 13:

    (a) the set of all integers
    (b) the set of all positive reals
    (c) the set of all real numbers whose square is less than or equal to one

1–3 THE ORDER AXIOMS

The field axioms listed in the previous section fail to characterize the real numbers. The fact that the examples in Problems 2 and 3 of the last section satisfy the field axioms shows this to be true. If the student is familiar with complex numbers, he can check to see that the set of complex numbers also satisfies the field axioms (this was Problem 7 of the last section).

A property of the real numbers that is not shared by the field of complex numbers, or one of the fields of the type seen in Problem 3 of the last section, is *order*. The order relation of the real numbers is linked to the field properties by certain axioms.

The Order Axioms for the Real Numbers

There exists an order relation on the real numbers. For every pair of real numbers a and b this relation is either true or false. If it is true, we say that a is less than b and write $a < b$. If it is not true, we write $a \nless b$. This relation satisfies:

1. ***The Trichotomy Law.*** For any pair of real numbers a and b, one and only one of the following holds:

$$\text{(a) } a < b, \qquad \text{(b) } a = b, \qquad \text{(c) } b < a.$$

2. ***The Transitive Law.*** If a, b, and c are real numbers such that $a < b$ and $b < c$, then $a < c$.

3. ***The Addition Law.*** If a, b, and c are real numbers and $a < b$, then $a + c < b + c$.

4. ***The Multiplication Law.*** If a, b, and c are real numbers such that $a < b$ and $0 < c$, then $ac < bc$.

From these axioms, all of the familiar properties of the order relation can be proved. For example:

Theorem 1–3. If $a < b$ and $c < d$, then $a + c < b + d$.

Proof: Since $a < b$, from Axiom 3 we have

$$a + c < b + c.$$

Similarly, since $c < d$, we have

$$b + c < b + d.$$

The transitive law applied to these two inequalities then gives the desired conclusion, $a + c < b + d$.

Other results can be proved just as easily. We will list a few of these without proof. The student should study them to be sure he knows and can apply the results. In the statement of these theorems, we will use a few symbols and conventions which have not been formally introduced, but this should cause no difficulty. The student knows, for example, that $a > b$ means $b < a$, that $a \leq b$ means that either $a < b$ or $a = b$, that $a - b$ means $a + (-b)$, and so forth.

Similarly, we will assume that all of the computational consequences of the axioms of the last section have been proved. For example, we may assume that $-a = (-1)a$, that $(-a)(-b) = ab$, and so on. It is not our purpose to give a detailed development of all of the properties of the real number system. Rather, we are only interested in showing how this might be done and pointing out that all of these properties depend on a very few axioms.

Theorem 1–4. If $a > 0$, then $-a < 0$.

Theorem 1–5. If $a < b$, then $b - a > 0$.

Theorem 1–6. If $b - a > 0$, then $a < b$.

Theorem 1–7. If $a < b$ then $-b < -a$.

Theorem 1–8. If $b < 0$, then $-b > 0$.

Theorem 1–9. If $a < b$ and $c < 0$, then $ac > bc$.

Theorem 1–10. $1 > 0$.

Theorem 1–11. If $0 < a < b$, then $0 < b^{-1} < a^{-1}$.

There is an entirely different way of looking at the order properties of the real numbers, typified by Theorems 1–4, 1–5, and 1–6. This method involves consideration of those real numbers which are *positive*, and leads to an alternative set of axioms to characterize the order properties.

Alternative Order Axioms

There exists a set P of positive elements in the set of all real numbers such that:

1. ***The Trichotomy Law.*** If a is any real number, then one and only one of the following is true:

   (a) $a \in P$,

   (b) $a = 0$,

   (c) $-a \in P$.

2. ***The Addition Law.*** If a and b are in P, then $(a + b) \in P$.

3. ***The Multiplication Law.*** If a and b are in P, then $a \cdot b \in P$.

These two sets of possible axioms are related by the assertion that $a < b$ if and only if $b - a$ is positive. Indeed, with this as the definition it is not difficult to prove these last three laws from the first set or conversely to prove the first set from these three. As an example, we can prove

Theorem 1–12. The transitive law is a consequence of the three alternative order axioms.

Proof: Suppose $a < b$ and $b < c$. This means that $(b - a)$ and $(c - b)$ are positive. Then the second axiom tells us that

$$(b - a) + (c - b) = c - a$$

is positive, and hence $a < c$.

From a theoretical point of view, a mathematician who is interested in abstract mathematics might prefer to use the second set of axioms to specify the properties of order, but the first set is probably of more practical use, and is a little easier to work with in the actual application of the order properties.

The fact that these two sets of axioms are equivalent and that either set can be used may be surprising to the student. He should realize that axioms are not intrinsically determined, but are chosen to accomplish a specific purpose.

PROBLEMS

1. Prove Theorems 1–4 through 1–11. Each may be used in the proof of any subsequent ones. The proofs should not make use of the alternative order axioms. The following hints may prove useful.

   Theorem 1–4: $a + (-a) = 0$. Use Axiom 1.

   Theorem 1–7: Use the previous theorems.

   Theorem 1–9: Use Axiom 4 and Theorem 1–7.

   Theorem 1–11: Prove in two parts. First prove that if $a > 0$, then $a^{-1} > 0$. Try applying Axiom 1 to a^{-1}.

2. Prove the alternative axioms from the first set. The truth of Theorems 1–3 through 1–11 may be assumed.

3. Prove the first set of order axioms from the alternative set. One has already been done for you (Theorem 1–12). Be careful not to use anything that is not given or has not yet been proved, starting from the alternative set.

4. If $a < b$, is $a^{-1} > b^{-1}$? What if $a < 0$? What if $b < 0$?

5. Prove that the field of Problem 3 in the last section cannot be ordered. [*Hint:* 0 and 1 are different numbers. Use the Trichotomy law, assuming that the field can be ordered. Add 1 to each side of the assumed order relation.]

1–4 THE COMPLETENESS AXIOM

The field axioms and the order axioms of the last two sections still do not characterize the real numbers completely. The set of all rational numbers (which can be represented in the form p/q, where p and $q \neq 0$ are integers) satisfies the field axioms and the order axioms, but not all real numbers are rational numbers. This fact was known to the early Greek mathematicians. Indeed, it is considered probable that the existence of such irrational numbers was one of the closely guarded secrets of the Pythagoreans.

To the Greek mathematicians, geometric facts were of primary importance, and in their view, numbers were closely related to the lengths of line segments. Let us try to see how this point of view operates. Imagine a straight line (extended indefinitely in both directions) and mark two distinct points on this line. Label one of these points 0 and the other 1. The line segment between these two points is taken as our unit length. By the construction methods of euclidean geometry this unit length can be laid out successively along the line to give us points we can label 2, 3, and so on.

If q is any positive integer, other construction methods allowed by euclidean geometry can be used to subdivide each of these segments of unit length into q segments of equal length. Doing this, we in effect construct a ruler having the initially given line segment as its unit distance, and with marks located at a distance $1/q$ apart.

In this way we see that by the euclidean "straightedge and compass" constructions we can find a line segment whose length is any (positive) rational number.

But we can also construct a line segment of length $\sqrt{2}$. If a square is erected with its base as the line segment between the points labeled 0 and 1, then by the Pythagorean theorem, the diagonal of this square is of length $\sqrt{2}$. This length can be transferred to the given line (Fig. 1-1) to yield a point which we can label $\sqrt{2}$. However, $\sqrt{2}$ is not a rational number, as we will now prove.

FIGURE 1-1

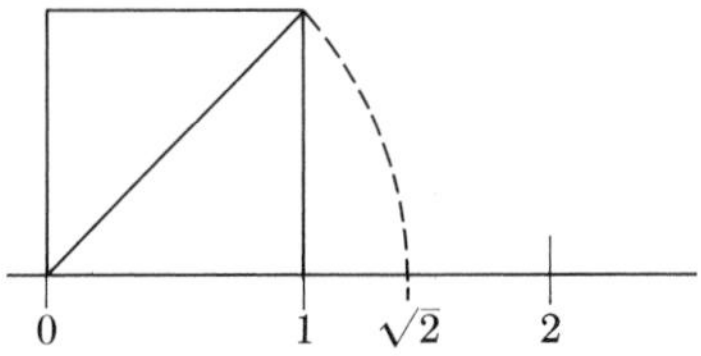

Suppose, on the contrary, that there exist two integers p and q such that $\sqrt{2} = p/q$. Then $2 = p^2/q^2$, or

$$p^2 = 2q^2.$$

The square of any odd number must be an odd number. This follows since any odd number is of the form $2k + 1$, where k is an integer, and its square is of the form $4k^2 + 4k + 1$, which leaves a remainder of one when divided by 2. Each of the numbers p and q contains some factors of two so that

$$p = 2^n k,$$
$$q = 2^m j,$$

where n and m are nonnegative integers (either could be zero) and k and j are odd numbers. Then $p^2 = 2^{2n}k^2$ and hence is an odd number times an even number of factors of 2. However, $p^2 = 2q^2 = 2 \cdot 2^{2m}j^2 = 2^{2m+1}j^2$ is at the same time an odd number times an odd number of factors of 2, which is impossible. The same number cannot contain both an even and an odd number of factors of 2.

We see therefore that there are points on the "measuring line" that we constructed which are not at a rational distance from the origin, or equivalently, that there are real numbers which are not rational numbers. Thus there must be still another property satisfied by the set of all real numbers which we have not yet listed. The missing property is the completeness property. This property can be explained intuitively as stating that if we assign numbers to the points on a line as described above, then every point on the line corresponds to a real number.

Before making a formal statement of the completeness axiom, we should remark about the way in which irrational numbers are used. First, consider $\sqrt{2}$. If you were asked, "What is the square root of two?," what would your answer be? If it is 1.414 or the like, you are wrong. The only correct answer which can be given to this question is "The real number whose square is two." Any other must be wrong. The square of 1.414, for example, is 1.999396, which is *not* 2.

Of course the student who says that the square root of 2 is 1.414 might argue that he meant 1.414 . . . , the three dots indicating additional decimal places which could be specified if necessary. This would be a semicorrect answer (if given this completely). It would be a correct answer if an explanation were also given of how the missing decimal places could be determined.

As another illustration, what is the value of π? The numbers $\frac{22}{7}$ or 3.1416 are commonly used in place of π, but they are of course not the same thing. The number π is also an irrational number and its decimal expansion goes on indefinitely. However, this is immaterial in actual practice. Many handbooks list ten or twelve decimal places of the value of π. How accurate is such a value? The circumference of a circle one meter in diameter is determined to within 10^{-10} meter by using 10 decimal places of π. This is one angstrom unit and is of the order of the distance between atoms in ordinary matter. It would hardly be of any practical concern to know the value of π any more accurately than this.

However, no finite number of decimal places suffice to determine such irrational numbers exactly. Even if the difference is too small to matter in any practical situation, it is still there. With regard to rational numbers, the situation is different. Many rational numbers also have nonterminating decimal expansions (e.g., $\frac{1}{3} = 0.33333\ldots$), but a group of digits repeats in these expansions, and it is always possible to determine the actual number being represented.

When we write $\pi = 3.14159\ldots$, what do we mean? Isn't it true that we mean that the rational number $3.14 = \frac{314}{100}$ is smaller than the real number π while 3.15 is larger than π? That $3.141 < \pi < 3.142$, and so on? Thus an infinite decimal expansion is nothing more than a sequence of rational numbers. The longer the expansion is carried out, the closer is its value to the desired number in terms of the decimal approximation from below.

With this as a background, we now give the final axiom for the real number system. In order to do so, however, we must first define some of the terms used in the axiom.

Definition 1–2. A set of real numbers A is said to be *bounded above* if there exists a number m such that $m \geq x$ for every x in the set A. The number m in this case is called an *upper bound* of the set A.

Definition 1–3. A number m is called the *least upper bound* of a set of real numbers A if and only if

(1) m is an upper bound of the set A,

and

(2) if k is any real number which is less than m, then there is some x in the set A such that $x > k$.

THE COMPLETENESS AXIOM: *If A is any set of real numbers which is bounded above, then there exists a real number m which is the least upper bound of A.*

We are not going to make formal use of this property of the real numbers in this book. We list it here only because it is the last of the axioms for the real number system. It so happens that the field axioms, the order axioms, and this single completeness axiom characterize the real number system completely. Students who go on to take advanced mathematics courses will probably see a proof of this fact.

In this book, we are only interested in the point of view, expressed above, that this axiom requires a correspondence between all the points on a line and the real numbers. Before leaving this section we would like to emphasize this point and formalize the discussion of the coordinates on a line.

When numbers were associated with the points on a line as described above, we considered only the points to the "right" of the point labeled zero. We can extend the labeling to the "left" of zero as well. Clearly, such points must correspond to the negative real numbers. When this is done, however, we find that we have a point on the line associated with every real number.

Definition 1–4. A *coordinate line* (or *coordinate axis*) is a line together with an association between the real numbers and the points on the line so that each point corresponds to a unique real number, called the *coordinate* of that point, and each real number corresponds to a unique point. Furthermore, this assignment of coordinates with points must be such that the distance between two points of the line (in terms of a particular unit of distance) is the difference of the coordinates of these points. The point associated with the real number zero is called the *origin* of the coordinate line.

Note that there is a tacit assumption of the existence of a concept of distance in the plane. Almost any suitable axiom scheme for euclidean geometry will make such a distance concept available.

Suppose that instead of two points on the line to start with, we were given a single point, which is to be the origin, and a unit distance (say as the length of an entirely separate line segment). Then there are two distinct ways in which the line can be turned into a coordinate line. There are two points on the line a unit distance from the origin, and either of these could be labeled 1 (the other would then be -1), giving us two distinct coordinate lines with the same origin and the same unit of distance.

PROBLEMS

1. Give an example of a set of numbers which is not bounded above.

2. (a) Given A, a set of numbers which is bounded above, exactly what would you mean by saying that the number m is the *maximum* of the set A?
   (b) If m is the maximum of A, how would m be related to the least upper bound of A?
   (c) Does every set A which is bounded above have a maximum?

3. A method used in many high school courses for approximating the square root of a number a is as follows: let x be an approximation to the square root of a. Then

$$y = \frac{x^2 + a}{2x}$$

is a closer approximation to $\sqrt{a}$. For the following problems, let $a = 2$.
   (a) Show that if x is a rational number, then y is a rational number.
   (b) Compute $y^2 - 2$ in terms of x.
   (c) Show that if $x > \sqrt{2}$, then $y > \sqrt{2}$.
   (d) Show that if $x > \sqrt{2}$, then

$$y^2 - 2 = (x^2 - 2)K,$$

where $0 < K < \frac{1}{4}$. What does this say about the closeness of the approximation of y to $\sqrt{2}$? Can you improve this result if x is quite close to $\sqrt{2}$?

4. Among all numbers of the form p/q, where p and q are integers and $0 < q < 10$, which is the closest to $\sqrt{2}$?

5. Let a and b be two real numbers with $a < b$. Prove that if $c = \frac{1}{2}(a + b)$, then $a < c < b$.

6. Using the results of Problem 5, prove that there is no largest negative number (that is, that the set of negative numbers does not have a maximum). [*Hint:* Assume that there is a maximum and arrive at a contradiction.]

1–5 ABSOLUTE VALUE

Let us open this section with a simple question:

Let a be a real number. Is $-a$ positive or negative?

The student should answer this question for himself before reading on. Many students will answer it incorrectly unless they pause to think about it a moment.

Did you say, or was your first thought that $-a$ is negative? This is the usual incorrect answer. What makes it negative? Where was it said that a is positive? If a is a negative number, then $-a$ must be positive. Actually of course this is an improper question. As worded, the correct answer would have to be that $-a$ may be positive, negative, or neither (the last if $a = 0$).

The point here is that after years of experience in seeing numbers of the type -2, -3, and recognizing them as negative, many students gain a deep-rooted feeling that a negative sign indicates a negative number. Yet this is true only if the quantity behind the negative sign is positive.

A negative sign does not indicate that a number is negative. Some of the difficulty comes from the common habit of reading $-a$ as "negative a." This is wrong. It should be read as "the negative *of* a." This small distinction is quite important.

Now, if the student has the above comments firmly in mind, we can proceed to give a definition of the absolute value.

Definition 1–5. Let a be a real number. Then the *absolute value* of a is the real number $|a|$ defined by

$$\begin{aligned} |a| &= a \qquad \text{if} \quad a \geq 0 \\ &= -a \qquad \text{if} \quad a < 0. \end{aligned}$$

Various other explanations of this same property are possible. For example, we could define

$$|a| = \sqrt{a^2},$$

where the square root symbol is understood (as always) to mean the positive square root. This definition is, however, less elementary and more difficult to work with.

The absolute value of a real number is frequently described as the "nonnegative magnitude of the number." This phrase is descriptive but too vague for use as a definition. It is sometimes also described as "the distance of the point having that coordinate from the origin on a coordinate line." Again, this is a descriptive phrase that leaves much to be desired in terms of usability.

Another possible definition would be: *the number* $|a|$ *is the maximum of the two numbers* a *and* $-a$. This definition is as good as the one given above. In fact, it is probably better from a theoretical point of view. However, as will be seen, the use of the definition given is probably easier. Proofs of results are not so short as they could be, but are easier to discover, since Definition 1–5 clearly calls for the breaking down of the problem into the various possible cases.

Let us list a few simple properties of the absolute value which can be proved directly from the definition.

Theorem 1–13. For any real number a, $|a| \geq 0$. $|a| = 0$ if and only if $a = 0$.

Proof: There are actually three separate results to be proved here. First, we must prove that if a is any real number, then $|a| \geq 0$. This result is obvious upon examination of the two possible cases in the definition.

Next, the theorem makes an "if and only if" statement. To prove this we must prove the two separate statements:

(1) $|a| = 0$ if $a = 0$.
(2) $|a| = 0$ only if $a = 0$.

Here, however, statement (1) is equivalent to the statement:

(1′) If $a = 0$, then $|a| = 0$,
and this too is obvious from the definition.

Statement (2) is equivalent to:

(2′) If $|a| = 0$, then $a = 0$.

We can prove this by considering the various possible cases.

Suppose $|a| = 0$. Then there are only three possibilities: $a > 0$, $a < 0$, or $a = 0$. If $a > 0$, then $|a| = a > 0$, which violates our supposition. If $a < 0$, then $|a| = -a > 0$, which also violates the assumption. Hence $a = 0$, since this is the only remaining possibility.

Theorem 1–14. For any real number a,

$$-|a| \leq a \leq |a|.$$

Proof: If $a \geq 0$, then $|a| = a$; therefore the conclusion of the theorem is true. If $a < 0$, then $|a| > 0$, and hence $-|a| = a < 0 < |a|$ (see Theorems 1–4 and 1–8).

Theorem 1–15. For any real numbers a and b,

$$|ab| = |a| \cdot |b|.$$

Proof: This can be proved by the most direct method possible, that is, by considering the four possible cases.

CASE I. $a \geq 0, b \geq 0$. Then $ab \geq 0$ and $|a| = a$, $|b| = b$, $|ab| = ab$; hence the theorem is true.

CASE II. $a \geq 0, b < 0$. Then $ab \leq 0$ and $|a| = a$, $|b| = -b$, $|ab| = -ab$. But in this case, $|a| \cdot |b| = a(-b) = -ab = |ab|$, and hence the theorem is again true.

The remaining two cases are left as an exercise.

Theorem 1–16. If $a^2 < b^2$, then $|a| < |b|$.

Proof: Suppose $a^2 < b^2$. Then $b^2 - a^2 > 0$. However, we know (Problem 1) that $b^2 = |b|^2$ and $a^2 = |a|^2$, and therefore $|b|^2 - |a|^2 > 0$. The expression on the left-hand side of this inequality can be factored to give

$$(|b| - |a|) \cdot (|b| + |a|) > 0.$$

Now $|b| + |a| > 0$ (why?), and hence the first factor cannot be negative or zero. Therefore $|b| - |a| > 0$, which is equivalent to the conclusion of the theorem.

These results demonstrate how the definition can be used to give rigorous proofs for the properties of the absolute value.

There is one more theorem which we wish to give in this section. This is a major result which will be used throughout the rest of the student's study of mathematics. In fact, it is the cornerstone of most proofs in calculus, and probably deserves to be called the fundamental theorem of analysis (although it never is). This result is the *triangle inequality*. The reason for this name is not obvious here, but will appear when we study vectors.

Theorem 1–17. (The Triangle Inequality) For any real numbers a and b,

$$|a + b| \leq |a| + |b|.$$

Proof: We note that

$$\begin{aligned} |a + b|^2 &= (a + b)^2 \\ &= a^2 + 2ab + b^2 \\ &= |a|^2 + 2ab + |b|^2. \end{aligned}$$

Using the fact that $ab \leq |ab| = |a|\,|b|$, we therefore have

$$\begin{aligned} |a+b|^2 &\leq |a|^2 + 2|a|\,|b| + |b|^2 \\ &= (|a| + |b|)^2. \end{aligned}$$

Theorem 1–16 then shows that this result implies the conclusion of the theorem. To see this, observe that what we have actually proved is

$$(|a+b|)^2 \leq (|a| + |b|)^2.$$

Putting this into Theorem 1–16 as a hypothesis gives us as a conclusion

$$|(|a+b|)| \leq |(|a| + |b|)|.$$

However, $|(|a+b|)| = |a+b|$ and $|(|a| + |b|)| = |a| + |b|$ (why?), which shows that we have completed the proof of the theorem.

We should remark on the usage of notations exhibited in this proof. When several lines are shown linked by equalities or inequalities we are to think of the expressions as being written sequentially on one line. Thus, for example, the lines

$$\begin{aligned} |a+b|^2 &= |a|^2 + 2ab + |b|^2 \\ &\leq |a|^2 + 2|a|\,|b| + |b|^2 \\ &= (|a| + |b|)^2 \end{aligned}$$

would be read

$$|a+b|^2 = |a|^2 + 2ab + |b|^2 \leq |a|^2 + 2|a|\,|b| + |b|^2 = (|a| + |b|)^2,$$

from which we conclude that $|a+b|^2 \leq (|a| + |b|)^2$.

In similar displays, some writers prefer to think of the top left-hand expression as being understood as the left-hand member of each line. To do so in the above display, the last equality would have to be replaced by the previous inequality. This, however, would interfere with the clarity of the relationship between successive lines.

Theorem 1–18. Let p be some positive number. Then $|a| < p$ if and only if $-p < a < p$.

Proof: Here again we have an "if and only if" theorem and hence must prove two results.

First, suppose that $|a| < p$. We wish to prove that this implies that $-p < a < p$. There are two possible cases. If $a \geq 0$, then $a = |a| < p$, and since at the same time we have $-p < 0 \leq a$, these two facts together give us $-p < a < p$. On the other hand, if $a < 0$, then we have

$-a = |a| < p$. From this we conclude, $a > -p$. Putting this together with $a < 0 < p$ gives the desired result $-p < a < p$.

Next, to prove the "if" part of the theorem, let us suppose that $-p < a < p$. We wish to prove from this assumption that $|a| < p$. However, if $a \geq 0$, then $|a| = a < p$, while if $a < 0$, then $|a| = -a < p$ (since $-p < a$ implies that $-a < p$). Thus, in either case, we have the desired result.

An example of the use of this theorem might be of interest. Suppose that we are given that x satisfies $|2x - 1| < 9$. From the above theorem we can conclude that $-9 < 2x - 1 < 9$. What is more, since the theorem said "if and only if," the set of all x which satisfy this last relation is the same as the set satisfying the first. Since we can add the same amount to both sides of an inequality, the last relation is equivalent to $-8 < 2x < 10$, which in turn is equivalent to $-4 < x < 5$. Thus we see that

$$\{x \mid |2x - 1| < 9\} = \{x \mid -4 < x < 5\}.$$

PROBLEMS

1. Prove from the definition of the absolute value that $|a|^2 = a^2$ for any real number a.

2. Complete the proof of Theorem 1–15.

3. Prove the converse of Theorem 1–16. That is, prove that if $|a| < |b|$, then $a^2 < b^2$.

4. In the proof of the triangle inequality, the inequality occurs at only one point. Under what conditions will $|a + b| = |a| + |b|$?

5. Prove the triangle inequality directly by considering the four cases:

   CASE I. $a \geq 0$ and $b \geq 0$;
   CASE II. $a \geq 0$, $b < 0$, and $a + b \geq 0$;
   CASE III. $a \geq 0$, $b < 0$, and $a + b < 0$;
   CASE IV. $a < 0$ and $b < 0$.

   Why is it sufficient to consider only these cases?

6. Prove that $|x| > b$ if and only if $x < -b$ or $x > b$.

7. Find numbers u and v for each of the following parts such that the given set is equal to $\{x \mid u < x < v\}$. Show these sets on a coordinate line.

   (a) $\{x \mid |x - 2| < 7\}$
   (b) $\{x \mid |x - 5| < \frac{3}{2}\}$
   (c) $\{x \mid |x + \frac{1}{2}| < \frac{5}{2}\}$
   (d) $\{x \mid |3x - 5| < 5\}$
   (e) $\{x \mid |5x + 3| < 8\}$

8. Show each of the following sets on a coordinate line.

   (a) $\{x \mid |x - 3| > 5\}$ (b) $\{x \mid |x + 4| > 4\}$ (c) $\{x \mid |2x - \frac{1}{2}| > \frac{3}{2}\}$

1–6 DETERMINANTS

In this section determinants of the second and third order will be discussed. Such determinants will be useful at various places in the remainder of the text in writing certain formulas in especially compact and easily remembered form. No attempt will be made to prove the existence of determinants of other orders or to give a rigorous discussion of determinants in general. At a later stage, when the required concepts have become familiar, it will be easy to come back and make a complete study of determinants. For our present needs, the discussion in this section will be enough.

Definition 1–6. A *determinant* is a real-valued function of a square array of numbers. The *value* of a determinant of order two is defined as

$$\begin{vmatrix} a_1 & a_2 \\ b_1 & b_2 \end{vmatrix} = a_1b_2 - a_2b_1,$$

and the value of a determinant of order three is defined as

$$\begin{vmatrix} a_1 & a_2 & a_3 \\ b_1 & b_2 & b_3 \\ c_1 & c_2 & c_3 \end{vmatrix} = a_1b_2c_3 + a_2b_3c_1 + a_3b_1c_2 - a_3b_2c_1 - a_2b_1c_3 - a_1b_3c_2.$$

The important thing to note about this definition is that in the expansion of the determinant, each term contains exactly one factor from each row and exactly one from each column. Furthermore, there is exactly one term for each possible combination. Thus the determinant of order three has six terms in its expansion, since there are three ways of choosing an element from the first row, and when this has been done, there remain two ways of choosing an element from the second row which is not in the column already used. After these two elements have been chosen, there is only one element in the third row which can be used.

A similar situation holds for determinants of higher orders. Thus, for example, the expansion of a determinant of order four will contain twenty-four terms (why?). The only difficulty in defining determinants of arbitrary orders is in giving a rule for the determination of the sign to be attached to each term.

If we group the terms in the expansion of the determinant of order three properly and factor out a_1, a_2, and a_3, we find

$$\begin{vmatrix} a_1 & a_2 & a_3 \\ b_1 & b_2 & b_3 \\ c_1 & c_2 & c_3 \end{vmatrix} = a_1(b_2c_3 - b_3c_2) - a_2(b_1c_3 - b_3c_1) + a_3(b_1c_2 - b_2c_1).$$

Comparing the terms in parentheses with the definition of a determinant of order two, we see that we have proved:

Theorem 1–19.

$$\begin{vmatrix} a_1 & a_2 & a_3 \\ b_1 & b_2 & b_3 \\ c_1 & c_2 & c_3 \end{vmatrix} = a_1 \begin{vmatrix} b_2 & b_3 \\ c_2 & c_3 \end{vmatrix} - a_2 \begin{vmatrix} b_1 & b_3 \\ c_1 & c_3 \end{vmatrix} + a_3 \begin{vmatrix} b_1 & b_2 \\ c_1 & c_2 \end{vmatrix}.$$

Note that the determinants of order two on the right-hand side of the equality in this theorem are obtained from the original determinant by deleting the top row and one of the columns. In fact, we delete the row and the column which contain the factor a_1, a_2, or a_3 which we then use to multiply the resulting smaller determinant. The fact that the middle term in this expansion takes a negative sign is something which must be remembered.

We may now proceed to prove a number of properties of determinants. We will state these results as theorems without reference to the order of the determinant since they are actually true for determinants of any order. The proofs given here, however, apply only to the cases of order two and three.

Theorem 1–20. If the rows and columns are interchanged in a determinant, the value of the determinant is unchanged.

REMARKS. For the case of order three, this says, for example, that

$$\begin{vmatrix} a_1 & a_2 & a_3 \\ b_1 & b_2 & b_3 \\ c_1 & c_2 & c_3 \end{vmatrix} = \begin{vmatrix} a_1 & b_1 & c_1 \\ a_2 & b_2 & c_2 \\ a_3 & b_3 & c_3 \end{vmatrix}.$$

This result can be proved by direct expansion of each of the determinants involved. This proof is trivial for a determinant of order two and not much more difficult in the case of order three. The student is invited to give the proofs as one of the problems at the end of this section.

The square array of numbers which results after interchanging the rows and columns in this way is usually called the *transpose* of the original array. Theorem 1–20 could thus be restated in the form: the determinant of an array is equal to the determinant of the transpose of that array.

Theorem 1–21. If in a determinant two rows (or columns) are interchanged, the value of the determinant is changed in sign.

REMARKS. In the case of a determinant of order three, an example of this fact is

$$\begin{vmatrix} a_1 & a_2 & a_3 \\ b_1 & b_2 & b_3 \\ c_1 & c_2 & c_3 \end{vmatrix} = -\begin{vmatrix} a_1 & a_2 & a_3 \\ c_1 & c_2 & c_3 \\ b_1 & b_2 & b_3 \end{vmatrix}.$$

It suffices to prove this theorem for either rows or columns. The remainder of the result would then follow by using Theorem 1–20. Thus, for example, if Theorem 1–21 had been proved for columns, its proof for rows would proceed as below:

Let A be a square array of numbers and let A' be the transpose of this array. Let B be the array which results from the interchange of two rows of A, and let B' be the transpose of B. Then it is clear that we can obtain B' also by interchanging two *columns* of A'. Hence, writing $|A|$ for the determinant of A, we have

$$|B| = |B'| = -|A'| = -|A|.$$

To prove this theorem for the interchange of columns of a determinant of order two is trivial. In the case of a determinant of order three, we can use the decomposition given in Theorem 1–19 to help us. The student should try writing out this decomposition for cases where the first and second columns have been interchanged and when the first and last columns have been interchanged to see how the proof may be accomplished.

Theorem 1–22. If two rows (columns) in a determinant are identical, the value of the determinant is zero.

Proof: Merely apply the previous theorem. If the two identical rows are interchanged, then on the one hand the value of the determinant is unchanged and on the other hand is changed in sign. The only number which is its own negative is zero.

Theorem 1–23. If all of the entries in a row (column) of a determinant are multiplied by a constant k, then the value of the determinant is also multiplied by this constant.

Proof: This says, for example, that

$$\begin{vmatrix} a_1 & a_2 & a_3 \\ kb_1 & kb_2 & kb_3 \\ c_1 & c_2 & c_3 \end{vmatrix} = k\begin{vmatrix} a_1 & a_2 & a_3 \\ b_1 & b_2 & b_3 \\ c_1 & c_2 & c_3 \end{vmatrix},$$

allowing us to factor a constant out of a row or a column. The proof is obviously trivial if the constant k multiplies the elements of the first row and if we look at the decomposition given by Theorem 1–19. To prove it for another row, we may use Theorem 1–21 as follows. Suppose we are given a square array of numbers A. Let B be the square array which results when the ith row of A is multiplied by k ($i \neq 1$). Let A^* be the square array obtained by interchanging the first and the ith rows of A, and let B^* be the array resulting from the interchange of the first and ith rows of B. Then B^* can be obtained from A^* by multiplying the top row of A^* by k. Therefore,

$$|B| = -|B^*| = -k|A^*| = k|A|.$$

The proof for columns is obtained by using Theorem 1–20 in a similar manner.

Theorem 1–24. Let two determinants of the same order be identical except in one given row (column). Then the sum of the values of the determinants is the value of the determinant with the common rows (columns) and the sum of the corresponding elements in the remaining row (column).

Proof: An example may help to make this clearer. This theorem asserts that

$$\begin{vmatrix} a_1 & a_2 & a_3 \\ b_1 + d_1 & b_2 + d_2 & b_3 + d_3 \\ c_1 & c_2 & c_3 \end{vmatrix} = \begin{vmatrix} a_1 & a_2 & a_3 \\ b_1 & b_2 & b_3 \\ c_1 & c_2 & c_3 \end{vmatrix} + \begin{vmatrix} a_1 & a_2 & a_3 \\ d_1 & d_2 & d_3 \\ c_1 & c_2 & c_3 \end{vmatrix} \cdot$$

The proof (using Theorem 1–19) is again quite simple if it is the top row which is different in the two determinants. It may then be done for an arbitrary row by interchanging rows just as in the proof of Theorem 1–23, and then for columns by using Theorem 1–20.

Actually, this theorem depends only on the fact that in the expansion of the determinant, each term contains one and only one (linear) factor from each row and column.

The next property of determinants is of considerable value in practice, since it yields a method for the simplification of determinants.

Theorem 1–25. In a given determinant, a constant multiple of the elements in one row (column) may be added to the elements of another row (column) without changing the value of the determinant.

Proof: That is, for example,

$$\begin{vmatrix} a_1 & a_2 & a_3 \\ b_1 + ka_1 & b_2 + ka_2 & b_3 + ka_3 \\ c_1 & c_2 & c_3 \end{vmatrix} = \begin{vmatrix} a_1 & a_2 & a_3 \\ b_1 & b_2 & b_3 \\ c_1 & c_2 & c_3 \end{vmatrix}.$$

The proof follows from the previous theorem. The value of the determinant on the left-hand side of the above is equal to

$$\begin{vmatrix} a_1 & a_2 & a_3 \\ b_1 & b_2 & b_3 \\ c_1 & c_2 & c_3 \end{vmatrix} + \begin{vmatrix} a_1 & a_2 & a_3 \\ ka_1 & ka_2 & ka_3 \\ c_1 & c_2 & c_3 \end{vmatrix}.$$

By Theorem 1–23, the constant k in the second row of the last determinant can be factored out, and then Theorem 1–22 shows that the value of this determinant is zero.

The final result of this section is of both theoretical and practical importance. In fact, it could be used to define higher-order determinants.

Definition 1–7. The *minor* of an element in a determinant is the determinant of lower order which results from the deletion of the row and the column containing that element.

For example, the minor of the element b_3 in the determinant

$$\begin{vmatrix} a_1 & a_2 & a_3 \\ b_1 & b_2 & b_3 \\ c_1 & c_2 & c_3 \end{vmatrix}$$

is the determinant

$$\begin{vmatrix} a_1 & a_2 \\ c_1 & c_2 \end{vmatrix}.$$

Definition 1–8. The *cofactor* of an element in a determinant is $(-1)^s$ times the value of the minor of that element, where $s = i + j$, the given element being in the ith row (counting from the top) and the jth column (counting from the left).

Thus, for example, the cofactor of the element b_3 in the above example is

$$(-1)^{2+3} \begin{vmatrix} a_1 & a_2 \\ c_1 & c_2 \end{vmatrix}.$$

The factor $(-1)^s$ is $+1$ for the element in the upper left-hand corner and is alternately $+1$ and -1 in a checkerboard pattern throughout the determinant.

Theorem 1–26. The value of a determinant is equal to the sum of the products of the elements of a given row (column) and their cofactors.

Proof: Two examples of this expansion are

$$\begin{vmatrix} a_1 & a_2 & a_3 \\ b_1 & b_2 & b_3 \\ c_1 & c_2 & c_3 \end{vmatrix} = a_1 \begin{vmatrix} b_2 & b_3 \\ c_2 & c_3 \end{vmatrix} - a_2 \begin{vmatrix} b_1 & b_3 \\ c_1 & c_3 \end{vmatrix} + a_3 \begin{vmatrix} b_1 & b_2 \\ c_1 & c_2 \end{vmatrix}$$

$$= -a_2 \begin{vmatrix} b_1 & b_3 \\ c_1 & c_3 \end{vmatrix} + b_2 \begin{vmatrix} a_1 & a_3 \\ c_1 & c_3 \end{vmatrix} - c_2 \begin{vmatrix} a_1 & a_3 \\ b_1 & b_3 \end{vmatrix}.$$

The result of this theorem applied to the top row (the first line in the above example) is exactly the statement of Theorem 1–19. We can prove it for the second row by interchanging rows one and two. This changes the sign of the determinant and each cofactor in the expansion will have its sign changed. To prove it for the third row (having proved it for the second), interchange rows two and three.

Note how simple this result is if all of the elements except one in a given row (or column) is zero. All determinants can be reduced to this form by the application of Theorem 1–25. Thus, for example,

$$\begin{vmatrix} 1 & 3 & -7 \\ 2 & 4 & 5 \\ -3 & 1 & 15 \end{vmatrix} = \begin{vmatrix} 1 & 3 & -7 \\ 0 & -2 & 19 \\ -3 & 1 & 15 \end{vmatrix}$$

$$= \begin{vmatrix} 1 & 3 & -7 \\ 0 & -2 & 19 \\ 0 & 10 & -6 \end{vmatrix}$$

$$= \begin{vmatrix} -2 & 19 \\ 10 & -6 \end{vmatrix}$$

$$= \begin{vmatrix} -2 & 19 \\ 0 & 89 \end{vmatrix}$$

$$= -178.$$

Here, in the first step, the top row was multiplied by 2 and subtracted from the second row. Next, the first row was multiplied by 3 and added to the third row (in practice these two steps could be done simultaneously to save writing). Then the determinant was expanded by the cofactors of the first column, only one term appearing because of the two zeros. The resulting second-order determinant could be expanded directly, or, as was done, the top row multiplied by 5 and added to the second row to give a simpler expansion.

At some future time the student will see a proper treatment of determinants of an arbitrary order. For the present, let us just state that the theorems listed above are true for determinants of any order. In particular, the theorem on expansion by cofactors could be used to define a determinant of nth order in terms of determinants of $(n - 1)$th order. With this type of definition, these theorems could all be proved. However, Theorem 1–20 would be quite difficult (and this is the main reason that we prefer to defer a complete discussion of determinants of an arbitrary order).

If a higher-order determinant must be evaluated, use the methods discussed above to reduce the order. Successive reductions of order will eventually lead to a second- or third-order determinant which can be evaluated.

PROBLEMS

1. Evaluate each of the following determinants, first by the definition, and then by the reduction technique illustrated at the end of this section.

(a) $\begin{vmatrix} 2 & -3 & 5 \\ 1 & 6 & 2 \\ 6 & 2 & -5 \end{vmatrix}$ (b) $\begin{vmatrix} 1 & 1 & 0 \\ 0 & 1 & 1 \\ 1 & 0 & 1 \end{vmatrix}$

(c) $\begin{vmatrix} 3 & 4 & 5 \\ 4 & 5 & 6 \\ 5 & 6 & 7 \end{vmatrix}$ (d) $\begin{vmatrix} 15 & 30 & -15 \\ 30 & -80 & 70 \\ 28 & 14 & -35 \end{vmatrix}$

2. Evaluate the following determinants:

(a) $\begin{vmatrix} 1 & 5 & -7 \\ 2 & 10 & 1 \\ 3 & 16 & 150 \end{vmatrix}$ (b) $\begin{vmatrix} 3 & -1 & 1 \\ 0 & 5 & -1 \\ 2 & 18 & -3 \end{vmatrix}$

(c) $\begin{vmatrix} 7 & 1 & -2 \\ 5 & 1 & 3 \\ 1 & -1 & -18 \end{vmatrix}$ (d) $\begin{vmatrix} 1 & 2 & 3 \\ 2 & 3 & 4 \\ 3 & 4 & 5 \end{vmatrix}$

3. For what values of x do the following determinants have a value of zero?

(a) $\begin{vmatrix} 3 & -1 & 2 \\ x & 5 & 0 \\ -6 & 2 & x \end{vmatrix}$ (b) $\begin{vmatrix} 1 & 5 & -1 \\ 1 & 3 & x \\ 1 & x & 3 \end{vmatrix}$

(c) $\begin{vmatrix} -x & 2 & 1 \\ 4 & 1 - x & 0 \\ 4 & -2 & 3 - x \end{vmatrix}$ (d) $\begin{vmatrix} x & 2x & -x \\ 1 & 0 & 3 \\ 5 & -1 & x \end{vmatrix}$

4. Prove Theorem 1–20 for determinants of order three.

5. Prove Theorem 1–21 for the interchange of the first and second columns.

6. Prove Theorem 1–21 for the interchange of the first and third columns.

7. Expand the determinants in Problem 1 by the cofactors of the second column.

8. Define a fourth-order determinant by

$$\begin{vmatrix} a_1 & a_2 & a_3 & a_4 \\ b_1 & b_2 & b_3 & b_4 \\ c_1 & c_2 & c_3 & c_4 \\ d_1 & d_2 & d_3 & d_4 \end{vmatrix} = a_1 \begin{vmatrix} b_2 & b_3 & b_4 \\ c_2 & c_3 & c_4 \\ d_2 & d_3 & d_4 \end{vmatrix} - a_2 \begin{vmatrix} b_1 & b_3 & b_4 \\ c_1 & c_3 & c_4 \\ d_1 & d_3 & d_4 \end{vmatrix}$$

$$+ a_3 \begin{vmatrix} b_1 & b_2 & b_4 \\ c_1 & c_2 & c_4 \\ d_1 & d_2 & d_4 \end{vmatrix} - a_4 \begin{vmatrix} b_1 & b_2 & b_3 \\ c_1 & c_2 & c_3 \\ d_1 & d_2 & d_3 \end{vmatrix}.$$

Prove Theorem 1–21 (for columns) for a fourth-order determinant.

9. Using the reduction method illustrated in the text, evaluate

$$\begin{vmatrix} 3 & 14 & 4 & 10 \\ 1 & -6 & -2 & -5 \\ -1 & 3 & 1 & 0 \\ 0 & 10 & 3 & 5 \end{vmatrix}.$$

2

Analytic Geometry and Trigonometry

2–1 THE CARTESIAN PLANE

Suppose that we are given a unit of distance in the plane. This unit of distance can be used on any line in the plane to turn that line into a coordinate line. Thus we can measure the distance between any two points of the plane by supposing that a line has been drawn which passes through these two points and then using the unit of distance to measure the distance.

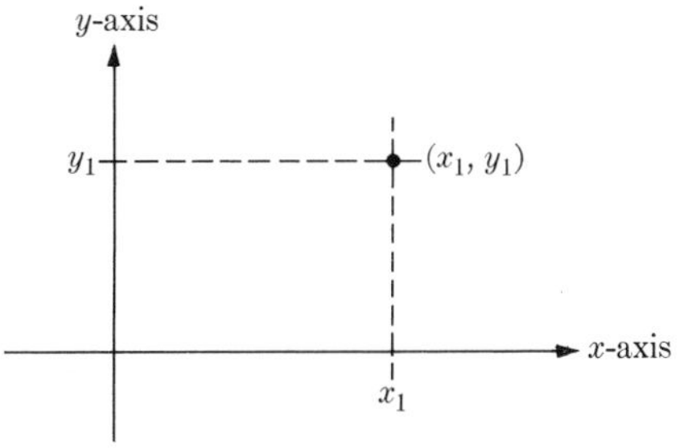

FIGURE 2–1

Suppose also that we are given two straight lines which intersect at right angles in the plane. We arbitrarily assign a sense of direction to each, and make each into a coordinate axis by making the point of intersection of the two lines the origin of the coordinates on each. One line is called the x-axis and the other the y-axis. While this can be done in a completely arbitrary fashion, we make a conventional choice of the orientation of these two axes for the purposes of illustration. This choice is as shown in Fig. 2–1. The x-axis is horizontal, with the positive direction being to the right. The y-axis is vertical, the positive direction being upward.

The plane of these two lines is called the *cartesian plane*. If a point P is given in the plane, unique lines parallel to the two axes can be drawn through this point. These lines will intersect the axes at a pair of well-determined points. Let the point at which the line parallel to the y-axis cuts the x-axis have coordinate x_1 (on the x-axis) and let the corresponding point on the y-axis have coordinate y_1. Then the pair of numbers (x_1, y_1) are called the *coordinates* of the point P. The coordinates are written in the order shown. The first number, x_1 in this case, is called the *x-coordinate* of the point, and the second is called the *y-coordinate* of the point.

Suppose conversely that an ordered pair of real numbers is given. The first will determine a unique point on the x-axis and the second a unique point on the y-axis. Through these points, perpendiculars can be drawn to the corresponding axes. These will intersect at a unique point.

In other words, each point in the cartesian plane determines a unique ordered pair of real numbers, and each ordered pair of real numbers determines a unique point. There is thus a one-to-one correspondence between the points and the pairs of real numbers. Thus, by common usage we will often speak of the point (x_1, y_1), meaning the point with coordinates (x_1, y_1).

The particular point $(0, 0)$ at which the coordinate axes intersect is called the *origin* of the coordinates, and hence also the *origin* of the plane.

In the next chapter, careful definitions will be given, and we will be able to prove many things while knowing exactly the foundation on which we are building. Here, however, we will assume a knowledge of the geometry of the plane upon which we superimpose the cartesian plane. One of the things we assume is the Pythagorean theorem. This allows us to determine the distance between two points of the cartesian plane.

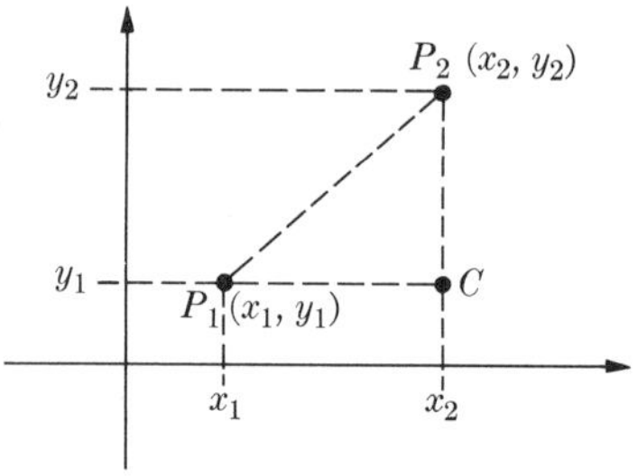

FIGURE 2–2

Suppose points P_1 and P_2 are given in the plane with coordinates (x_1, y_1) and (x_2, y_2) respectively. Let the lines through P_1 and P_2 parallel to the x- and y-axes intersect at C, as shown in Fig. 2–2. Then the triangle whose vertices are P_1, P_2, and C is a right triangle with its right angle at C. The length of the side P_1C is $|x_1 - x_2|$ (as measured on the x-axis) and the side P_2C has length $|y_1 - y_2|$. From the Pythagorean theorem, we see that the distance between P_1 and P_2 is

$$[(x_1 - x_2)^2 + (y_1 - y_2)^2]^{1/2}.$$

Definition 2-1. The *distance* between two points P_1 and P_2 in the cartesian plane is denoted by $|P_1P_2|$.

Thus we have shown that if $P_1 = (x_1, y_1)$ and $P_2 = (x_2, y_2)$, then

$$|P_1P_2| = [(x_1 - x_2)^2 + (y_1 - x_2)^2]^{1/2}. \tag{2–1}$$

For example, if A and B are the points with coordinates $(3, -4)$ and $(1, 2)$ respectively, then

$$\begin{aligned} |AB| &= [(3 - 1)^2 + (-4 - 2)^2]^{1/2} \\ &= [2^2 + (-6)^2]^{1/2} \\ &= [4 + 36]^{1/2} \\ &= \sqrt{40}. \end{aligned}$$

Now suppose a positive real number R and a point P_0 with coordinates (x_0, y_0) are given. What are the points which lie on the circle with radius R and center P_0? Suppose P is such a point. Then $|PP_0| = R$. Hence if P has coordinates (x, y), then $[(x - x_0)^2 + (y - y_0)^2]^{1/2} = R$, or equivalently,

$$(x - x_0)^2 + (y - y_0)^2 = R^2. \tag{2–2}$$

Conversely, suppose that the coordinates of some point $P = (x, y)$ satisfy the relation (2–2). Comparing the equation with (2–1), we see that $|PP_0|^2 = R^2$, or equivalently, $|PP_0| = R$. That is, the point P is at a distance R from the point P_0, but this means that the point P is on the circle of radius R with center P_0. Thus we have shown that the set of points on this circle is exactly the same as the set of points whose coordinates satisfy Eq. (2–2). Putting this into the form of a theorem, we have

Theorem 2-1. The circle with radius R and center $P_0 = (x_0, y_0)$ in the cartesian plane is

$$\{(x, y) \mid (x - x_0)^2 + (y - y_0)^2 = R^2\}. \tag{2–3}$$

An important point must be noted here. We see in (2–3) that a circle is a set of points which satisfy a certain equation. This notation is completely accurate but rather cumbersome. For this reason, a very common usage eliminates any mention of the set and we find phrases such as "the circle $(x - x_0)^2 + (y - y_0)^2 = R^2$." Such a phrase is clearly incorrect, since the circle is the set of points which satisfy this equation and not the equation itself. However, this is not a serious objection since the meaning of the phrase could not be misunderstood.

In mathematics accuracy of thinking is essential. It is safest to be careful and always use accurate language. When the student is aware of the exact meaning needed, he may be allowed to use shorter terminology and phrases which are not quite precise, provided that *the meaning is not lost or altered.*

Definition 2–2. The set of all points (x, y) in the cartesian plane which satisfy a given equation in the variables x and y is called the *locus* of that equation, and the equation is called the equation of that locus. Two equations are called *equivalent* if they have the same locus.*

Thus, the locus of Eq. (2–2) is a circle. In using the terminology of this definition, the word "locus" is sometimes replaced by the name applied to that point set. In particular, we would say, for example, that (2–2) is the equation of a circle.

For example, the circle with center $(2, -1)$ and radius 3 would have the equation

$$(x - 2)^2 + [y - (-1)]^2 = 3^2$$

or

$$(x - 2)^2 + (y + 1)^2 = 9.$$

Let us look again at the equation of a circle, (2–2). This equation is equivalent to the equation

$$x^2 + y^2 - 2x_0x - 2y_0y + (x_0^2 + y_0^2 - R^2) = 0,$$

that is, to an equation of the form

$$x^2 + y^2 - 2ax - 2by + c = 0. \tag{2–4}$$

Thus the equation of the circle with center $(2, -1)$ and radius 3, given above, becomes

$$x^2 - 4x + 4 + y^2 + 2y + 1 = 9$$

or

$$x^2 + y^2 - 4x + 2y - 4 = 0$$

when transformed to the form (2–4).

* The phrase "truth set" or "solution set" is often used instead of "locus" in modern texts. The meaning is the same. We use "locus" here because it is in such common use that the student should be aware of it. Besides, it is shorter.

Is any equation of the form (2–4) the equation of a circle? The answer is clearly no, since, for example, the equation

$$x^2 + y^2 - 2x - 2y + 4 = 0$$

is equivalent to

$$(x - 1)^2 + (y - 1)^2 = -2,$$

and no points in the plane would have coordinates which could satisfy this equation. The sum of two squares cannot be negative.

Given an equation of the form (2–4), it is easy enough to tell whether or not it is the equation of a circle and, if it is, to identify the circle. All that needs to be done is to complete the square in both x and y. For example, given the equation

$$x^2 + y^2 - 6x + 14y + 33 = 0,$$

we would proceed by the following steps

$$\begin{aligned} x^2 - 6x + \quad y^2 + 14y \qquad &= -33, \\ x^2 - 6x + 9 + y^2 + 14y + 49 &= -33 + 9 + 49, \\ (x - 3)^2 + (y + 7)^2 &= 25, \\ (x - 3)^2 + (y + 7)^2 &= 5^2. \end{aligned}$$

This last equation can immediately be identified from (2–3) as the equation of the circle of radius 5 with center at the point (3, −7). Note how the *numbers* appearing in this form are the *negative of the coordinates* of the center.

Suppose we were asked to find the circle which passes through three given points, say the points (0, −4), (−5, 1), and (4, 4). We know that the equation of any circle can be brought into the form (2–4), and hence if we can find a, b, and c in this equation we can find the circle. To do this, all that needs to be done is to put the values of x and y for the given points into (2–4) and solve the resulting set of equations for a, b, and c.

When the coordinates of the three points given above are put into (2–4), we have

$$\begin{aligned} 16 + 8b + c &= 0, \\ 26 + 10a - 2b + c &= 0, \\ 32 - 8a - 8b + c &= 0, \end{aligned}$$

or equivalently,

$$\begin{aligned} 8b + c &= -16, \\ 10a - 2b + c &= -26, \\ 8a + 8b - c &= 32. \end{aligned} \tag{2–5}$$

This set of equations can then be solved for a, b, and c. The resulting values can be used to find the center and the radius of the circle in the manner described above.

Similarly, by assuming an equation for the circle with unknown parameters, we could find the equations for circles with other given conditions.

PROBLEMS

1. Make a sketch locating the following points in the cartesian plane:

   (a) $A = (1, 5)$ (b) $B = (5, 1)$
   (c) $C = (-6, 2)$ (d) $D = (3, -5)$
   (e) $E = (-2, -7)$ (f) $F = (2, 7)$
   (g) $D = (-2, 7)$ (h) $H = (2, -7)$

2. If a and b are two nonzero real numbers, what is the relationship between the points (a, b) and $(-a, b)$? between the points (a, b) and $(a, -b)$? between the points (a, b) and $(-a, -b)$? What happens to these relationships if a or b is zero?

3. Using the points A through H of Problem 1, find the distances

   (a) $|AB|$ (b) $|AC|$
   (c) $|EF|$ (d) $|FG|$
   (e) $|FH|$ (f) $|DE|$

4. Using the points in Problem 1, find the distances:

   (a) $|AE|$ (b) $|AF|$
   (c) $|CG|$ (d) $|BC|$

5. Write the equations of the circles with the following centers and radii, both in the form (2–2) and in the form (2–4). Make a sketch showing the circle.

   (a) Center $(1, 2)$; radius 4
   (b) Center $(3, 4)$; radius 5
   (c) Center $(-5, 3)$; radius 1

6. Follow the instructions given for Problem 5 for the following circles:

   (a) Center $(0, 2)$; radius 2
   (b) Center $(6, -2)$; radius 6
   (c) Center $(-2, -2)$; radius 8

7. Identify whether or not the following are equations of circles. If they are, give the centers and the radii.

   (a) $x^2 + y^2 + 2x - 4y - 4 = 0$
   (b) $x^2 + y^2 - 20y + 84 = 0$
   (c) $x^2 + y^2 - 6x - 2y + 14 = 0$

8. Follow the same instructions as in Problem 7.

   (a) $x^2 + y^2 + 2x - 3y + 1 = 0$
   (b) $x^2 + y^2 + 7x - 8y + 3 = 0$ (c) $3x^2 + 3y^2 + 4x + 18y + 7 = 0$

9. What is the locus of the equation

$$(x - x_0)^2 + (y - y_0)^2 = 0,$$

where x_0 and y_0 are specified real numbers?

10. Solve equations (2–5) and find the center and the radius of the circle.

11. Find the equations of the circles satisfying the conditions below, and give the centers and the radii.

 (a) The circle passes through the points (0, 0), (3, 1), (7, 0).
 (b) The circle passes through the points (9, 1), (8, —4), (1, 13).
 (c) The circle passes through the points (0, 4), (0, —2), (4, 2).

12. Find the equations of the circles of radius 10 which pass through the points (—4, 0) and (12, 0). How many of them are there? Make a sketch.

13. Find the equation of the circle with center at (3, —7) which passes through the point (6, 2).

2–2 STRAIGHT LINES

In Chapter 4 we will consider the problem of defining exactly what is meant by a straight line. In this section we will assume that we know what a straight line is, and concentrate on its properties.

First, let us consider a very special case. Suppose L is a straight line in the cartesian plane which is parallel to the y-axis. Then by the very way in which we introduced the coordinates of a point, we see that every point on this line has the same x-coordinate, namely the coordinate of the point at which this line cuts the x-axis. Furthermore, every point which has this value for the x-coordinate is on the line. Thus, for each point (x, y) on the line, we must have

$$x = c, \qquad (2\text{–}6)$$

where c is the coordinate of the point on the x-axis at which the given line crosses. We therefore see that we have proved:

Theorem 2–2. L is a straight line in the cartesian plane which is parallel to the y-axis if and only if there is some real number c such that

$$L = \{(x, y) \mid x = c\}.$$

Note that this statement is the same (using our conventions) as saying that the equation of L is $x = c$. Students sometimes find it difficult to think of $x = c$ as defining a set of points in the plane since y does not appear in this equation; but if we recall that this is just a short way of stating the set relation in this theorem, there should be no such difficulty.

Now if L is any line in the cartesian plane which is not parallel to the y-axis, then it must cut every line parallel to the y-axis at a single point. That is, given any real number x_0, there will be one and only one point on the line with x_0 as its x-coordinate.

Let b be the coordinate of the point at which the line cuts the y-axis, and draw the line parallel to the x-axis through the point $(0, b)$. In a similar manner as above, we see that this line could be identified as the line whose equation is $y = b$. Next, if we choose any $c \neq 0$, and also draw in the line $x = c$, we will have formed a right triangle. All such triangles have a common angle at the point $(0, b)$ and hence are similar.

In fact, if we take any two points (x_1, y_1) and (x_2, y_2) on the line which are such that $x_1 < x_2$ and draw in the lines $y = y_1$ and $x = x_2$, we will have formed a right triangle which is also similar to any of the above triangles (see Fig. 2–3).

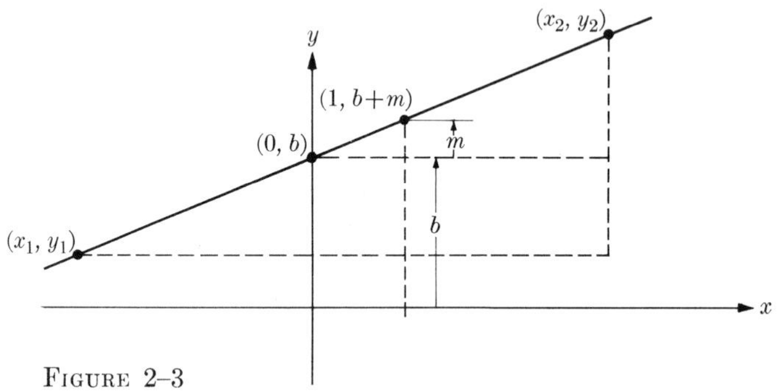

FIGURE 2–3

Let us fix a particular triangle as the one to refer all of the others to. We will use the triangle determined by the given line and the lines $y = b$ and $x = 1$. The length of the base of this triangle is 1. Let the height of this triangle be $|m|$, where the sign of m is so chosen that the point $(1, b + m)$ is on the line. Thus, m is positive if the line "rises," as does the line in Fig. 2–3, and m is negative if the line "falls." For this triangle, the ratio of the height to the base is $|m|/1 = |m|$.

On the other hand, for the triangle determined by the points (x_1, y_1) and (x_2, y_2), the base is of length $(x_2 - x_1)$ and the height is $|y_2 - y_1|$ (why?). The fact that this triangle is similar to the triangle fixed above means that

$$|m| = \frac{|y_2 - y_1|}{(x_2 - x_1)}.$$

Note, however, that m has been chosen to be positive or negative so that it has the same sign as $(y_2 - y_1)$ in this case when we are assuming $x_1 < x_2$.

We can therefore conclude:

Theorem 2–3. If L is a straight line which is not parallel to the y-axis, then there exists a real number m such that if (x_1, y_1) and (x_2, y_2) are any two distinct points of the line, then

$$m = \frac{y_2 - y_1}{x_2 - x_1}.$$

As stated, this theorem does not require that $x_1 < x_2$. The student is asked to verify that this restriction is not necessary in one of the problems at the end of this section.

Let us apply this theorem to the point $(0, b)$ at which the line cuts the y-axis and a general point (x, y), $x \neq 0$, on the line. The result of this theorem gives

$$m = \frac{y - b}{x}.$$

This equation is easily seen to be equivalent to the equation

$$y = mx + b \tag{2–7}$$

except when $x = 0$. We see that the point $(0, b)$ satisfies (2–7), however. Therefore, every point on the line satisfies (2–7). Hence we have

Theorem 2–4. If L is a straight line in the cartesian plane, not parallel to the y-axis, then there are real numbers b and m such that

$$L = \{(x, y) \mid y = mx + b\}.$$

Conversely, the locus of an equation of the form (2–7) is a straight line not parallel to the y-axis.

Strictly speaking, the last half of this theorem has not been proved. However, exactly the same discussion as above can be used to show that if a point (x, y) satisfies this equation, then (x, y) must lie on the line through the points $(0, b)$ and $(1, b + m)$.

Definition 2–3. If the line L has equation $y = mx + b$, then b is called the *y-intercept* of L and m is called the *slope* of L.

Equation (2–7) is called the *slope-intercept form* of the equation of a line. A line which is parallel to the y-axis is often said to have infinite slope (see Problem 3), but it is more correct to say that it has no slope. Note that the lines for which $m = 0$, that is, those with equation $y = b$, are parallel to the x-axis.

Equations (2–7) and (2–6) can be combined into a single case. Either one can be written in the form

$$ax + by + c = 0, \tag{2–8}$$

where not both a and b are zero. Equation (2–8) is called the *general form* of the equation of a line. We see that if $b = 0$ in an equation of this form, we can divide through by a and get the equation of a line of the type (2–6). If $b \neq 0$, then we can divide by b and get the slope-intercept form of an equation of a line. In this case, the slope is $m = -a/b$.

The student will find it essential to be able to find the equation of a line satisfying given conditions. There are two types of conditions which appear very frequently in practice, and which must therefore be familiar to the student. These conditions are: a pair of points which are to be on the line, and a given point and slope. Let us look at this second condition first.

If the slope m is given, we know that the line will have an equation of the form

$$y = mx + b,$$

and hence all that needs to be determined is the correct value for b. Suppose that the point (x_1, y_1) is given and is to be on the line. Then the coordinates must satisfy the equation, giving

$$y_1 = mx_1 + b,$$

and hence $b = y_1 - mx_1$. The required equation is therefore

$$y = mx + (y_1 - mx_1). \tag{2–9}$$

This equation can be put into a slightly different form which is often useful. Equation (2–9) is equivalent to

$$y - y_1 = m(x - x_1), \tag{2–10}$$

which is called the *point-slope form* of the equation of a line. Note that each side of the equation is zero at the point (x_1, y_1).

The point-slope form of the equation could also be derived directly from Theorem 2–3. Indeed, Eq. (2–10) is equivalent to

$$m = \frac{y - y_1}{x - x_1}, \tag{2–11}$$

except for the point (x_1, y_1) which is on the line and satisfies (2–10) but not (2–11). Equation (2–11) can be derived immediately from Theorem 2–3. This result is easily remembered, particularly in the form (2–11), and the student is advised to be sure he learns it, since it is used quite often.

Let us look at an example of the use of this result. What is the equation of the line with slope $\frac{1}{2}$ which passes through the point (1, −3)? From (2–10) we have

$$y - 1 = \tfrac{1}{2}(x + 3).$$

We can find an equivalent equation in the form (2–8) from the above equation. Such an equation is

$$x - 2y + 5 = 0.$$

Next, let us consider the problem of finding the equation of the line passing through two given points. This can be done in several ways. We could assume the general form

$$ax + by + c = 0$$

and use the coordinates of the two given points to obtain the pair of equations

$$ax_1 + by_1 + c = 0, \qquad ax_2 + by_2 + c = 0.$$

These two equations contain three unknowns, but they can be solved nonetheless. The method is to eliminate one of the unknowns, leaving a single equation in two unknowns. This can be solved for one of the unknowns in terms of an assumed value of the other. A solution set can be obtained for each such assumed value. But the different solution sets for different assumed values are multiples of each other. This does not matter, since the locus of Eq. (2–8) is unchanged when all of the coefficients are multiplied by the same nonzero constant.

For example, let us find the equation of the line passing through the points (1, 2) and (4, 4). Assuming the equation $ax + by + c = 0$, we find that at (1, 2)

$$a + 2b + c = 0,$$

and that at (4, 4)

$$4a + 4b + c = 0.$$

Subtracting the first of these equations from the second, we find

$$3a + 2b = 0.$$

We now assume any convenient value for a and solve for b. The value $a = 2$ is useful here, since it makes $b = -3$ (an integer). These values can now be put into one of the equations given above. In particular, from the first equation,

$$\begin{aligned} c &= -a - 2b \\ &= -2 + 6 \\ &= 4. \end{aligned}$$

The desired equation is therefore

$$2x - 3y + 4 = 0.$$

The method described above is not the only one which can be used to find an equation of the line through two points. The results of Theorem 2–3 can also be utilized.

If the two given points have the same x-coordinate, but different y-coordinates, then the line is parallel to the y-axis and must have the equation $x = x_1$ (x_1 being the common x-coordinate). Let us suppose that for the two given points $x_1 \neq x_2$, and solve for the point-slope form of the equation. All we need is the slope, since we know a point already. From Theorem 2–3 we have the slope

$$m = \frac{y_2 - y_1}{x_2 - x_1}, \tag{2–12}$$

and putting this into the point-slope form of the equation as given by (2–10), using (x_1, y_1) as the point, gives

$$y - y_1 = \frac{(y_2 - y_1)}{(x_2 - x_1)} (x - x_1).$$

This result can be written in several equivalent forms, two of which are:

$$\frac{(y - y_1)}{(y_2 - y_1)} = \frac{(x - x_1)}{(x_2 - x_1)},$$

$$(x_2 - x_1)(y - y_1) = (y_2 - y_1)(x - x_1). \tag{2–13}$$

The student should check to see that the two given points actually satisfy these equations.

Both are called the *point-point forms* of the equation of the line. The first is easier to remember, but the second is of greater generality, since it remains valid even when $x_1 = x_2$.

In practice, most students find it easier to determine the slope first, using (2–12), and then to use the point-slope form (2–10) rather than trying to memorize formulas (2–13). For example, to find the line through the points (1, 3) and (5, −5), we first find the slope

$$m = \frac{-5 - 3}{5 - 1} = \frac{-8}{4} = -2,$$

and then using (2–10) we have the equation

$$y - 3 = -2(x - 1),$$

or, equivalently,

$$2x + y - 5 = 0.$$

PROBLEMS

1. Explain why Theorem 2–3 holds even if $x_2 < x_1$.

2. Let c be a fixed real number. Find the equation of the line with slope m which cuts the x-axis at the point $x = c$. Write this equation in the general form (2–8) with $a = 1$. What happens to this equation if m becomes increasingly large?

3. Find the equation of the line which passes through the two points $(a, 0)$ and $(0, b)$, where neither a nor b is zero. These points are called the *intercepts* of the line. Make a sketch showing these points and how the line is determined. Show that this equation can be brought into the form

$$\frac{x}{a} + \frac{y}{b} = 1.$$

4. Find the equation of the line with the given slope, passing through the given point. Make a sketch showing the line. Give the equation in the general form (2–8), and in the slope-intercept form (2–7).

   (a) Slope 2, point (7, 3) (b) Slope -1, point $(1, -1)$
   (c) Slope 5, point (0, 10) (d) Slope $\frac{1}{5}$, point (0, 10)
   (e) Slope $-\frac{3}{5}$, point $(-4, 5)$

5. Follow the same directions as in Problem 4.

   (a) Slope $-\frac{1}{2}$, point $(3, -8)$ (b) Slope 50, point (1, 0)
   (c) Slope $-\frac{1}{50}$, point (1, 0) (d) Slope -50, point (1, 0)
   (e) Slope 1, point $(0, -1)$

6. Find the equation of the line passing through the given points. Give the equation in the general form (2–8), and give the slope of the line. Make a sketch.

   (a) (3, 1), $(2, -1)$ (b) $(-7, 8)$, (15, 20)
   (c) (4, 2), (4, 17) (d) $(-1, 10)$, $(1, -12)$
   (e) $(-3, 5)$, (7, 5)

7. Follow the directions of Problem 6.

   (a) (10, 5), (7, 2) (b) $(-2, 15)$, $(-2, 0)$
   (c) $(4, -8)$, $(8, -4)$ (d) $(-2, -7)$ $(6, -7)$
   (e) (7, 32), $(8, -62)$

8. Show that the equation of the line through the points (x_1, y_1) and (x_2, y_2) is given by

$$\begin{vmatrix} x & y & 1 \\ x_1 & y_1 & 1 \\ x_2 & y_2 & 1 \end{vmatrix} = 0.$$

   Can you turn this into a formula which can be used to determine whether or not three points are all on the same line?

2–3 FUNCTIONS AND GRAPHS

We have mentioned functions a few times already, expecting that the student would have no trouble understanding what was meant, but in this section we will give the formal definition of a function and try to make clear how we think about and work with the function concept.

Up until quite recently (within the last century), when functions were mentioned in the mathematical literature they were usually considered to be formulas, that is, algebraic expressions which could be written down more or less explicitly, involving one or more variables. By the turn of the century it had become obvious that this concept was too narrow and that a better understanding of a function was needed.

In particular, it was realized that functions could not be restricted to having arguments and values among just the real and complex numbers. In fact, it seemed that there should be no such restrictions at all. The elements of any set had to be allowable. Eventually what was arrived at was the following formal definition.

Definition 2–4. Let D and R be any two sets. A *function* with *domain* D and *range* R is a set F of ordered pairs (x, y) with the properties:

(1) For every $(x, y) \in F$, $x \in D$ and $y \in R$,
(2) For every $x \in D$ there is one and only one $y \in R$ such that $(x, y) \in F$.

The set D is called the *domain* of the function and the set

$$\{y \mid (x, y) \in F \text{ for some } x \in D\}$$

is called the *image* of the function.

This formal definition becomes necessary for certain difficult problems. But in general it is too clumsy for actual use in the ordinary situation. In fact, it is usually better to think of functions as some "rule" that associates to each element of the set D a unique element of the set R.

Note that in the above definition, the range can be any set which contains the image. Strictly speaking we should not speak of *the* range, since this is not unique. The concept of range is useful when considering a function in which it is difficult or impossible to determine the exact image. In such a case, the range is defined to be the smallest set which we are sure contains the image. For example, we might have a function in which the domain was the set of all people in the world and which associated to each person the number of hairs on his head. We certainly cannot determine the image of this function, but we know that the range is a subset of the nonnegative integers. We could say that the range is the set of all real numbers, or the smaller set of all integers, but these sets are clearly too big. Can you put an upper limit on the integers in the range?

A special notation is used for functions. We will usually denote the function by a letter and when we are talking about functions in general, we will usually use the letter f. The way in which we use the functional notation is explained by the following definition:

Definition 2–5. If the function f is a set F of ordered pairs as defined above, then by the *value* of the function at $x \in D$ we mean the element $y \in R$ such that $(x, y) \in F$. This value will be denoted by $f(x)$.

We sometimes will speak of "the function $f(x)$" instead of "the function f." This happens especially when the function can be defined by a simple formula, such as

$$f(x) = x^2.$$

This is a function which associates to each real number x the value x^2, and is therefore the set of ordered pairs $\{(x, x^2) \mid x \text{ is a real number}\}$. We will say that this is the function x^2, even though x^2 is really the value of the function at x and not the function itself.

The logical confusion in letting $f(x)$ represent both the function and the value of the function never causes difficulty in any normal context. Essentially, it merely amounts to thinking of x as being a variable point in D and thinking of $f(x)$ then as representing the set of all pairs $(x, f(x))$ in the above definition.

Although most of the functions we shall consider will have real values and will be defined on some subset of the real numbers, it is worthwhile to give a few examples showing other types of functions.

In a library, every book is assigned a call number. This gives rise to a function which assigns a call number to each book. We might write this function as $C(x)$. The domain of this function is the set of all books in the library. The x in $C(x)$ thus ranges over all of these books. The value of $C(x)$ is a call number, and the image of $C(x)$ is the set of all call numbers of the books.

Let P be the set of all people in the United States and let D be the collection of all subsets of P. Then we can define a function on D by specifying the value of the function to be the number of people in each subset. This is a type of function which is of interest to the census bureau, although they only consider certain special subsets, such as the set of all men, the set of all residents of a given state, the set of all unemployed, etc. The image of this function would be the set of all integers from zero to the total population of the United States.

Every rational number can be written in the form p/q, where p is an integer and q is a positive integer so that p and q have no factors in common (we say p/q is in lowest terms). For every rational number x, we can define a function $f(x)$ to be $f(x) = 1/q$, where $x = p/q$ in lowest terms. What is the image of this function?

For a final example of a nonstandard type of function, suppose that on the domain of all real numbers we define

$$f(x) = \begin{cases} 0 & \text{if } x \text{ is rational,} \\ 1 & \text{if } x \text{ is irrational.} \end{cases}$$

What is the image of this function? Is the function completely defined?

Next, we wish to define the *graph* of a function.

Definition 2–6. The *graph* of a function $f(x)$ with domain D is the set of all ordered pairs $(x, f(x))$ where $x \in D$.

A comparison of Definition 2–4 with this definition seems to show that the function and its graph are the same thing. Each is the same set of ordered pairs. This is true, but we actually distinguish between the two concepts.

In the first place, we do not normally think of the function as the set of ordered pairs. We usually think of it as the association (or mapping) between the elements of the domain and the elements of the range.

However, even when we use the formal definitions, we still distinguish between the function and the graph. The function is considered to be the set of ordered pairs F, while the graph is considered to be the same set F, thought of as a subset of the set of all ordered pairs (x, y) with x in the domain and y in the range of F.

This becomes easier to see when we have a function whose domain is the set of real numbers (or a subset of the set of real numbers) and whose range is the set of real numbers. The ordered pairs of the graph are ordered pairs of real numbers, and hence can be identified with points of the cartesian plane. The graph will then be a point set in the cartesian plane. For each value of x, we can mark the point $(x, f(x))$ on the cartesian plane and obtain a picture of the graph of the function.

Not every point set in the cartesian plane is the graph of a function. The requirements that a point set be the graph of a function can be deduced from Definition 2–4 and will serve to clarify the meaning we assign to the term function. For each real number c which is in the domain of the function $f(x)$, there is a unique real number $f(c)$ such that $(c, f(c))$ is on the graph. This means that for each c in the domain, the line $x = c$ cuts the graph at one and only one point.

Thus, for example, Fig. 2–4 shows the locus of the equation

$$x = y^2,$$

but it is not the graph of a function whose domain is a subset of the x-axis. There is an obvious function (or rather two such functions) associated with this locus, however. The function defined by

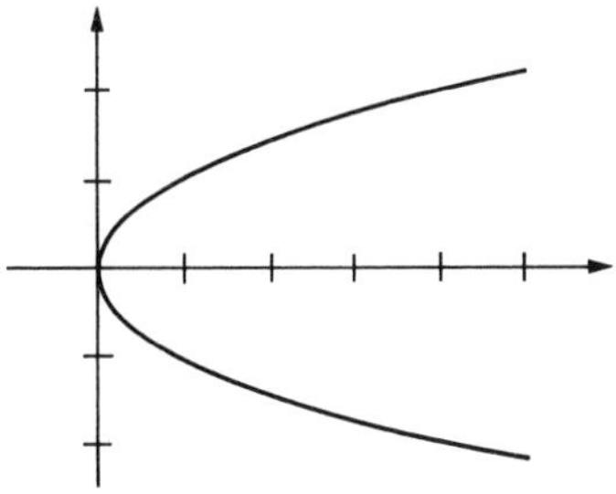

FIGURE 2–4

$$y = \sqrt{x}$$

has as its domain the set of all nonnegative real numbers and as its image the set of all nonnegative real numbers. What is its graph?

Note that when we think of the graph of a function in the cartesian plane, we usually write the function in the form

$$y = f(x),$$

since we are thinking of a point set of ordered pairs (x, y) in our standard notation.

As another example, we show in Fig. 2–5 the graph of the function

$$y = |x|.$$

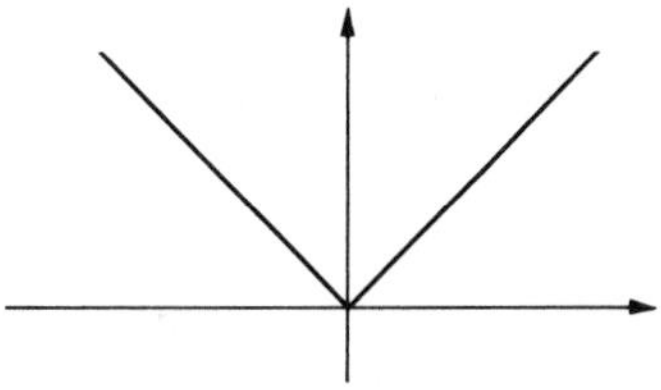

FIGURE 2–5

What is the domain of this function? What is the image of this function?

There are two special types of functions which occur frequently enough to deserve special comment. These are the *polynomial functions* and the *rational functions*.

A polynomial function is one whose value at each x is given by a linear combination of powers of x. That is, a polynomial function, $p(x)$, is defined by some finite number, $n + 1$, of real numbers $a_0, a_1, \ldots, a_n$ such that for every x,

$$p(x) = a_0 + a_1x + a_2x^2 + \cdots + a_nx^n.$$

We will assume that the student is already well acquainted with the basic properties of polynomials, and turn to rational functions.

A rational function is a function whose value at each x is given by the quotient of two polynomials. The domain of a rational function is therefore the set of all real numbers, less those real numbers for which the denominator is zero. We will assume that the student is familiar with the graphs of polynomial functions, but we will make a few remarks about the problems which arise in sketching the graphs of rational functions. This may best be done by showing how a particular example can be analyzed.

Let us sketch the graph of the function

$$y = f(x) = \frac{x^2 - 1}{x^2 - x - 6} = \frac{(x-1)(x+1)}{(x-3)(x+2)}.$$

The first thing we do is (as shown above) factor the numerator and the denominator. It is then clear that the domain of this function is the set of all real numbers less the numbers 3 and -2. The zeros of the numerator tell us that the function is zero at 1 and -1 (and only at these values).

The function cannot change sign between any of these values for x. This fact involves questions of continuity which we cannot discuss here, but the student may accept it without question. To determine the sign of the function $f(x)$ between these values, we merely need to calculate values of the function at intermediate points. These values will help us make the sketch later. In this example, we find

$$f(-3) = \tfrac{4}{3}, \quad f(-\tfrac{3}{2}) = -\tfrac{5}{9}, \quad f(0) = \tfrac{1}{6},$$
$$f(2) = -\tfrac{3}{4}, \quad f(4) = \tfrac{5}{2}.$$

Next, we determine the behavior of the function near the zeros of the denominator. Suppose that x is near but smaller than -2 in this example.

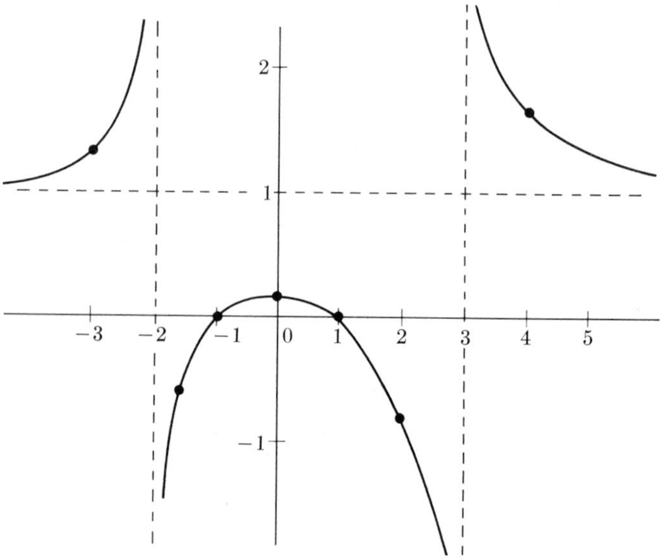

FIGURE 2–6

Then $(x - 1)$ is near -3, $(x + 1)$ is near -1, and $(x - 3)$ is near -5. Therefore $f(x)$ must be near

$$-\frac{3}{5(x + 2)}.$$

Since x is smaller than -2, $(x + 2)$ is negative. What happens if x gets very close to -2? The factor $(x + 2)$ stays negative, but gets close to zero, and hence $|f(x)|$ must become very large. That is, "$f(x)$ gets close to $+\infty$." A common way of writing this down is

$$f(x) \to +\infty \quad \text{as} \quad x \to -2 \ (x < -2).$$

This is a purely symbolic statement which we interpret as saying that the values of $f(x)$ for x very close to, but less than, -2 are "near $+\infty$"; that is, they are very large in absolute value and are positive. For this example we see that

$$\begin{aligned} f(x) &\to +\infty \quad \text{as} \quad x \to -2 \ (x < -2), \\ f(x) &\to -\infty \quad \text{as} \quad x \to -2 \ (x > -2), \\ f(x) &\to -\infty \quad \text{as} \quad x \to 3 \ (x < 3), \\ f(x) &\to +\infty \quad \text{as} \quad x \to 3 \ (x > 3). \end{aligned}$$

Note that in order to write the above expressions we do not need to give all of the analysis which has been carried out. All we need to do is to note what the sign of $f(x)$ is near the point in question; and we determine this sign by calculating intermediate values.

Finally, we would like to determine the behavior of $f(x)$ as x becomes very large in absolute value. We do this by dividing the numerator and denominator through by the highest power of x in $f(x)$. In this case

$$f(x) = \frac{x^2 - 1}{x^2 - x - 6} = \frac{1 - 1/x^2}{1 - 1/x - 6/x^2}.$$

As $|x|$ becomes increasingly large, $1/x$, $1/x^2$, and $6/x^2$ become very close to zero, and hence $f(x)$ gets close to 1.

With all of the above information available, we can now make a sketch of the graph of the function. First, we draw dashed lines $x = -2$, $x = 3$, and $y = 1$. These lines are called the asymptotes of the function, since the graph gets very close to these lines at distances far from the origin. Next, we plot the points that have been determined and sketch in a smooth graph which makes use of all of the information on the behavior of the function that we have been able to determine. For this example, we obtain the graph shown in Fig. 2–6.

PROBLEMS

1. Under what conditions is a straight line in the cartesian plane the graph of a function? If it is the graph of a function, what formula will give the values of the function?

2. The set of points on the circle whose equation is
$$x^2 + y^2 = R^2$$
for which $y \geq 0$ is the graph of a function. What is a formula for $f(x)$? What is the domain of this function? What is the image of this function?

3. What is the domain of the function defined by $f(x) = 1/x$ on the real numbers? What is its image? Sketch the graph of this function.

4. If $f(x)$ is a function whose domain is some subset of the real numbers and whose range is in the set of real numbers, when is $1/f(x)$ a function and what is its domain?

5. Sketch the graph of each of the following functions, whose domains are the real numbers or subsets of the real numbers:

(a) $f(x) = 1 + x$ (b) $f(x) = x + |x|$
(c) $f(x) = [16 - x^2]^{1/2}$ (d) $f(x) = 4 - [16 - x^2]^{1/2}$
(e) $f(x) = \begin{cases} 0 & \text{if } x \text{ is rational} \\ 1 & \text{if } x \text{ is irrational} \end{cases}$

6. Sketch the graph of each of the following functions:

(a) $f(x) = x^2 - 4x + 3$ (b) $f(x) = (x - 1)(x^2 - 4)$
(c) $f(x) = (x + 1)(x^2 + 1)$ (d) $f(x) = \dfrac{x}{x^2 + 1}$
(e) $f(x) = \dfrac{(x - 1)}{(x - 2)}$ (f) $f(x) = \dfrac{(x - 1)^2}{(x - 2)^2}$
(g) $f(x) = \dfrac{(x + 3)(x - 1)}{(x - 2)(x + 2)}$ (h) $f(x) = \dfrac{x(x + 1)(x + 2)}{(3x + 2)(x + 3)(x - 1)}$
(i) $f(x) = \dfrac{x^3}{x^2 - 4}$ (j) $f(x) = \dfrac{(x + 1)^2}{x(x - 1)(x + 2)}$

2–4 TRANSLATIONS

The euclidean concept of translation is connected with the idea of a "rigid motion," that is, the moving of the points of the plane so that the distance between any two points is the same after the motion as it was before. The euclidean rigid motions are translation, rotation, and reflection. The particular feature that distinguishes a translation from one of the other rigid motions is that every point is moved in the same direction and through the same distance.

Definition 2–7. A *euclidean rigid motion* of the cartesian plane is a function $m(P)$ whose domain and image are the set of all points in the cartesian plane and which preserves the distance between points; i.e., for any two points A and B, if $A' = m(A)$ and $B' = m(B)$, then

$$|A'B'| = |AB|.$$

A *translation* is a rigid motion in which the distance between any point and its image is always the same.

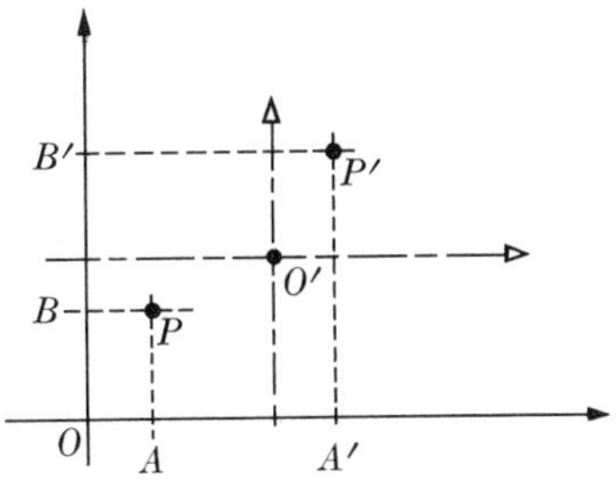

FIGURE 2–7

Suppose that a translation carries the origin, O, to the point O' with coordinates (h, k). We do not prove it here, but it follows from the above definition that the points on a line are mapped by the translation to the points of a line parallel to the original one. Then if the point P is mapped to the point P', we see as in Fig. 2–7 that the broken lines through O' are the images of the axes and that the dashed lines through P' are the images of the dashed lines through P. All of these lines are parallel to one or the other of the axes, and we conclude that P' has been moved a horizontal distance h and a vertical distance k from P. That is:

Theorem 2–5. If the points of the cartesian plane are translated so that the point which is at the origin goes to the point with coordinates (h, k), then a point with coordinates (x, y) is translated to the point (x', y'), where

$$x' = x + h,$$
$$y' = y + k.\text{*} \qquad (2\text{–}14)$$

Note that under a translation, every point of the plane is moved, but that the coordinate axes remain fixed. We "slide" the plane along under the axes. Formula (2–14) gives us the relationship between the coordinates of the point before and after the translation. It is sometimes useful to

* This theorem could just as well be made the definition of a translation.

write this in the following manner:

$$\begin{aligned}
(x, y) &\to (x', y') \\
(0, 0) &\to (h, k), \\
(a, b) &\to (a + h, b + k), \\
(1, -1) &\to (1 + h, -1 + k).
\end{aligned}$$

Suppose now that we are given a locus in the plane. For a concrete example, consider a circle with radius R and center O, that is, the locus of

$$x^2 + y^2 = R^2. \tag{2–15}$$

We know that a translation which carries the point at the origin to the point with coordinates (h, k) will carry this circle to a circle of the same radius, but with center at the point (h, k). How could this be determined directly from Eq. (2–15)? If a point (x, y) is on the original circle, x and y satisfy (2–15). The point $(x', y') = (x + h, y + h)$ is on the translated circle. From (2–14) $x = x' - h$ and $y = y' - k$, and hence the translated point (x', y') must satisfy the equation

$$(x' - h)^2 + (y' - k)^2 = R^2, \tag{2–16}$$

which we recognize as the equation of the translated circle. Looking at this closely, we see that in general:

Theorem 2–6. Let C be the locus of an equation

$$f(x, y) = 0,$$

and let C' be the set obtained from C by a translation which carries the point at the origin to the point with coordinates (h, k); then C' is the locus of the equation

$$f(x' - h, y' - k) = 0.$$

In the second expression of this theorem we have used x' and y' as the variables to emphasize the relations (2–14) and the fact that we are assuming the points of C' to have coordinates (x', y'). In practice, after making this transformation, we would drop the primes, leaving the equation of the translated locus in usual form.

Note that the identification obtained above can also be read from:

$$\begin{aligned}
(x, y) &\to (x' y'), \\
(x, y) &\to (x + h, y + k), \\
(x' - h, y' - k) &\to (x', y').
\end{aligned}$$

In the last line, the coordinates of the point on the right are the same as the coordinates on the right of the top line. Therefore, the corresponding coordinates on the left must be the same also. When (x, y) satisfies a given equation, we therefore must have the pair of numbers $(x' - h, y' - k)$ satisfying the same equation.

The concept of translation can be used in several different ways. First, if we are given the equation of a locus, we can ask for the equation of the translated locus. This was the problem solved by the above theorem. Suppose, to give a specific example, we have the locus

$$K = \{(x, y) \mid y = 8x^2\},$$

and we wish to make the translation which sends the point at the origin to the point with coordinates $(1, -3)$. Then

$$\begin{aligned} (0, 0) &\to (1, -3), \\ (x, y) &\to (x', y'), \\ (x, y) &\to (x + 1, y - 3), \\ (x' - 1, y' + 3) &\to (x', y'), \end{aligned}$$

so that the locus K translates to

$$\begin{aligned} K' &= \{(x', y') \mid y' + 3 = 8(x' - 1)^2\} \\ &= \{(x, y) \mid y + 3 = 8(x - 1)^2\}. \end{aligned} \tag{2–17}$$

Sometimes we would like to find the equation of a locus whose equation we would know if the locus were properly positioned. For example, what is the equation of the locus consisting of the point of intersection of the two lines $y = x + 1$ and $y = -x + 3$, together with all points on the two lines "above" this point? That is, the locus

$$A = \{(x, y) \mid y = x + 1 \text{ or } y = -x + 3, \text{ and } y \geq 2\}.$$

In the last section, we saw that if this locus is translated so that the point of intersection is at the origin, then the translated locus would have the equation $y' = |x'|$; so we write

$$\begin{aligned} (x, y) &\to (x', y'), \\ (1, 2) &\to (0, 0), \\ (x, y) &\to (x - 1, y - 2), \end{aligned}$$

and obtain the desired equation

$$A = \{(x, y) \mid y - 2 = |x - 1|\}.$$

Finally, we can use translations to simplify equations. Having the locus

$$E = \{(x, y) \mid 4(x - 1)^2 + 3(y + 5)^2 = 12\},$$

for example, we can introduce the translation

$$(x, y) \to (x', y'), \qquad (x, y) \to (x - 1, y + 5),$$

so that $x' = x - 1$, and $y' = y + 5$. Then, under this translation,

$$E' = \{(x', y') \mid 4x'^2 + 3y'^2 = 12\}.$$

We still may not know what this new locus is, but at least it has a simpler equation.

PROBLEMS

1. Why are the two sets in (2–17) the same?

2. Suppose that we have translations T and T' such that T takes $(x, y) \to (x + h, y + k)$ and T' takes $(x, y) \to (x + h', y + k')$.
   (a) Is the result of translating the plane by translation T and then translating the resulting points by translation T' itself a translation? What happens to the coordinates of a point under these circumstances?
   (b) Are translations commutative? That is, is the result of T followed by T' the same as T' followed by T? (Be careful here.)
   (c) Given T, does there always exist a T' which is the inverse of T; that is, such that T followed by T' returns all points to where they started from? If so, what is it?

3. Sketch the graphs of
   (a) $y = |x - 3|$ (b) $y = |x + 4| - 2$
   (c) $y + 2 = \sqrt{x - 1}$ (d) $y = |4x - 8| - 3$

4. Find the equation of the locus resulting from the translation of

$$D = \{(x, y) \mid |x| + |y| = 1\}$$

   in such a way that the point which is at the origin moves to the point whose coordinates are $(2, -4)$.

2–5 ANGLES

Euclid defined an angle to be the inclination of one line to another. Since inclination is undefined, this is not a definition at all. A study of Euclid's proofs shows, however, that he considered an angle to be the geometric configuration of two intersecting lines, with two angles being equal if the two geometric configurations are congruent (i.e., if they can be made to coincide by means of rigid motions).

While this form of the definition of an angle was sufficient for Euclid's work, it has been found necessary to use a more complex definition in modern mathematics. Given two intersecting lines L and L', we must be able to distinguish between the angle from L to L' and the angle from L' to L, and we must be able to assign real number values to angles. In this section we will try to make these ideas precise.

Definition 2–8. Let P and Q be two distinct points of the plane and let L be the line through P and Q. Make L a coordinate axis by letting P be the origin and letting Q have a positive coordinate. Then the *ray* from P through Q is the set of all points on L which have nonnegative coordinates. We call this the ray PQ.

Note that it does not matter what unit of length is used in defining the coordinates on the line. Only the direction chosen for the positive coordinates matters. For a given line through a point P there are two rays, one for each way of choosing a sense of direction on L. From a given point there are infinitely many possible rays, two for every line through P.

Definition 2–9. A *geometric angle* is a pair of rays originating from the same point. An *oriented* geometric angle is an ordered pair of rays originating from the same point. If PR and PQ, in that order, are the pair of rays making up an oriented geometric angle, then the ray PR is called the initial side and the ray PQ is called the terminal side of the oriented geometric angle RPQ.

In this definition the two rays may coincide or may lie in opposite directions along the same line. This conflicts with the definition used in many geometry courses, but we will find it useful not to have to distinguish these special cases. Note that a given geometric angle determines two oriented geometric angles, depending upon which of the two rays we call the initial side of the angle.

Before we continue, we must make some observations about orientation in the plane. The two rays consisting of the points of the x- and y-axes with nonnegative coordinates divide the plane into two regions, one of which is "three times as large" as the other. We can get from the x-axis to the y-axis by moving along the unit circle (the circle with radius one and center at the origin) in two distinct ways. One of these ways is shorter than the other, the shorter path being in the counterclockwise direction.

As far as the mathematics goes, it is unimportant whether the shorter path from the x-axis to the y-axis is counterclockwise or clockwise, but it is important that we are able to fix one such sense of rotation and refer to it as needed. Observe that the assignment of an orientation in this way depends on our being "on one side" of the plane. If we have an angle formed by two rays in space, we could find a plane containing these rays, but we cannot decide whether to call a rotation from one ray to the other clockwise or counterclockwise unless we know which side of the plane we observe it from.

Let us assume that we have fixed an orientation in the cartesian plane so that we can speak of a "clockwise" or "counterclockwise" rotation in this plane; the orientation is to be so chosen that the counterclockwise route is the shorter one in going from the positive x-axis to the positive y-axis.

The concept of angle which we wish to develop is to be independent of translation and rotation (but not of reflection), and hence it will suffice to consider only angles at the origin which are such that the initial side is the positive portion of the x-axis (Fig. 2–8). Note that in Fig. 2–8 we show an arrow on an arc between the two rays to indicate which is the terminal side of the angle.

Since we work with the real numbers, we would like to assign real number values to angles. This has, of course, been done since the earliest times. The Babylonians measured angles by dividing a full circle into 360 equal parts and we still use their system when we measure angles in degrees. In military usage, angles are measured in mils, which are defined to be $\frac{1}{6400}$ of a full circle. This particular system has a computational simplicity which is useful in the particular applications made of it.

It would appear that we are at liberty to assign almost any desired unit to a system of angular measurement. However, for mathematical purposes, one particular method of measuring angles turns out to be the most valuable. This is the so called *radian* measure of angles, which assigns the value 2π to the full circle.

It is convenient to have angles with all possible real numbers as their values, but it is clear that any pair of rays could have an angular measurement only between 0 and 2π if we assign the value 2π to the full circle. We avoid this and other difficulties by defining the configuration of rays which corresponds to a given numerical value of an angle rather than by defining the numerical value of an angle defined by a pair of rays. We will do this by means of another undefined concept, that of arc length along the circumference of a circle.

When we say that we want angles to be independent of euclidean motion, this implies an ability to subdivide angles (dividing the whole circle into 360 degrees, for example). We can imagine a method of subdividing the circle, using the euclidean notion of congruence, so as to assign a rational multiple of the entire length of the circle to any arc on the circle. Just as the rational numbers can be completed to the reals, we could then complete these arc length measurements so as to be able to measure any arc. Conversely, we will also assume that given any real number we can measure off a circular arc of that length. To do so, we must make an agreement about what to do with negative numbers.

To fix our thoughts, let us use the unit circle; that is, the circle centered at the origin whose radius is one. Let the point P be the point $(1, 0)$ on this circle (Fig. 2–9). The entire length of circumference of this circle is 2π (by the definition of π). Just as we could measure off coordinates on a line, we now assume we can measure off coordinates on the circle, starting at P and proceeding in the counterclockwise direction for positive coordinates. Thus, for example, the point A in Fig. 2–9 would correspond to the coordinate $+1$ while the point B would correspond (as shown) to the coordinate -2.

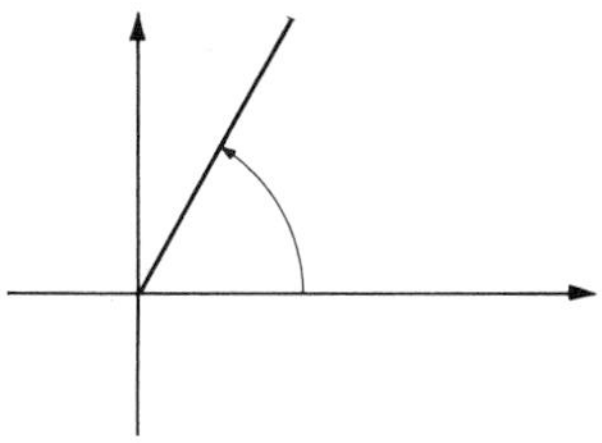

FIGURE 2–8

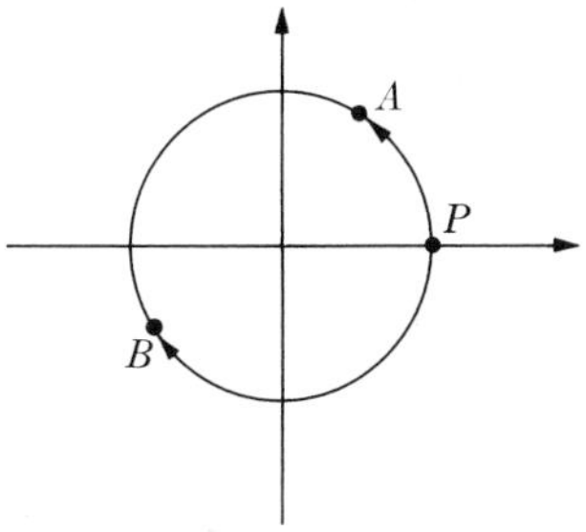

FIGURE 2–9

The point $(0, 1)$ corresponds to the coordinate $\pi/2$ but also to the coordinate $-3\pi/2$ (why?). Each real number would give us only one point, but each point will have many coordinates. The point P in particular has the coordinate zero, but since the total length of the circumference of the circle is 2π, it also has the coordinates 2π, -2π, 4π, -4π, etc. Indeed, it is easily seen that if any point has a coordinate α, then it has coordinates $\alpha + 2\pi k$ for $k = 0, \pm 1, \pm 2, \ldots$ The coordinates of a given point all differ by integral multiples of 2π.

Definition 2–10. Let α be any real number. Let P be the point $(1, 0)$ on the unit circle, and A the point with coordinate α, measured as arc length from P on the unit circle, positive coordinates being measured counterclockwise from P. Then the ray from the origin through A is said to make an *angle with value* α with the ray from the origin through P.

By virtue of this definition, the same ray OA will make an angle with many different measures with the ray OP. If we are given a real number α, then the ray OA will be uniquely determined, but the same ray can also be said to make an angle with measure $\alpha + 2\pi k$ with the ray OP, where k can be any integer.

Once we have a clear understanding of this ambiguity, we may use looser terminology without creating confusion. We often see a phrase such as "an angle of $\pi/2$," and we need to decide exactly what is meant by a phrase such as this.

First of all, we will assume that the above definition has been extended so that we can speak of the ray QR making an angle whose measure is α with the ray QS, where Q is an arbitrary point in the plane and QS is an arbitrary ray from that point. This can be done with the help of translation and rotation, two of the euclidean motions which we will assume known.

Definition 2–11. Let α be any real number. Then by an *angle of* α, we mean any oriented geometric angle which is such that the terminal ray makes an angle with value α with the initial ray in the sense of the definition above. The number α will then be called a *value* or *measure* of the angle.

The phrase "an angle of α" introduced in this definition is merely a short way of saying "an oriented geometric angle in which the terminal ray makes an angle with measure α with the initial ray." The student will find that the word *angle* is in common use to mean either the geometric angle or the numerical value attached to that angle. Usually, this dual usage will give no difficulty, and the student can determine the particular meaning desired by the context.

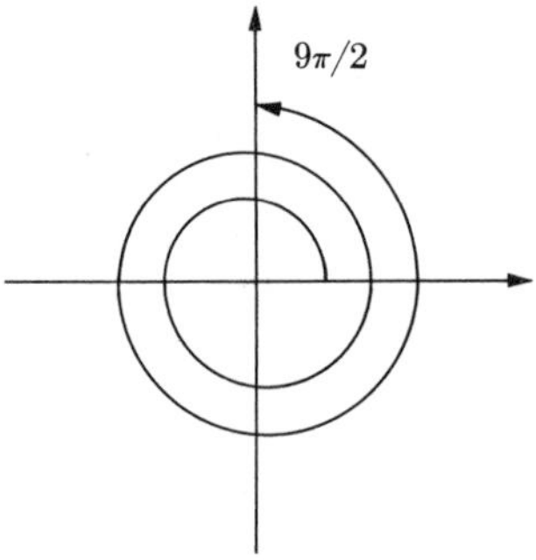

FIGURE 2–10

For pictorial purposes it is convenient to show the measurement of the angle along a spiral rather than the unit circle, as in Fig. 2–10. This figure illustrates the angle with measure $9\pi/2$. The spiral allows us to count the amount of rotation needed to obtain this angle.

A given geometric angle determines many angles in the sense of this definition, but each real number determines only one geometric angle. The different numerical values for a given geometric angle differ by integral multiples of 2π. Of all these, exactly one, α, will lie in the interval

$$0 \leq \alpha < 2\pi.$$

This is most easily seen by thinking of the pair of rays cutting the unit circle, and noting that we can get from the first to the second by moving counterclockwise through some arc of less than 2π in length. If the two rays coincide, the value 0 for the angle can be used. The numerical value for the angle in this interval can be used as a standard value.

Sometimes, however, it is more convenient to use the interval

$$-\pi < \alpha \leq \pi$$

for the standard value. The student should satisfy himself that angles can be reduced to this range as well as to the range $0 \leq \alpha < 2\pi$.

Angles can be added geometrically or numerically with the same results. Thus, for example, if the angle from the ray OP to the ray OA has the value α and the angle from the ray OA to OB has the value β, then the angle from OP to OB has the value $\alpha + \beta$. Note that when we use the terminology of the definition and say that the angle from OP to OA has the value α, what we really mean is that α is one of the infinite number of possible values that can be given as the value of this angle. The number α determines a unique geometric angle, but not conversely. So long as this is remembered, no confusion need arise.

In a similar way, we see how angles can be subtracted. In particular, we can take the negative of an angle. Thus, in Fig. 2–11, β is the value of the angle from OA to OB while the angle from OB to OA would have the value $-\beta$.

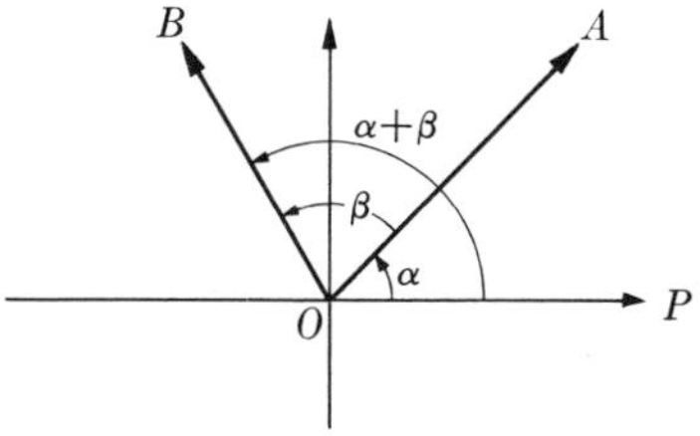

FIGURE 2–11

We have defined angles in great generality—as signed angles in the plane. In actual practice, there are times when the full amount of generality is not needed. For example, while we have defined only the angle *from* one ray *to* another, it is sometimes unnecessary to distinguish between the rays. Then we need only speak of the angle *between* the two rays. The value of such an angle is usually taken to be positive and in the interval $0 \leq \alpha \leq \pi$. This would be the absolute value of β, where β is the standard value for the angle, chosen so that $-\pi < \beta \leq \pi$. When we consider the angle between two rays in space, we cannot use signed values, since a sense of direction of rotation cannot be given as it can in the plane.

There are many possible units of measurement of length. We have assumed a natural unit of measurement in the cartesian plane, and in terms of this unit of length, a circle whose radius is one will have a circumference of length 2π. We could, however, introduce other units of arc length and use them to measure angles. For example, if we assign the length of 360 to the circumference of the unit circle, then in using Definition 2–10 we would obtain other numerical values for the same angles. In this particular case we would obtain a measurement of the angles in *degrees*. We indicate this by means of a symbol which shows the unit of measurement we use. For an angle measured in degrees, we use the symbol °.

This point needs to be stressed. Whenever a particular unit of measurement is used in describing an angle, that unit must be given or implied. Thus, we can describe an angle as having the value 45°, but the degree sign is essential and cannot be omitted. After all, we recognize the statement, "This board is 10 long" as nonsense. On the other hand, we do speak of a line segment of length 2 in the cartesian plane. Two what? Two units of length—the unit of length that is given as part of the cartesian plane. In this case we understand the unit. Similarly we do not indicate the unit when we measure an angle in radians. This makes it even more important to give the unit when we measure the angle in any other way.

PROBLEMS

1. Make sketches showing angles of

(a) $\pi/2$	(b) π	(c) $3\pi/2$	(d) 2π
(e) $-\pi/2$	(f) $-\pi$	(g) $-3\pi/2$	(h) -2π
(i) $\pi/4$	(j) $-7\pi/4$	(k) $\pi/3$	(l) $5\pi/6$
(m) $15\pi/4$	(n) $-9\pi/2$	(o) 127π	(p) $253\pi/4$

2. For each of the angles in Problem 1, give a value in the range $0 \leq \alpha < 2\pi$ for the same oriented geometric angle.

3. The angle of 2π (radians) is the same as the angle of 360°.
   (a) If α is the value of an angle given in the radians, what is the formula for the value of the angle in degrees? That is, if an angle has values α and $a°$, then $a = ?$
   (b) Given an angle with a value of a degrees, what is its measurement in terms of radians?

4. Convert each of the angles in Problem 1 to degrees.

5. How many degrees is an angle of 1 radian?

6. Using the approximation $\pi = 3.1416$ and the fact that an angle of 6400 mils is the same as an angle of 2π, find the angle of one mil in radians to three significant figures. What do you think "mil" stands for?

7. Suppose that the angle from the ray OP to the ray OA has the value α, the angle from OA to OB has the value β, and the angle from OP to OB has the value γ. Why is it not necessarily true that $\alpha + \beta = \gamma$? How does this situation differ from that of the statements made about Fig. 2–11?

2–6 THE TRIGONOMETRIC FUNCTONS

The student is probably familiar with the standard trigonometric functions of angles. In this section we will give a definition of these functions which may appear different from that which the student has seen before. The functions are the same, however; we only change the definitions so as to make the particular properties which we wish to emphasize as easy to see as possible.

Definition 2–12. Let α be any real number, let P be the point $(1, 0)$ on the unit circle, and let $A = (x_\alpha, y_\alpha)$ be the point on the unit circle such that the angle from OP to OA has the value α. Then the *sine* and *cosine* functions of α are defined by

$$\cos \alpha = x_\alpha,$$
$$\sin \alpha = y_\alpha.$$

The functions sine and cosine as defined here are functions whose domain is the set of all real numbers. Since the points on the unit circle never have coordinates outside of the range -1 to $+1$, the range of these functions is the interval from -1 to $+1$ (inclusive of the endpoints). It is easy to picture the behavior of these functions. Starting at $\alpha = 0$, as α increases we can follow the x-coordinate, for example, and observe the behavior of $\cos \alpha$. In this way, we see that the functions $\sin \alpha$ and $\cos \alpha$ have graphs as shown in Fig. 2–12.

In Fig. 2–12, the horizontal axis is the α-axis. A feature of these graphs which should be noted is the fact that they repeat with a period of 2π. The functions $\sin \alpha$ and $\cos \alpha$ are examples of *periodic* functions since they satisfy the conditions that for any α,

$$\cos (2\pi + \alpha) = \cos \alpha,$$
$$\sin (2\pi + \alpha) = \sin \alpha. \tag{2–18}$$

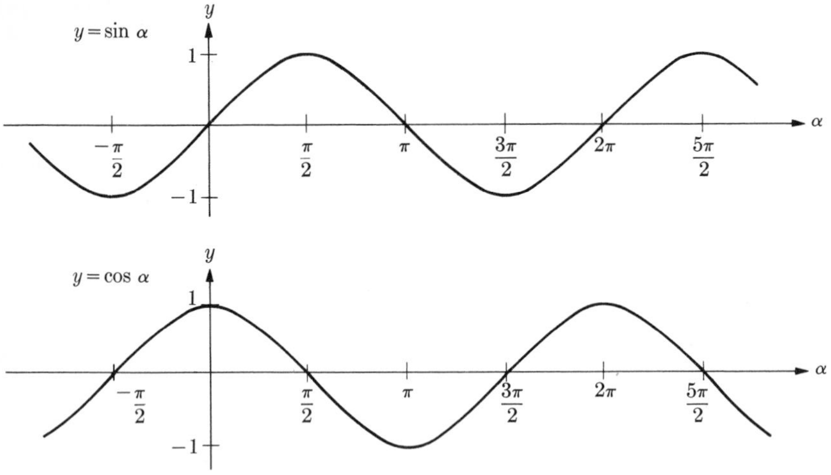

FIGURE 2–12

This follows from the fact that increasing the angle by 2π does not change the geometric configuration of the rays, and it is the oriented geometric angle that determines the values of the functions.

Definition 2–13. Let $f(x)$ be a function defined for all real x. Then $f(x)$ is said to be a *periodic function* with *period p* if for every x

$$f(x + p) = f(x).$$

In terms of this formal definition, we see that Eqs. (2–18) state that the sine and cosine functions are periodic with period 2π.

If the ray from the origin through A makes the angle α with the positive x-axis, then the continuation of this ray through to the other side of the origin makes the angle $\pi + \alpha$ with the positive x-axis. If A is the point (x_0, y_0), this opposite ray cuts the circle at the point $(-x_0, -y_0)$ (make a sketch and verify this, noting the similar triangles formed). This shows that for any α,

$$\cos(\pi + \alpha) = -\cos\alpha,$$
$$\sin(\pi + \alpha) = -\sin\alpha. \tag{2–19}$$

Next, imagine the plane reflected in the x-axis. Any point (x, y) will be reflected to the point $(x, -y)$ (why?), and the points on the unit circle will be reflected to the points also on the unit circle (why?). If A is a point such that the arc from P to A is of signed length α, then A will be reflected to a point A' such that the arc from P to A' is of signed length

$-\alpha$. But $A = (\cos\alpha, \sin\alpha)$ and $A' = (\cos\alpha, -\sin\alpha)$, so we have that for any α,

$$\cos(-\alpha) = \cos\alpha,$$
$$\sin(-\alpha) = -\sin\alpha. \tag{2-20}$$

From Eqs. (2–20) we see that if we know the values of $\cos\alpha$ and $\sin\alpha$ for every positive α, then we would know the values for every α. However, use of Eqs. (2–18), repeated as many times as necessary, shows that it suffices to know the values for α between 0 and 2π. With the help of (2–19) we see that we need only the values between 0 and π. We can reduce this still further by the following reasoning.

Observe Fig. 2–13. We show the two rays OA and OA' where OA makes the angle α with the positive x-axis, and OA' makes the same angle α with the positive y-axis. Thus OA' makes the angle $\pi/2 + \alpha$ with the positive x-axis. The y-coordinate of A is $\sin\alpha$ and is indicated by the vertical arrow in Fig. 2–13. It is clear that the displacement of A' in the horizontal direction, as indicated by the horizontal arrow, is of the same numerical value but of opposite sign (since this displacement starts in the negative direction). Hence we see that $\cos(\pi/2 + \alpha) = -\sin\alpha$.

In exactly the same way it can be seen that $\sin(\pi/2 + \alpha) = \cos\alpha$. That is, we have the relations

$$\cos\left(\frac{\pi}{2} + \alpha\right) = -\sin\alpha,$$
$$\sin\left(\frac{\pi}{2} + \alpha\right) = \cos\alpha. \tag{2-21}$$

Although our diagram indicates this only for α between 0 and $\pi/2$, it can be seen that the argument is valid for any value of α by observing what happens in Fig. 2–13 as α is allowed to change to any value. By means of these equations we can reduce the problem of finding the sine or cosine of any α to the same problem for α between 0 and $\pi/2$. Indeed, it suffices to know the values between 0 and $\pi/4$, since we can combine (2–20) and (2–21) to see that

$$\cos\left(\frac{\pi}{2} - \alpha\right) = \cos\left[\frac{\pi}{2} + (-\alpha)\right] = -\sin(-\alpha) = \sin\alpha$$

and

$$\sin\left(\frac{\pi}{2} - \alpha\right) = \sin\left[\frac{\pi}{2} + (-\alpha)\right] = \cos(-\alpha) = \cos\alpha.$$

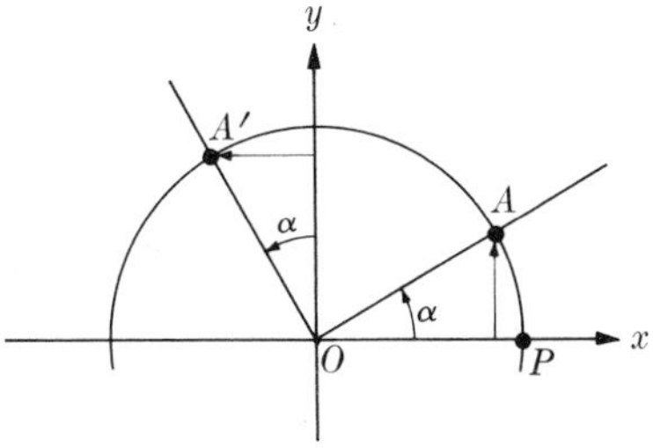

FIGURE 2–13

If α is between $\pi/4$ and $\pi/2$, then $\pi/2 - \alpha$ is between 0 and $\pi/4$. Hence the relations

$$\cos\left(\frac{\pi}{2} - \alpha\right) = \sin \alpha,$$
$$\sin\left(\frac{\pi}{2} - \alpha\right) = \cos \alpha, \tag{2–22}$$

serve to complete the proof of the observation that the values of $\sin \alpha$ and $\cos \alpha$ for α between 0 and $\pi/4$ serve to define these functions for all possible α. This is the reason that trigonometric tables are normally given only for this range (except that the last relations are usually built into the tables).

The use of these relations in practice is fairly simple. For example, if we wish to find $\sin(-197\pi/3)$ we first observe that this is $-\sin(197\pi/3)$ from (2–20). Now $197\pi/3 = 65\pi + 2\pi/3$, and $2\pi/3 = \pi/2 + \pi/6$, so

$$\begin{aligned} \sin(-197\pi/3) &= -\sin(197\pi/3) && \text{by (2–20)}\\ &= -\sin(64\pi + \pi + 2\pi/3) &&\\ &= -\sin(\pi + 2\pi/3) && \text{by (2–18)}\\ &= \sin(2\pi/3) && \text{by (2–19)}\\ &= \sin(\pi/2 + \pi/6) &&\\ &= \cos \pi/6 && \text{by (2–21).} \end{aligned}$$

The student might find it difficult to memorize all of these relations. Luckily, there is a simple pair of formulas from which the above set of formulas can all be obtained. These "addition formulas" will be derived in the next section. However, some of these relations are so important that they should be learned in their own right. The equations (2–18) *must* be known without question. The equations (2–20) are also so useful that they should be known. It helps in learning these relations to recall the geometric picture.

The formulas in (2–22) are of frequent utility, and since they are fairly easy to learn, it is recommended that the student learn these also.

There is still another relationship between these functions which is immediately available from the definition and which is of fundamental importance. For any α, the values of $\cos \alpha$ and $\sin \alpha$ are the coordinates of a point on the unit circle. This point is at a distance 1 from the origin, and hence

$$\sin^2 \alpha + \cos^2 \alpha = 1.$$

This relation is one of the fundamental properties of the trigonometric functions and is important enough to be restated as a theorem.

Theorem 2–7. For any real number α, the functions $\sin\alpha$ and $\cos\alpha$ satisfy the relation

$$\sin^2\alpha + \cos^2\alpha = 1. \tag{2–23}$$

Note that the sine and cosine functions have been defined as functions on the real numbers, but they are also, in a natural way, defined as functions on oriented geometric angles. Relation (2–18) is what is important in this regard. The convention we introduced for writing the measure of an angle in radians as a pure real number (without units) permits us to think of the trigonometric functions as functions of either angles or real numbers.

We also allow the use of notation such as $\sin 45°$. Here we write the function as a function of the angle, indicating this by the use of a degree symbol to show the units. With such a convention, note that we can write

$$\sin 60° = \sin\frac{\pi}{3}$$

and other similar relations.

An important question which comes up frequently is the extent to which an angle is determined by the trigonometric functions. The answers to this question can be summarized as follows:

Theorem 2–8. If two numbers a and b are given such that $a^2 + b^2 = 1$, then there is a unique α in the interval $0 \leq \alpha < 2\pi$ such that $a = \cos\alpha$ and $b = \sin\alpha$.

Theorem 2–9. If a number a with $|a| \leq 1$ and a sign $+1$, or -1 are given, then there is a unique α in the interval $0 \leq \alpha < 2\pi$ such that $a = \cos\alpha$ and $\sin\alpha$ has the given sign (or is zero). Likewise there is a unique α' with $0 \leq \alpha' < 2\pi$ such that $a = \sin\alpha$ and $\cos\alpha$ has the given sign (or zero).

Theorem 2–10. If a number a with $|a| \leq 1$ is given, then there is a unique α in the interval $0 \leq \alpha \leq \pi$ such that $\cos\alpha = a$.

The first of these results is evident when we note that the given condition on a and b is exactly what is required to have the point (a, b) be a point on the unit circle.

The second result follows from the observation that the line $x = a$ cuts the unit circle at exactly two points (unless $a = +1$ or -1, in which case there is only one point). The y-coordinates of these two points have opposite signs, and only one of them has the given sign and thus determines α. The second half of this result follows in the same way by considering the line $y = a$.

The third result follows from the second when we note that $\sin \alpha > 0$ for $0 < \alpha < \pi$ and $\sin \alpha < 0$ for $\pi < \alpha < 2\pi$. Hence, although the line $x = a$ cuts the unit circle at two points in general, only one of these points will correspond to an angle in the required range. This particular result can also be interpreted as saying that the cosine alone serves to determine the geometric angle (but not, of course, the oriented geometric

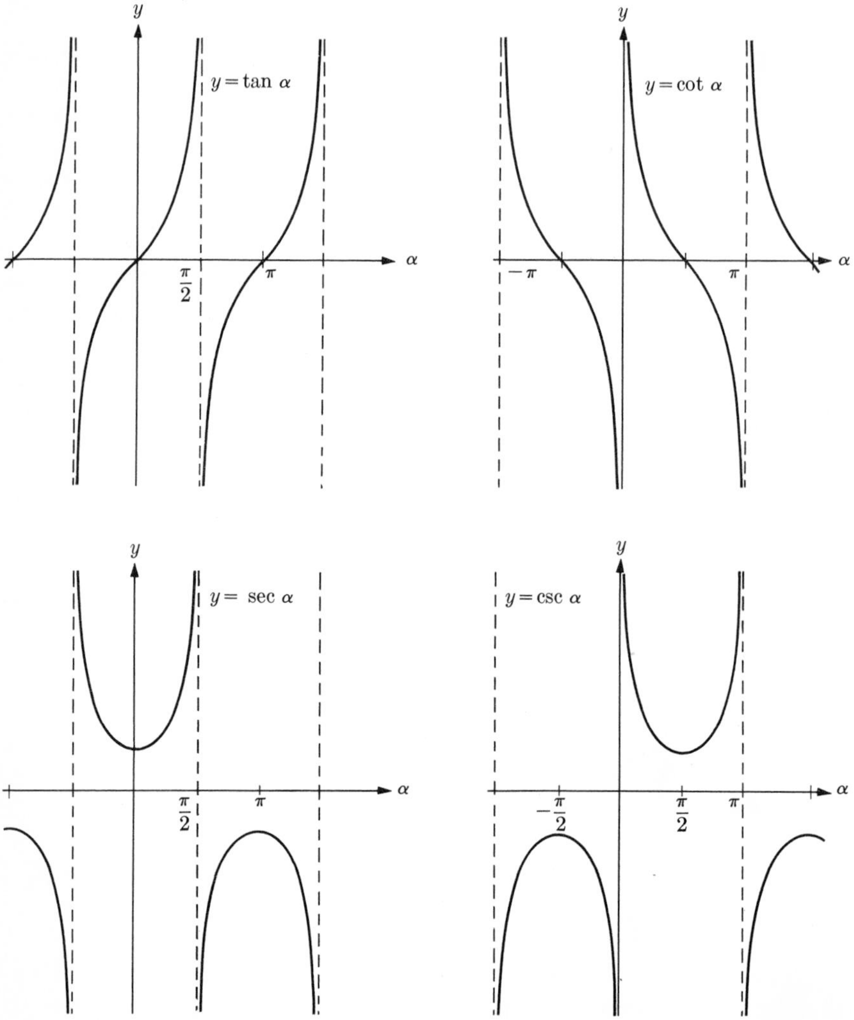

FIGURE 2–14

angle). Note that the converse of this results also holds. A geometric angle has a single cosine. This follows from (2–20), since the two choices of an oriented geometric angle would have measures which are negatives of each other.

The remaining trigonometric functions can be defined in terms of the sine and cosine. They are useful in practice and should be known. At this time it is sufficient to know the definitions of these functions.

These remaining functions are the tangent, cotangent, secant, and cosecant functions. They are defined as follows:

Definition 2–14. For any α for which the denominator of the given expression is not zero,

$$\tan \alpha = \frac{\sin \alpha}{\cos \alpha}, \qquad \cot \alpha = \frac{\cos \alpha}{\sin \alpha},$$

$$\sec \alpha = \frac{1}{\cos \alpha}, \qquad \csc \alpha = \frac{1}{\sin \alpha}.$$

The graphs of these functions are sketched in Fig. 2–14.

All of the relations (2–18) through (2–22) clearly hold when the cosine is replaced by the secant and the sine is replaced by the cosecant (why?). For the tangent and cotangent, however, somewhat different relations hold. Putting the relations (2–20) into the definition, we see that

$$\begin{aligned} \tan(-\alpha) &= -\tan \alpha, \\ \cot(-\alpha) &= -\cot \alpha. \end{aligned} \tag{2–24}$$

From relations (2–19) we have

$$\begin{aligned} \tan(\pi + \alpha) &= \tan \alpha, \\ \cot(\pi + \alpha) &= \cot \alpha, \end{aligned} \tag{2–25}$$

which shows that the functions $\tan \alpha$ and $\cot \alpha$ are periodic with period π (half of that of the remaining trigonometric functions).

Finally from (2–21) and (2–22) we deduce that

$$\tan\left(\frac{\pi}{2} + \alpha\right) = -\cot \alpha, \qquad \tan\left(\frac{\pi}{2} - \alpha\right) = \cot \alpha, \tag{2–26}$$

and

$$\cot\left(\frac{\pi}{2} + \alpha\right) = -\tan \alpha, \qquad \cot\left(\frac{\pi}{2} - \alpha\right) = \tan \alpha. \tag{2–27}$$

A few other relations will be given as problems.

PROBLEMS

1. For what values of α is

(a) $\sin \alpha = 0$? (b) $\cos \alpha = 0$?
(c) $\sin \alpha = 1$? (d) $\cos \alpha = 1$?
(e) $\sin \alpha = -1$? (f) $\cos \alpha = -1$?

2. What conclusion can be made from Eqs. (2–22) when $\alpha = \pi/4$? Show that (2–23) then can be used to find the values of $\sin \pi/4$ and $\cos \pi/4$. What is $\tan \pi/4$?

3. Reduce each of the following to a trigonometric function of an angle between 0 and $\pi/4$.

(a) $\sin (7\pi/5)$ (b) $\cos (-17\pi/2)$
(c) $\sin (315\pi/3)$ (d) $\sin (-111\pi/10)$
(e) $\cos (218\pi)$ (f) $\sin (-15\pi/2)$
(g) $\tan (35\pi/3)$ (h) $\cot (-12\pi/5)$

4. Rewrite relations (2–18) through (2–22) in terms of angles expressed in degrees.

5. Reduce each of the following to a trigonometric function of an angle (expressed in degrees) between 0° and 45°.

(a) $\sin (337°)$ (b) $\cos (-1000°)$
(c) $\sin (-2345°)$ (d) $\cos (112°)$
(e) $\tan (535°)$ (f) $\cot (1800°)$
(g) $\sec (215°)$ (h) $\csc (-7000°)$

6. Prove from (2–23) that

$$1 + \tan^2 \alpha = \sec^2 \alpha \quad \text{and} \quad 1 + \cot^2 \alpha = \csc^2 \alpha$$

for any α for which the functions are defined.

7. Let OA be the ray which makes an angle of α with the positive x-axis. Prove that the line through O and A has slope $\tan \alpha$. What is the meaning of the relation (2–25) in this context?

8. Let OA be the ray which makes an angle of α with the positive x-axis. Prove that the line through O and A intersects the line $x = 1$ at the point $(1, \tan \alpha)$. Make a sketch showing this for angles in all four quadrants 0 to $\pi/2$, $\pi/2$ to π, π to $3\pi/2$, and $3\pi/2$ to 2π.

9. Let Q be a point on the ray from the origin which makes an angle α with the positive x-axis. Suppose that Q is a distance c from the origin. Prove that Q has coordinates

$$(c \cos \alpha, c \sin \alpha).$$

10. Show that if $f(x)$ is periodic with period p, then it is also periodic with period kp, where k is any nonzero integer.

2-7 TRIANGLE FORMULAS

A right triangle has two sides which meet at a right angle. The other two angles formed by the sides of the triangle are taken as unoriented angles to which we can assign values between 0 and $\pi/2$. Suppose that the triangle is placed on the cartesian plane so that one side is on the x-axis and a vertex (not at the right angle) is at the origin, as in Fig. 2-15. Let α be the value of the angle between the hypotenuse and the side along the x-axis. Let a be the length of the side of the triangle opposite this angle, let c be the length of the hypotenuse, and let b be the length of the remaining side.

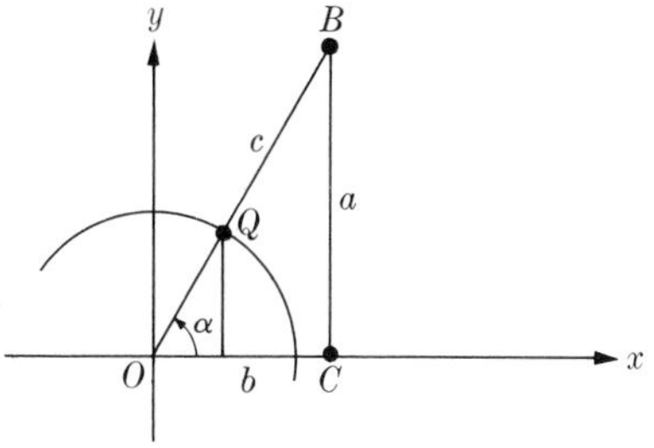

FIGURE 2-15

Extend the hypotenuse if necessary, and locate the point Q which is the intersection of the hypotenuse with the unit circle. Drop a perpendicular from Q to the x-axis. This forms another right triangle which is similar to the given triangle. But this new triangle has sides of length $\sin\alpha$ (the vertical side), $\cos\alpha$ (the horizontal side), and 1 (the hypotenuse). From the similarity, we can conclude that

$$\begin{aligned} \cos\alpha &= \frac{b}{c}, \\ \sin\alpha &= \frac{a}{c}, \\ \tan\alpha &= \frac{a}{b}. \end{aligned} \tag{2-28}$$

The first two of these can be written in the form

$$\begin{aligned} a &= c\sin\alpha, \\ b &= c\cos\alpha, \end{aligned} \tag{2-29}$$

which allows us to compute the length of the sides of the right triangle if we know the length, c, of the hypotenuse and the value of one of the base angles, α.

If a line segment AB is given in the plane along with a line L, then we may draw lines AA' and BB' through the respective points A and B, perpendicular to the line L and meeting L at A' and B' respectively. The line segment $A'B'$ is called the *projection* of AB on L. What is its length? By adding the dashed line in Fig. 2–16, it is easy to see with the help of (2–29) that

$$|A'B'| = |AB| \cos \alpha, \tag{2–30}$$

where α is the angle between the line L and the line through A and B. When two lines intersect, four rays are determined. These determine $4 \cdot \frac{3}{2} = 6$ geometric angles. Two of these are straight angles, and the remaining four are equal (in value) in pairs. The two values will be α and $\pi - \alpha$. Use the smaller in (2–30). The other would give the negative of the correct result, since

$$\cos (\pi - \alpha) = -\cos \alpha$$

from the formulas of the last section. The concept of projection will be discussed more fully in the next chapter.

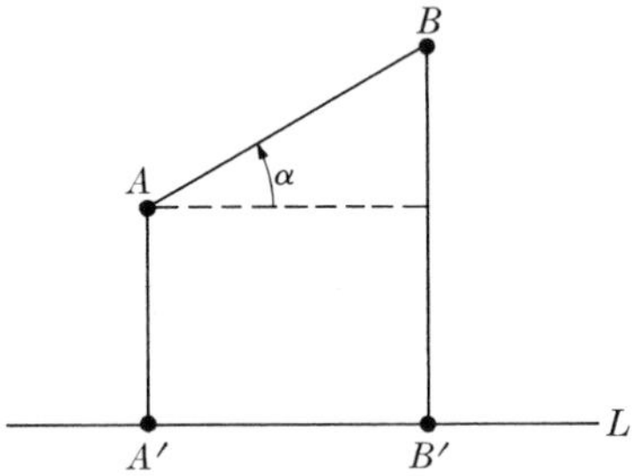

FIGURE 2–16

Suppose now we have an arbitrary triangle, not necessarily a right triangle. Suppose that it has interior angles whose values are α, β, and γ (all taken as positive angles in the interval from 0 to π), and that the sides opposite the angles α, β, and γ are of lengths a, b, and c respectively. We know that the area of a triangle is given by $\frac{1}{2}$ the product of the length of one of the sides with the altitude perpendicular to that side. Thus, if we drop a perpendicular from the vertex with angle β to the opposite side, as illustrated in Fig. 2–17, and if the length of this altitude is h, then the area of the triangle is

$$A = \tfrac{1}{2}bh.$$

However, the altitude drawn is a side of a right triangle. Hence

$$h = c \sin \alpha,$$

and thus

$$A = \tfrac{1}{2}bc \sin \alpha = \frac{abc}{2} \frac{\sin \alpha}{a}.$$

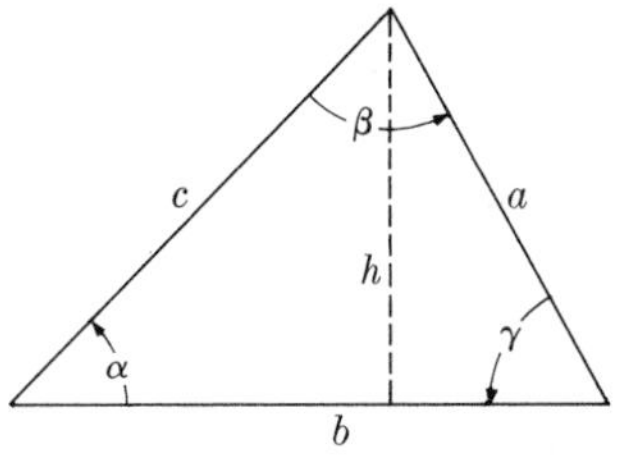

FIGURE 2–17

In exactly the same way, using the same altitude, we have

$$h = a \sin \gamma$$

and

$$A = \tfrac{1}{2}ba \sin \gamma$$
$$= \frac{abc}{2} \frac{\sin \gamma}{c}.$$

By dropping an altitude from one of the other vertices we can show in the same way that

$$A = \frac{abc}{2} \frac{\sin \beta}{b}.$$

If one of the angles is greater than $\pi/2$, as in Fig. 2–18, it is necessary to note that

$$\sin (\pi - \beta) = \sin \beta \qquad (2\text{–}31)$$

in proving that

$$h = c \sin \beta$$

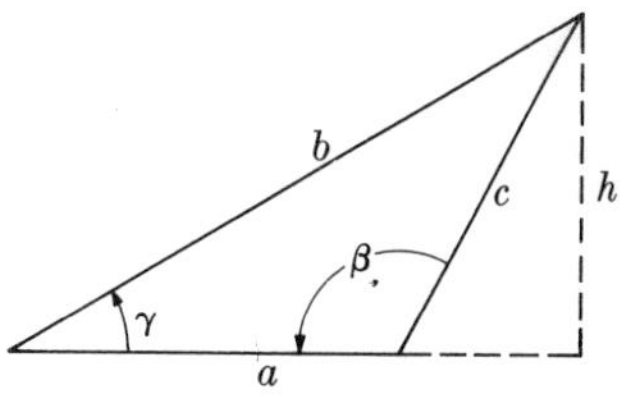

FIGURE 2–18

by the method described. Since this relation follows from the results of the last section, we can conclude that these three representations of the area are valid. They are equal, and hence dividing through by $abc/2$, we have

$$\frac{\sin \alpha}{a} = \frac{\sin \beta}{b} = \frac{\sin \gamma}{c}. \qquad (2\text{–}32)$$

The relations (2–32) are valid for any triangle. This result is known as the *Law of Sines*, and can be used for several purposes. In particular, when two angles of a triangle are known, the third angle is also known since the sum of the angles in any triangle is π, and then if any side is known, the relations (2–32) can be used to find the two remaining sides.

For example, if we know that $\sin \alpha = \frac{1}{3}$, $\sin \beta = \frac{2}{5}$, and $a = 3$, then we can compute b from the law of sines by

$$b = \frac{a}{\sin \alpha} \sin \beta = \frac{3}{(\frac{1}{3})} \left(\frac{2}{5}\right)$$
$$= \frac{18}{5}.$$

If the law of sines is used to determine an angle of a triangle, ambiguity results. Since $\sin (\pi - \alpha) = \sin \alpha$, finding the sine of an angle does not completely determine the angle. There are always two possibilities (except when $\sin \alpha = 1$), one less than $\pi/2$ and one greater than $\pi/2$. Thus, for

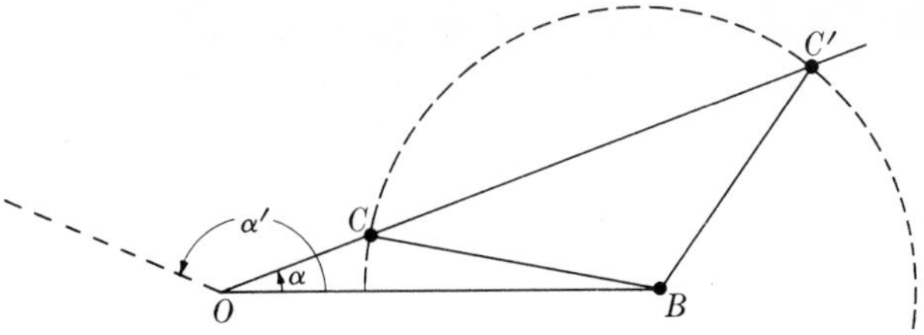

FIGURE 2-19

example, if $a = 2$, $c = 3$, and $\sin\alpha = \frac{1}{3}$, then

$$\sin\gamma = \frac{\sin\alpha}{a}\,c = \frac{(\frac{1}{3})}{2}\,(3) = \frac{1}{2}\,.$$

Hence, as we will prove in one of the problems at the end of this section, $\gamma = \pi/6$, or $\gamma = 5\pi/6$.

This example is illustrated in Fig. 2-19. Both the angle labeled α and the angle labeled α' have a sine whose value is $\frac{1}{3}$. However, the dashed line cannot be the side of a triangle meeting the required conditions, since no point of this ray is at a distance 2 from the point B. The points C and C' are both at a distance 2 from B. The two triangles which satisfy the given conditions are therefore OBC and OBC'.

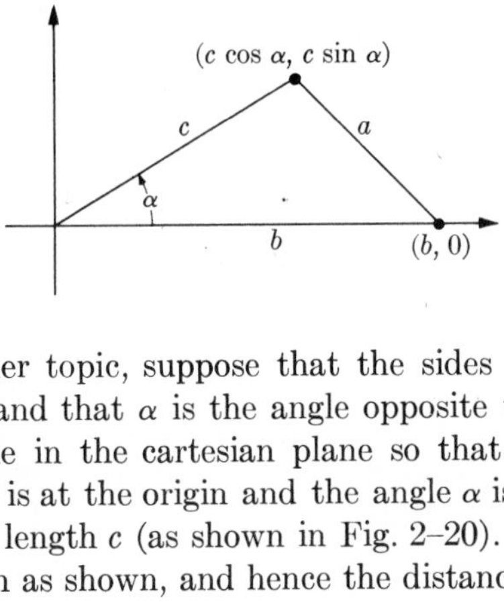

FIGURE 2-20

Turning to another topic, suppose that the sides of a triangle are of lengths a, b, and c and that α is the angle opposite the side of length a. Position this triangle in the cartesian plane so that the vertex opposite the side of length a is at the origin and the angle α is measured from the x-axis to the side of length c (as shown in Fig. 2-20). The coordinates of the vertices are then as shown, and hence the distance formula gives us

$$\begin{aligned} a^2 &= (c\cos\alpha - b)^2 + c^2\sin^2\alpha \\ &= c^2\cos^2\alpha - 2bc\cos\alpha + b^2 + c^2\sin^2\alpha \\ &= b^2 + c^2(\sin^2\alpha + \cos^2\alpha) - 2bc\cos\alpha, \end{aligned}$$

or, since $\sin^2\alpha + \cos^2\alpha = 1$,

$$a^2 = b^2 + c^2 - 2bc\cos\alpha. \tag{2-33}$$

This result is called the *Law of Cosines*. Like the law of sines it can be used to determine missing parts of a triangle. When used to determine an angle (when all three sides are known) there is no ambiguity, since the angle α must lie between 0 and π and there is only one such angle for a given value of the cosine.

As it is written, this relation can be used to determine the third side of a triangle when two sides and the included angle are given. If two sides and an angle other than the included angle are given, this relation results in a quadratic equation in the length of the third side. There are in general two possible solutions.

Note that there are two other versions of the law of cosines in addition to (2–33). There is one for each angle in the triangle. These relations are easy to remember, since the equation says that the square of a side is equal to an expression involving the cosine of the angle opposite the side and the other two sides. All that is necessary is to remember the form of the expression.

Let us now give a few examples showing how the law of cosines can be used to find the missing parts of triangles.

First, suppose we are given that $a = 4$, $b = 4$, and $c = 1$. We wish to find the angles of the triangle. Actually, it suffices to find the cosines of the angles, and so we use the law of cosines. To find $\cos\beta$, for example, we use

$$b^2 = a^2 + c^2 - 2ac\cos\beta,$$

or

$$\cos\beta = \frac{a^2 + c^2 - b^2}{2ac} = \frac{4 + 1 - 4}{8}$$
$$= \frac{1}{8}.$$

The cosines of the other angles could be found in a similar way.

For our next example, suppose that $a = 3$, $b = 5$, and $\cos\gamma = \frac{1}{2}$. Then we can solve for c by direct use of the law of cosines in the following way:

$$\begin{aligned} c^2 &= a^2 + b^2 - 2ab\cos\gamma \\ &= 9 + 25 - 15 \\ &= 19. \end{aligned}$$

Therefore, we find that $c = \sqrt{19}$. The other angles can be found as above.

As a last example, suppose we are given that $a = 2\sqrt{13}$, $c = 6$, and $\cos\alpha = \frac{1}{2}$. We attempt to find b from the law of cosines, using

$$a^2 = b^2 + c^2 - 2bc\cos\alpha.$$

Putting in these values, we find

$$b^2 - 6b - 16 = 0, \qquad \text{or} \qquad (b - 8)(b + 2) = 0.$$

Of the two roots, only the positive one has a meaning in this case, so that we conclude that $b = 8$. The student should make a sketch to see why there is only the one solution in this particular case.

Observe that in this section we are interested in the theoretical rather than the practical use of these formulas. For this reason we do not include, or consider the use of, tables of trigonometric functions. We consider an angle of a triangle as being known when we know its cosine, since there is a unique correspondence between the cosine and the angle when the angle is restricted to the range $0 \leq \alpha < \pi$.

This is not meant to imply that the student should not know how to use the trigonometric tables. He should. In working actual problems, it is usually easier to work with the tables than to use the methods we discuss below. We are interested, however, in the existence of analytic methods which do not require the use of tables.

There is no difficulty, in theory, in finding the sine of an angle if its cosine is known since $\sin^2 \alpha = 1 - \cos^2 \alpha$, and the sine of any angle between 0 and π is positive. There is, of course, some ambiguity in going the other way. The real difficulty we find in trying to use the cosines of the angles is in applying the fact that the sum of the angles of a triangle is π. If we know $\cos \alpha$ and $\cos \beta$ and we wish to find $\cos \gamma$, then using the results of the last section, we find

$$\begin{aligned} \cos \gamma &= \cos [\pi - (\alpha + \beta)] \\ &= -\cos (\alpha + \beta); \end{aligned}$$

but how do we find $\cos (\alpha + \beta)$ in terms of $\cos \alpha$ and $\cos \beta$?

The answer is in the use of the trigonometric addition formulas. These are

$$\begin{aligned} \cos (\alpha + \beta) &= \cos \alpha \cos \beta - \sin \alpha \sin \beta, \\ \sin (\alpha + \beta) &= \sin \alpha \cos \beta + \cos \alpha \sin \beta. \end{aligned} \tag{2–34}$$

Let us now prove the first of these.

In Fig. 2–21(a), we show the unit circle cut by rays so that the value of the angle from OP to OA is α and the value of the angle from OA to OB is β. Then the value of the angle from OP to OB is $\alpha + \beta$. We assume that the point P has coordinates $(1, 0)$. Then the point B has coordinates $\big(\cos (\alpha + \beta), \sin (\alpha + \beta)\big)$, and therefore,

$$\begin{aligned} |PB|^2 &= [\cos (\alpha + \beta) - 1]^2 + \sin^2 (\alpha + \beta) \\ &= \cos^2 (\alpha + \beta) + \sin^2 (\alpha + \beta) + 1 - 2 \cos (\alpha + \beta) \\ &= 2 - 2 \cos (\alpha + \beta). \end{aligned}$$

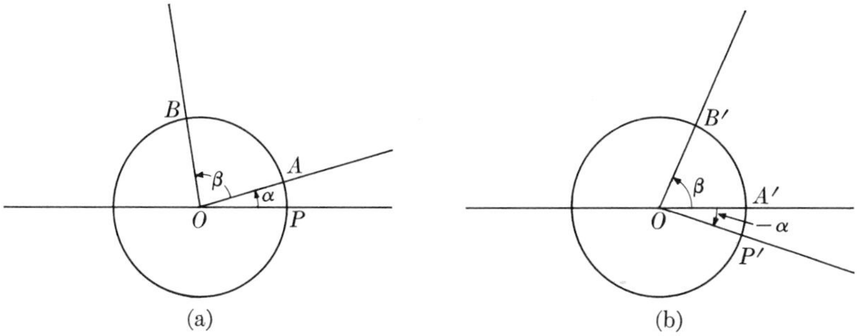

FIGURE 2–21

Consider the same figure, but rotated so that the point A is moved to A' on the x-axis. In the resulting figure, Fig. 2–21(b), the point P' has coordinates $(\cos(-\alpha), \sin(-\alpha)) = (\cos\alpha, -\sin\alpha)$, and the point B' has coordinates $(\cos\beta, \sin\beta)$. Therefore, we can compute

$$\begin{aligned}|P'B'|^2 &= (\cos\beta - \cos\alpha)^2 + (\sin\beta + \sin\alpha)^2 \\ &= \cos^2\beta + \sin^2\beta + \cos^2\alpha + \sin^2\alpha - 2\cos\alpha\cos\beta + 2\sin\alpha\sin\beta \\ &= 2 - 2[\cos\alpha\cos\beta - \sin\alpha\sin\beta].\end{aligned}$$

However, $|PB|^2 = |P'B'|^2$, and hence we can conclude that

$$\cos(\alpha + \beta) = \cos\alpha\cos\beta - \sin\alpha\sin\beta,$$

which is what we wished to prove.

It is useful to obtain a similar formula for the cosine of the difference of two angles. This is easily done as follows:

$$\begin{aligned}\cos(\alpha - \beta) &= \cos[\alpha + (-\beta)] \\ &= \cos\alpha\cos(-\beta) - \sin\alpha\sin(-\beta) \\ &= \cos\alpha\cos\beta + \sin\alpha\sin\beta.\end{aligned}$$

The second formula in (2–34) can now be obtained with the help of formula (2–22),

$$\begin{aligned}\sin(\alpha + \beta) &= \cos\left[\frac{\pi}{2} - (\alpha + \beta)\right] \\ &= \cos\left[\left(\frac{\pi}{2} - \alpha\right) - \beta\right] \\ &= \cos\left(\frac{\pi}{2} - \alpha\right)\cos\beta + \sin\left(\frac{\pi}{2} - \alpha\right)\sin\beta \\ &= \sin\alpha\cos\beta + \cos\alpha\sin\beta,\end{aligned}$$

which is the second equation of (2–34).

Thus we see that if the values of $\cos\alpha$ and $\cos\beta$ are known for two angles in a triangle, then the cosine of the third angle is given by

$$\begin{aligned}\cos\gamma &= -\cos(\alpha+\beta)\\ &= -\cos\alpha\cos\beta + \sin\alpha\sin\beta.\end{aligned}$$

In using this result, it is necessary to recall that the sine of an angle in a triangle is always taken to be positive.

As an example of the use of these equations, let us find the missing sides and angles of the triangle in which $a = 1$, $\cos\beta = \frac{11}{16}$, and $\cos\gamma = -\frac{1}{4}$. We see that we can use the law of sines to determine the missing sides once we have determined the third angle. To this end we compute

$$\begin{aligned}\sin\beta &= [1 - \tfrac{121}{256}]^{1/2} = [\tfrac{135}{256}]^{1/2} = \tfrac{3}{16}\sqrt{15},\\ \sin\gamma &= [1 - \tfrac{1}{16}]^{1/2} = \tfrac{1}{4}\sqrt{15},\\ \cos\alpha &= -\cos\beta\cos\gamma + \sin\beta\sin\gamma\\ &= \tfrac{11}{64} + \tfrac{45}{64}\\ &= \tfrac{7}{8}.\end{aligned}$$

We could compute $\sin\alpha$ from this, or from

$$\begin{aligned}\sin\alpha &= \sin[\pi - (\beta+\gamma)]\\ &= \sin(\beta+\gamma)\\ &= \sin\beta\cos\gamma + \cos\beta\sin\gamma\\ &= -\tfrac{3}{64}\sqrt{15} + \tfrac{11}{64}\sqrt{15}\\ &= \tfrac{1}{8}\sqrt{15}.\end{aligned}$$

With these values, we can then use the law of sines to compute

$$b = a\,\frac{\sin\beta}{\sin\alpha} = \frac{3}{2}$$

and

$$c = a\,\frac{\sin\gamma}{\sin\alpha} = 2.$$

PROBLEMS

1. Let a right triangle have sides a, b, and c opposite the angles α, β, and γ respectively, γ being the right angle. For each of the following write an expression for the required side in terms of the given quantities.

   (a) Given $a = 7$, $\alpha = \pi/4$. Find c
   (b) Given $a = 3$, $\beta = 3\pi/5$. Find b.
   (c) Given $a = 5$ and α. Find b.
   (d) Given $c = 7$ and α. Find a.
   (e) Given c and β. Find a.
   (f) Given b and α. Find c.
   (g) Given a and b. Find c.

2. In an equilateral triangle, all three sides are of the same length and all three angles are $\pi/3$.
   (a) Use (2–33) to find $\cos \pi/3$.
   (b) Find $\sin \pi/3$.
   (c) Use (2–22) to find $\sin \pi/6$ and $\cos \pi/6$.

In each of the following problems, a, b, and c are the sides of a triangle opposite the angles α, β, and γ respectively. Using the values given, find the lengths of the missing sides and the cosines of the missing angles. If there is more than one triangle satisfying the given conditions, give the values for each of the possible triangles. If there are no triangles satisfying the given conditions, explain why.

3. (a) $a = 2, \quad b = 4, \quad c = 5$ (b) $a = 2, \quad b = 11, \quad c = 10$
   (c) $a = 3, \quad b = 4, \quad c = 6$ (d) $a = 3, \quad b = 8, \quad c = 4$
4. (a) $a = 5, \quad b = 6, \quad \cos \gamma = \frac{13}{15}$ (b) $b = 7, \quad c = 6, \quad \cos \alpha = \frac{7}{12}$
   (c) $a = 2, \quad c = 4, \quad \cos \beta = -\frac{5}{16}$ (d) $a = 1, \quad c = 2, \quad \cos \beta = \frac{1}{4}$
5. (a) $a = 3, \quad b = 5, \quad \cos \alpha = -\frac{3}{5}$ (b) $a = 7, \quad c = 6, \quad \cos \alpha = -\frac{3}{8}$
   (c) $a = 2, \quad b = 3, \quad \cos \beta = \frac{1}{3}$ (d) $b = 5, \quad c = 4, \quad \cos \gamma = \frac{3}{5}$
   (e) $a = 3, \quad b = 6, \quad \cos \alpha = \frac{13}{15}$
6. (a) $c = 5, \quad \cos \alpha = \frac{13}{20}, \quad \cos \beta = \frac{37}{40}$
   (b) $b = 6, \quad \cos \alpha = \frac{23}{72}, \quad \cos \gamma = \frac{7}{12}$
   (c) $a = 4, \quad \cos \beta = -\frac{15}{16}, \quad \cos \gamma = \frac{1}{16}$
   (d) $b = 10, \quad \cos \beta = \frac{12}{13}, \quad \cos \gamma = \frac{5}{13}$
7. Construct another proof of the law of sines along the following lines: Let A, B, and C be the vertices of a triangle with angles α, β, and γ at these vertices respectively. Let O be the center of the circle circumscribed about the triangle. For some vertex, say A, choose another vertex, say B, and draw the line from B through the center O of the circle to intersect the circle again at A'. Draw $A'C$. Show that the angle $BA'C$ is the same as α. Show that the triangle $BA'C$ is a right triangle. Compute $|BC|$ in terms of α and the diameter of the circle. Repeat the same process for the other vertices and use the results to obtain the law of sines.

3

Vectors

3–1 CARTESIAN COORDINATES IN THREE-DIMENSIONAL SPACE

Just as the geometry of the plane is characterized by two real coordinates, so the geometry of three-dimensional space can be characterized by three real coordinates. In order to do this, we need to have a fixed set of coordinate axes in space. These may conveniently be chosen to be a set of three mutually perpendicular lines intersecting in a single point.

Suppose that we have such a set of lines. We will assume that each is directed and that we have a fixed unit of distance in our three-dimensional space which can be applied to each of the lines to make it a coordinate line or axis. On each of the lines, a point is determined by a single real number, or coordinate. Through that point a unique plane can be constructed perpendicular to that coordinate axis. And since the three coordinate lines are mutually perpendicular, three points, one on each axis, determine three mutually perpendicular planes. Any two of these planes intersect in a line, and the third cuts this line at a point. In this manner three real numbers determine three distinct points on the axes, which in turn determine a unique point in the three-dimensional space (see Fig. 3–1).

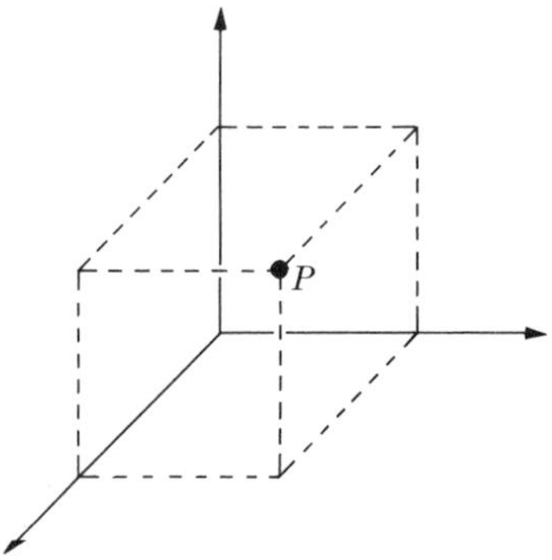

FIGURE 3–1

Conversely, given any point in space, it determines three planes, respectively perpendicular to the three axes, and these three planes cut the axes in unique points which then correspond to three coordinates. Therefore, there is a one-to-one correspondence between the points of space and sets of three real numbers.

Note that we are making use of the properties of euclidean three-dimensional space. If we start from the axioms of euclidean geometry, it can be shown that three mutually perpendicular directed lines do exist and that the above discussion is valid. This is not done here since our point of view is going to be the opposite. We will treat the mathematical system we develop as an independent entity, which can be thought of as a model of euclidean geometry. Throughout the discussion, however, we will base this development on the comparison with euclidean space as we usually understand it. The discussion should help the student to see the relationship between mathematics and the physical world. While the student should concentrate on building a geometric picture of the mathematical system, he should also realize that the validity of this picture is not being proved. Indeed, it is more accurate to say that we are postulating the fact that the geometry of space is determined by the mathematical system which we shall develop.

There is one point, however, on which agreement must be reached before a physical picture of the mathematical system can be said to be known. Suppose we have three mutually perpendicular directed lines passing through a single common point, and we wish to label these as the axes of our system, say the x-, y-, and z-axes. There are six possible ways of assigning these labels (why?), but these six fall into only two groups which need to be distinguished.

Note the three ways of labeling the axes shown in (a), (b), and (c) of Fig. 3–2. Each can be changed into any other by the rigid euclidean

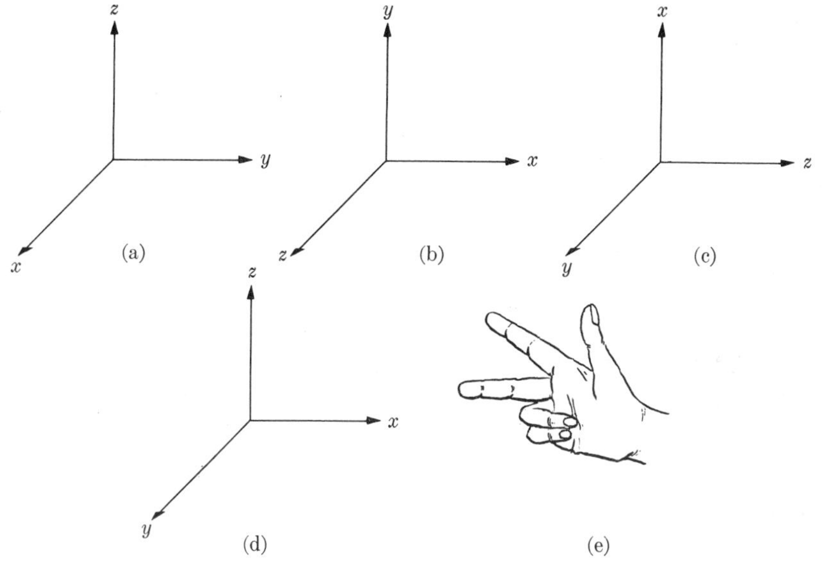

FIGURE 3–2

motion of rotation; however, the arrangement shown in (d) cannot be so transformed without using reflection. For, if we leave the x-axis fixed and attempt to transform Fig. 3–2(d) into Fig. 3–2(b) by rotating about the x-axis until the y-axes coincide, then the z-axes of the two figures will be pointing in opposite directions.

Extend the index finger of your right hand, hold the thumb perpendicular to the index finger but in the same plane as the rest of the hand, and turn the middle finger inward so that it is perpendicular to the palm and both the index finger and thumb. In this position, the hand can be rotated so as to bring the thumb into the position of the positive x-axis, the index finger into the position of the positive y-axis, and the middle finger into the position of the positive z-axis for any of the three arrangements shown in Fig. 3–2(a), (b), or (c). However, the arrangement of Fig. 3–2(d) cannot be obtained. This arrangement of axes would require the left hand.

Henceforth, we will agree on the arrangement of axes shown in Figs. (a), (b), and (c). This is called a *right-handed coordinate system*, since the thumb and the first two fingers of the right hand can be put into the positions of the x-, y-, and z-axes respectively as described above. Although this convention is immaterial to the mathematical development, it would be essential in any consideration of applications to know exactly which system was being used.

Let us assume now that we have a fixed right-handed coordinate system. As described above, three coordinates serve to identify uniquely one point in space. We shall use the convention of writing down the coordinates in the order of the x-, y-, z-coordinates respectively and enclosing the resulting triple of numbers in parentheses. Thus a triple of numbers such as $(1, 2, -1)$ represents the coordinates of some point, but we will actually go further and identify this triple with the point. That is, when it is understood that a coordinate system has been fixed, we may speak of a point (x_1, y_1, z_1) rather than having to say the point with coordinates (x_1, y_1, z_1). Moreover, we will use a single letter to label the point. This letter then would represent both the point and the triple of numbers giving the coordinates of the point.

Definition 3–1. A *point* of *three-dimensional space* is an ordered triple of numbers. Points will be denoted by capital italic letters, e.g., $P = (x_1, y_1, z_1)$. The particular point $(0, 0, 0)$ is called the *origin*.

This definition is the start of the construction of a *mathematical model* of three-dimensional space. We are not saying that the points of the space in which we live are really triples of numbers, but that the set of all triples of numbers can be used to represent this space. The mathematical model will give us something that we can work with algebraically. It is

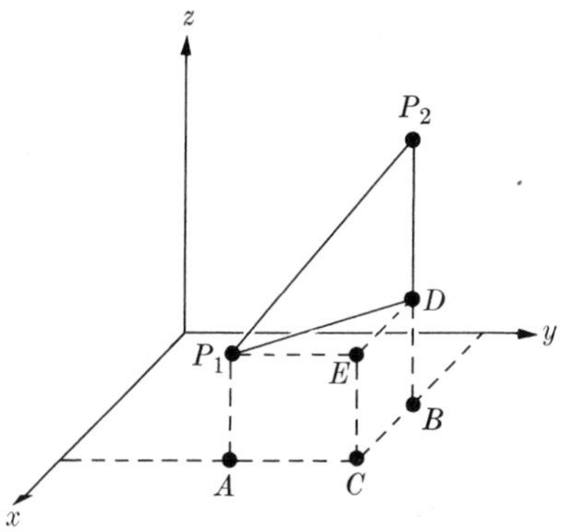

FIGURE 3–3

actually three-dimensional cartesian space with a fixed intrinsic coordinate system.

Suppose we have two points given, say $P_1 = (x_1, y_1, z_1)$ and $P_2 = (x_2, y_2, z_2)$. We would like to give a formula for the distance between these two points which would coincide with the euclidean concept of distance. Observe the set of points shown in Fig. 3–3. It is clear from the figure how these points are obtained, but they can be completely defined in terms of their coordinates. Thus $A = (x_1, y_1, 0)$, $B = (x_2, y_2, 0)$, $C = (x_1, y_2, 0)$, $D = (x_2, y_2, z_1)$, and $E = (x_1, y_2, z_1)$. (Verify all of these.) The points P_1 and E lie on a line parallel to the y-axis since only their y-coordinates differ. The distance between these two points is therefore the absolute value of the difference of their y-coordinates, or $|y_1 - y_2|$. Likewise the distance between the points D and E is $|x_1 - x_2|$. The triangle P_1ED is a right triangle, and hence from the Pythagorean theorem, the distance between P_1 and D would be

$$[(x_1 - x_2)^2 + (y_1 - y_2)^2]^{1/2}.$$

Similarly, the triangle P_1P_2D is a right triangle, the distance between P_2 and D is $|z_1 - z_2|$, and the Pythagorean theorem finally gives the distance between the points P_1 and P_2. Thus we have:

Definition 3–2. Given two points $P_1 = (x_1, y_1, z_1)$ and $P_2 = (x_2, y_2, z_2)$, the *distance* between them is defined to be:

$$|P_1P_2| = [(x_1 - x_2)^2 + (y_1 - y_2)^2 + (z_1 - z_2)^2]^{1/2}.$$

Thus, for example, if $A = (7, 3, -9)$ and $B = (11, -5, -8)$, then

$$\begin{aligned} |AB| &= [(7 - 11)^2 + (3 + 5)^2 + (-9 + 8)^2]^{1/2} \\ &= [(-4)^2 + 8^2 + (-1)^2]^{1/2} \\ &= [16 + 64 + 1]^{1/2} \\ &= 9. \end{aligned}$$

From this distance formula we may obtain the algebraic conditions satisfied by the points on a sphere. Since by definition a sphere is the set of all points which are at some fixed distance from a fixed point, we have:

Definition 3–3. A *sphere* with *center* (x_0, y_0, z_0) and *radius* $R > 0$ is

$$\{(x, y, z) \mid (x - x_0)^2 + (y - y_0)^2 + (z - z_0)^2 = R^2\}.$$

For short, we say that

$$(x - x_0)^2 + (y - y_0)^2 + (z - z_0)^2 = R^2$$

is the equation of the sphere.

From this formula, it is easy to write down the equation of any sphere if we are given its center and the radius. Conversely, if we are given an equation which can be brought into this form, we can recognize it as the equation of a sphere and obtain the center and radius.

The equation of the sphere of radius 4 whose center is located at the point $(1, 3, -2)$ is thus

$$(x - 1)^2 + (y - 3)^2 + (z + 2)^2 = 16,$$

or

$$x^2 + y^2 + z^2 - 2x - 6y + 4z - 2 = 0.$$

On the other hand, if we are given the equation

$$x^2 + y^2 + z^2 + 3x - 6z + 11 = 0,$$

we can identify this as the equation of a sphere by completing the square:

$$\begin{aligned} x^2 + 3x + \phantom{\tfrac{9}{4} +{}} y^2 + z^2 - 6z \phantom{{}+9} &= -11, \\ x^2 + 3x + \tfrac{9}{4} + y^2 + z^2 - 6z + 9 &= -11 + \tfrac{9}{4} + 9, \\ (x + \tfrac{3}{2})^2 + y^2 + (z - 3)^2 &= \tfrac{1}{4}. \end{aligned}$$

Therefore, we conclude that this is the equation of a sphere of radius $\frac{1}{2}$ whose center is located at the point $(-\frac{3}{2}, 0, 3)$.

The concept of translation will prove to be most important in our development. Let us investigate how this concept fits into the algebraic model we are developing. A *translation* (or *parallel translation*) of the points of space is a rigid motion of the points—that is, a motion which leaves the distance between any two points unchanged—and is such that every point is moved exactly the same distance and in the same direction.

Suppose that under such a translation the point which is originally at the origin is moved to the point (h, j, k), and that a point (x, y, z) is moved to the point (x', y', z'). What is the relationship between these sets of coordinates? See Fig. 3–4. Through the point (h, j, k) we have drawn dashed lines parallel to the original axes. The point (x', y', z') will be a signed distance x from the plane through the point (h, j, k) perpendicular to the x-axis. But this plane cuts the x-axis at the point with coordinate h. Therefore, x', the first coordinate of (x', y', z'), must be $x + h$. Similarly, we see that $y' = y + j$ and $z' = z + k$. This then is the background for the following definition:

Definition 3–4. A *translation* of the points of three-dimensional space is a function whose domain and range are the space, and for which there are three real numbers h, j, and k such that if the *translate* of a point (x, y, z) is the point (x', y', z'), then

$$\begin{aligned} x' &= x + h, \\ y' &= y + j, \\ z' &= z + k. \end{aligned} \tag{3–1}$$

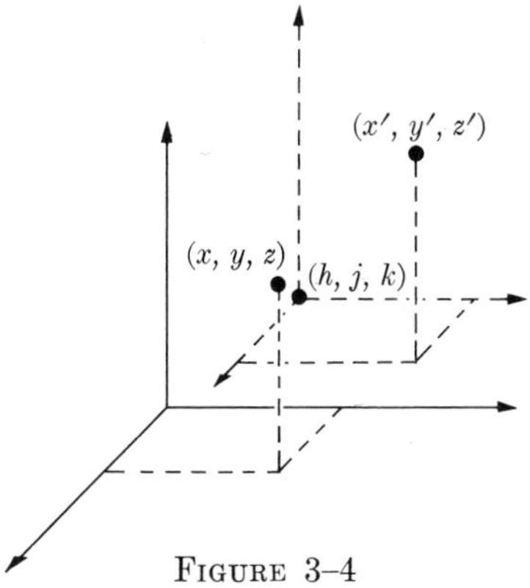

FIGURE 3–4

A translation is therefore a mapping which carries the points in one copy of three-dimensional space into the points of another copy of the same space. We might prefer to think of there being only a single three-dimensional space, and the translation as being a motion of the points of this space. Every point is moved from its original position to its new translated position.

An entirely different point of view can also be taken. Our definition of the points of space as being triples of numbers is merely a useful mathematical device. The more "physical" point of view would be that three-dimensional space has an intrinsic existence, and that the coordinates of a point result from the (arbitrary) introduction of a coordinate system. In this picture, a translation results from the introduction of a new coordinate system in a "translated position." The translation given by Eqs. (3–1) would be obtained by introducing the new x'-, y'-, z'-coordinate system with its axes parallel to the original axes, but all intersecting at the point $(-h, -j, -k)$, where the coordinates of this point are given in terms of the original coordinate system. Whatever geometric point of view is taken, the algebraic form of a translation is the same. It is given by Eqs. (3–1).

Let us note that translation as defined above actually does preserve the distance between points. If we have two points, (x_1, y_1, z_1) and (x_2, y_2, z_2), which are translated to (x'_1, y'_1, z'_1) and (x'_2, y'_2, z'_2), then

$$x'_1 = x_1 + h,$$
$$x'_2 = x_2 + h,$$

but then

$$(x'_2 - x'_1) = (x_2 + h) - (x_1 + h)$$
$$= (x_2 - x_1).$$

In the same way, we can see that

$$y'_2 - y'_1 = y_2 - y_1,$$
$$z'_2 - z'_1 = z_2 - z_1,$$

and inserting these values into the distance formula of Definition 3–2, we find that the distance between the translated points is the same as the distance between the original points.

It is important to note the distinction between a point as a physical location and a point as an algebraic entity. In our intuitive discussions, we think of a point as a physical location, that is, as a "geometric point." In our formal mathematical development, we will mean the algebraic entity of Definition 3–2. Our development assumes a complete correspondence between these two points of view.

PROBLEMS

1. Find the distance between the following pairs of points:
   (a) (1, 1, 2) and (3, 7, 5)
   (b) (1, 0, 7) and (6, 2, —1)
   (c) (—1, 4, —5) and (5, —3, —8)

2. Find the coordinates of a point whose distance from the origin is $\sqrt{6}$, and whose distances from the points (0, 0, 1) and (2, 2, 2) are $\sqrt{3}$ and $\sqrt{2}$ respectively. Is there more than one such point? If so, how many such points are there, and what are their coordinates?

3. Write the equations of the spheres:
   (a) with radius 5 and center (3, 1, —2)
   (b) with radius 2 and center (1, 0, 1)
   (c) with radius 10 and center (8, —6, 0)

4. Show that the equation of any sphere can be brought into the form

$$x^2 + y^2 + z^2 + Bx + Cy + Dz + E = 0,$$

and that any equation of the form

$$Ax^2 + Ay^2 + Az^2 + Bx + Cy + Dz + E = 0$$

with $A \neq 0$ can be brought into the form of the equation of a sphere. State the conditions under which this would be the equation of a sphere. If it is a sphere, what is its center and radius?

5. Find the center and radius of each of the spheres with the following equations:
   (a) $x^2 + y^2 + z^2 - 6x + 2y + 4z + 5 = 0$
   (b) $2x^2 + 2y^2 + 2z^2 + 4x - 20z + 32 = 0$
   (c) $3x^2 + 3y^2 + 3z^2 - 5x + 6y - 12z - 8 = 0$

6. Find the equation, center, and radius of the sphere which passes through the four points $(3, 0, 4)$, $(-1, 3, -1)$, $(-2, 0, -1)$, and $(3, -4, 2)$.

7. Find the equation of the sphere with center $(1, 5, -2)$ which passes through the point $(2, 0, 4)$.

8. What is the result of two successive translations? How could this problem be handled algebraically?

9. If B is a set of points which satisfy an equation $f(x, y, z) = 0$, what equation is satisfied by the set of points obtained from B by a translation? Apply this to the equation of a sphere. What happens to a sphere when it is translated?

3–2 DIRECTION COSINES AND DIRECTION NUMBERS

By a ray we mean a half-line; that is, the set of all points which are on one side of a given point on a line. A sense of direction is automatically assigned to the ray, the positive direction being away from the given point. This description is not adequate in terms of the algebraic framework we are erecting, for as yet we do not know (algebraically) what a straight line is. Again, we proceed by letting our geometric intuition be our guide. Let us consider the points on a ray originating from the origin.

Let a point $P = (l, m, n)$, not the origin, be assumed to be on the ray we wish to discuss and let $X = (x, y, z)$ be any other point on the ray. From these two points drop lines perpendicular to the x-axis. The one from P will meet the x-axis at the point with coordinate l, the other at the point with coordinate x. Suppose now that $l \neq 0$. (See Fig. 3–5.) The two right triangles formed are similar and hence the ratio of $|x|$ to $|l|$ is the same as the ratio of the distance $|OX|$ to $|OP|$. Let $|OX|/|OP| = t$. Then $|x|/|l| = t$. However, these two points on the x-axis are both on the same side of the origin and we can conclude that $x/l = |x|/|l|$, and so $x = lt$.

In case l happened to be zero, the ray must have been perpendicular to the x-axis, in which case $x = 0$ and the equation $x = lt$ would still hold.

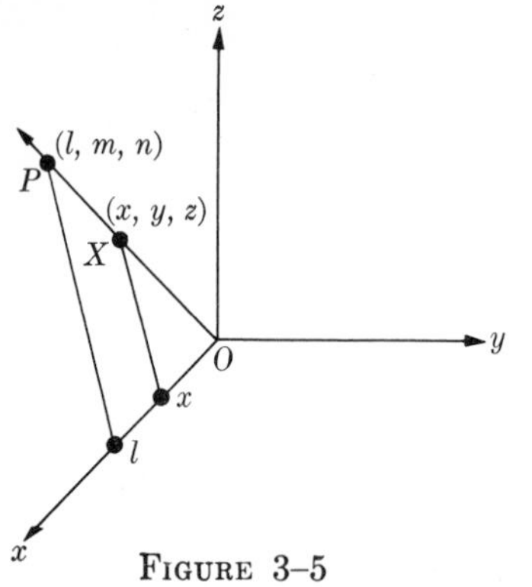

FIGURE 3–5

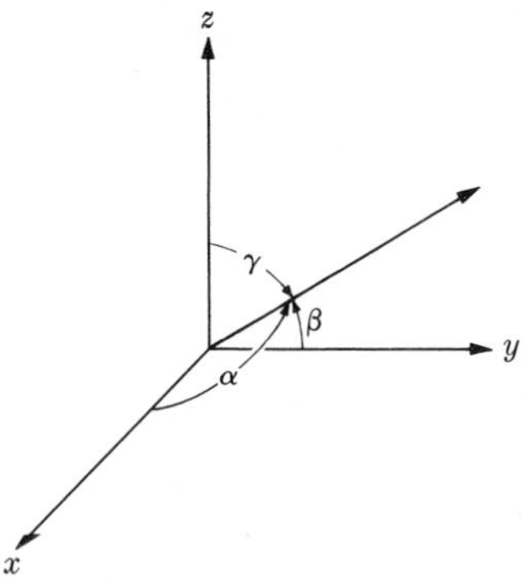

FIGURE 3–6

In the same way, we could drop perpendiculars to the y- and z-axes and conclude that $y = mt$ and $z = nt$, the ratio t being the same in each case. The above analysis then is the motivation for the definition:

Definition 3–5. A *ray* from the origin through the point (l, m, n), not the origin, is

$$\{(x, y, z) \mid x = lt, y = mt, z = nt, \text{ for all } t \geq 0\}.$$

The coordinates of any point of the ray, other than the origin, are called a set of *direction numbers* for the ray.

The reader can try to exercise his critical sense on this definition. Although complete as it stands, it raises an important question. After trying to discover this question, check with Problem 3 at the end of this section.

Note that the number t which appears in this definition is the ratio $|OX|/|OP|$. This fact can be used, for example, to find the point two-thirds of the way from the origin to the point $(6, -9, 5)$. The desired point would be $(4, -6, \frac{10}{3})$. Why?

Suppose now we have a ray, with direction numbers l, m, n. Let this ray cut the unit sphere (the sphere of radius 1, centered at the origin, with equation $x^2 + y^2 + z^2 = 1$) at the point (λ, μ, ν). We might remark here that the postulates of euclidean geometry are sufficient to show that this point exists,* but the proof is quite difficult. In our case, this is easy to show. We merely need to set $t = 1/[l^2 + m^2 + n^2]^{1/2}$ in the

---

* Euclid's postulates are not sufficient to show this, but later extensions, such as the postulate system of Hilbert, are sufficient for a rigorous proof of this fact.

definition above. It is simple to verify that the point (λ, μ, ν) with

$$\lambda = \frac{l}{[l^2 + m^2 + n^2]^{1/2}}, \qquad \mu = \frac{m}{[l^2 + m^2 + n^2]^{1/2}},$$
$$\nu = \frac{n}{[l^2 + m^2 + n^2]^{1/2}}, \tag{3-2}$$

is common to the ray and the unit sphere.

It is clear geometrically that there is only one such point on each ray. Conversely, we see that there is a unique ray from the origin through each point of the unit sphere. Thus, the three coordinates of this point on the unit sphere suffice to determine the ray completely.

A given ray determines three angles, one between it and each of the positive directions along the axes. Let α, β, and γ be the values of these angles, as shown in Fig. 3-6. Consider α, the value of the angle between the positive direction of the x-axis and the ray. The perpendicular from the point (λ, μ, ν) to the x-axis meets the x-axis at the point with coordinate λ. But at the same time, since the length of the segment from the origin to (λ, μ, ν) is one, the point λ on the x-axis also has coordinate $\cos \alpha$. That is, $\lambda = \cos \alpha$. (See Fig. 3-7.) In exactly the same way, if β and γ are the values of the angles between the ray and the y-axis and z-axis respectively, then it is seen that $\mu = \cos \beta$ and $\nu = \cos \gamma$. This leads to the following definition:

Definition 3-6. If (l, m, n) is a set of direction numbers for a ray, then the set of numbers

$$\lambda = \frac{l}{[l^2 + m^2 + n^2]^{1/2}}, \qquad \mu = \frac{m}{[l^2 + m^2 + n^2]^{1/2}},$$
$$\nu = \frac{n}{[l^2 + m^2 + n^2]^{1/2}}$$

is called the set of *direction cosines* of the ray.

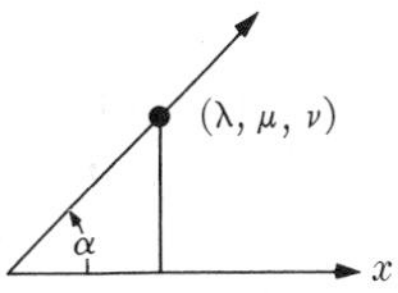

FIGURE 3-7

For example, the ray from the origin through the point $(8, -1, -4)$ has direction numbers $(8, -1, -4)$, or $(16, -2, -8)$, or $(4, -\frac{1}{2}, -2)$, or any other set of positive multiples. But this ray has only the single set of direction cosines, $(\frac{8}{9}, -\frac{1}{9}, -\frac{4}{9})$.

Our next step is to introduce the notion of a directed line segment. The essential idea is to consider a directed line segment as the translate of a portion of a ray from the origin. For example, suppose $P = (l, m, n)$ is some point other than the origin. Then the set of all points on the ray from O through P which lie between O and P is

$$R = \{(x, y, z) \mid x = lt, y = mt, z = nt, 0 \leq t \leq 1\},$$

and if we make a translation which carries the point at the origin to (x_0, y_0, z_0), then R is translated to a set R' which can be seen to be

$$\begin{aligned} R' &= \{(x', y', z') \mid x' = x + x_0, y' = y + y_0, z' = z + z_0, \text{and } (x, y, z) \in R\} \\ &= \{(x', y', z') \mid x' = x_0 + lt, y' = y_0 + mt, z' = z_0 + nt, 0 \le t \le 1\} \\ &= \{(x, y, z) \mid x = x_0 + lt, y = y_0 + mt, z = z_0 + nt, 0 \le t \le 1\}. \end{aligned}$$

The last step here follows from the fact that the symbols used in defining a set are "dummy variables." The set is the same no matter what letters are used for variables.

The ray from the origin through $P = (l, m, n)$ has direction numbers (l, m, n). We assign these same direction numbers to the directed line segment obtained in this way by translation of the segment from O to P. Observe that these direction numbers are then merely the differences of the values of the coordinates at the two ends of the segment. Indeed, if $P_1 = (x_1, y_1, z_1)$ is the point corresponding to $t = 1$, then $x_1 = x_0 + l$ and hence $x_1 - x_0 = l$. Similarly, $y_1 - y_0 = m$ and $z_1 - z_0 = n$.

Definition 3–7. A *directed line segment* P_0P_1 whose initial point is at $P_0 = (x_0, y_0, z_0)$ and whose terminal point is at $P_1 = (x_1, y_1, z_1)$ is the set of points

$$\{(x, y, z) \mid x = x_0(1 - t) + x_1t, y = y_0(1 - t) + y_1t,$$

$$z = z_0(1 - t) + z_1t, \text{for all } t \text{ with } 0 \le t \le 1\},$$

together with the sense of direction determined by increasing t. This directed line segment is said to have direction numbers

$$(x_1 - x_0, y_1 - y_0, z_1 - z_0)$$

and length

$$d = [(x_1 - x_0)^2 + (y_1 - y_0)^2 + (z_1 - z_0)^2]^{1/2}.$$

Its direction cosines are $\lambda = (x_1 - x_0)/d$, $\mu = (y_1 - y_0)/d$, and $\nu = (z_1 - z_0)/d$.

For short, we will speak of the directed line segment P_0P_1 as being from P_0 to P_1 rather than always referring to its initial and terminal points.

While the coordinates of any point on a ray from the origin form a set of direction numbers for that ray, we say that a directed line segment whose initial point is at the origin and whose terminal point is at (l, m, n) has direction numbers (l, m, n) and *only these.* That is, a directed line segment will have only a single set of direction numbers. Note also that the length of a directed line segment is the square root of the sum of the squares of its direction numbers, which is exactly our formula for the distance between the initial and terminal points.

The direction numbers of a directed line segment determine completely its direction in space and its length. Also, if we make any parallel translation, the direction numbers of a given directed line segment remain unchanged. This is usually expressed by saying that the direction numbers of a directed line segment are *invariant* under translation.

As an example, consider the directed line segment from $A = (7, -3, 2)$ to $B = (1, 0, 4)$. Its direction numbers are $(1 - 7, 0 + 3, 4 - 2)$ or $(-6, 3, 2)$. The length of this line segment is $|AB| = [36 + 9 + 4]^{1/2} = 7$. Therefore its direction cosines are $(-\frac{6}{7}, \frac{3}{7}, \frac{2}{7})$.

The parameter t in Definition 3–7, just as in Definition 3–5, represents a ratio of distances. In fact, making use of the definition of distance we can prove

Theorem 3–1. Let $P_0 = (x_0, y_0, z_0)$ and $P_1 = (x_1, y_1, z_1)$ be two distinct points. Let t be any real number between zero and one. Then the point

$$X = (x_0(1 - t) + x_1t, y_0(1 - t) + y_1t, z_0(1 - t) + z_1t) \qquad (3\text{–}3)$$

on the directed line segment P_0P_1 has the property $|P_0X|/|P_0P_1| = t$.

Proof: To prove this theorem, we merely need to compute

$$\begin{aligned} |P_0X|^2 &= (x_1t - x_0t)^2 + (y_1t - y_0t)^2 + (z_1t - z_0t)^2 \\ &= t^2[(x_1 - x_0)^2 + (y_1 - y_0)^2 + (z_1 - z_0)^2] \\ &= t^2|P_0P_1|^2, \end{aligned}$$

which is equivalent to the desired result.

Observe that the point X given in this theorem can also be characterized by the fact that it divides the line segment P_0P_1 in the ratio $t/(1 - t)$. Noting this fact makes it easier for some students to remember (3–3) in the form

$$X = (x_0 + t(x_1 - x_0), y_0 + t(y_1 - y_0), z_0 + t(z_1 - z_0)). \qquad (3\text{–}4)$$

It is worthwhile learning this formula for the special case when $t = \frac{1}{2}$. The point in question is then the midpoint of the line segment P_0P_1, and from (3–3) we see that the coordinates of this midpoint are the averages of the corresponding coordinates of the endpoints of the segment.

For example, the midpoint of the segment AB, where $A = (7, -3, 2)$ and $B = (1, 0, 4)$ is $C = (4, -\frac{3}{2}, 3)$. This result can be written down by inspection, but other division points usually take more computation. Thus, the point D, one-third of the way from A to B, has coordinates

$$(7 + \tfrac{1}{3}(-6), -3 + \tfrac{1}{3}(3), 2 + \tfrac{1}{3}(2)) = (5, -2, \tfrac{8}{3})$$

as calculated from formula (3–4).

The above definition can be extended easily to define a straight line. The formal discussion of straight lines will be postponed until Section 4–4, but we give the definition here so that we will be able to speak of straight lines if necessary.

Definition 3–8. Let $P_0 = (x_0, y_0, z_0)$ and $P_1 = (x_1, y_1, z_1)$ be two distinct points. Then the straight line through P_0 and P_1 is

$$\{(x, y, z) \mid x = x_0(1 - t) + x_1 t,\ y = y_0(1 - t) + y_1 t,\ z = z_0(1 - t) + z_1 t,\ t \text{ any real number}\}.$$

PROBLEMS

1. What are the direction cosines of the directed ray from the origin through the following points?

   (a) (2, 6, 3) (b) (7, 3, −5)
   (c) (−1, −1, 5) (d) (2, −2, −1)

2. Find the direction numbers, length, and direction cosines of the directed line segments:

   (a) From (3, 1, 7) to (−2, 5, 3) (b) From (1, 1, 1) to (7, 2, 5)
   (c) From (0, 1, 1) to (1, 0, 1) (d) From (1, 1, 1) to (−1, 0, −1)

3. Let R be the ray from the origin through the point (l, m, n). Let (l', m', n') be any point (other than the origin) on this ray. Prove that the ray, R', from the origin through the point (l', m', n') is identical to R.

   Remark: Definition 3–5 defines a ray as a certain set of points, depending on a given point. What you are asked to show is that the resulting set of points is the same, no matter what point of the ray we start with. Note that in order to show that two sets R and R' are the same, you must show that any point in R is also in R' and, conversely, that any point in R' is also in R.

4. In each of the coordinate axes, the set of all points which have nonnegative coordinates constitutes a ray. What are the direction cosines of these three rays?

5. Show that the direction numbers of a directed line segment are invariant under translation.

6. Find the midpoints of the directed line segments of Problem 2. Also find the points which are $\frac{1}{3}$ and $\frac{2}{3}$ of the distance from the initial point to the terminal points.

7. Let R be a ray from the origin through (l, m, n). Let λ, μ, and ν be defined as in (3–2).
   (a) Show that (λ, μ, ν) is at distance 1 from the origin.
   (b) Show that any other point of the ray is at a distance other than 1 from the origin. [*Hint:* Use the result of Problem 3 above to express the points of the ray in terms of λ, μ, and ν.]

8. Let $A = (a_1, a_2, a_3)$, $B = (b_1, b_2, b_3)$, and $C = (c_1, c_2, c_3)$ be three distinct noncollinear points in space. Consider these three points as the vertices of a triangle and let A', B', and C' be the midpoints of the sides opposite the vertices A, B, and C, respectively. The line segments AA', BB', and CC' are therefore the medians of the triangle. Let A'', B'', and C'' be the points two-thirds of the way from A to A', B to B', and C to C', respectively.
   (a) Find the coordinates of A', B', and C'.
   (b) Find the coordinates of A'', B'', and C''. What can you conclude?

9. What happens to the conclusion of Theorem 3–1 if the point X in (3–3) is such that t does not lie between 0 and 1? State and prove a theorem about the location of X in relation to P_0 and P_1 for $t > 1$ or $t < 0$.

3–3 VECTORS

The concept of a vector is a consequence of physical fact. It has long been observed that a single number is insufficient to characterize certain physical phenomena. For example, a moving object may have a known speed, but until we also know its direction we cannot say that we can describe its motion. Similarly, force requires both a number (the magnitude of the force) and a direction (the direction of application of the force) to characterize it.

Physicists long ago found it useful to introduce a single symbol to represent a quantity, such as force, which has both a magnitude and a direction. They called such a quantity a *vector*. From the observed physical behavior of such quantities, algebraic operations on vectors were defined.

For example, if **F** represented a certain force, say a force of 100 dynes directed straight downward, it was found useful to be able to represent a force of some different magnitude, say 200 dynes, but still in the same direction. It seemed logical to write this second force as 2**F**, the number 2 being thought of as doubling the force without changing its direction. Such a multiple of a vector was called a *scalar multiple* of a vector, pure numbers being called *scalars* to distinguish them from vectors.

A second algebraic operation, that of *vector addition*, was defined in terms of the result of applying two forces simultaneously. If a force is applied to an object, that object will move unless a second force of exactly equal magnitude but pointed in the opposite direction is also applied at the same time. A simple physical experiment serves to show how simultaneous forces must be combined. Suppose two strings are tied together at a point P, and a weight is suspended by a third string from the same point P (see Fig. 3-8). The forces on the point P are applied through the strings, and hence must be in the direction of the strings. The weight exerts a known force through the vertical string on the point P. Since the point P is not moving, the resultant of the forces exerted by the two supporting strings must exactly match the downward force exerted by the weight. That is, it must be as shown by the dashed arrow in Fig. 3-8, where the length of the arrow represents the magnitude of the force.

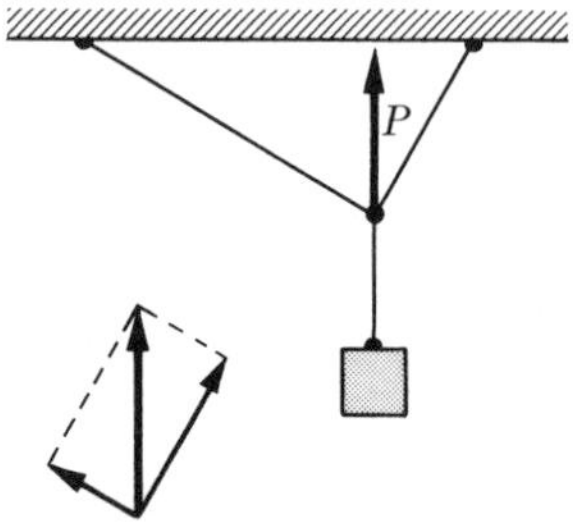

FIGURE 3-8

If the forces exerted by the two supporting strings are measured by introducing spring balances into the strings for example, it is found that the forces line up as shown in the insert of Fig. 3-8. In other words, if we draw lines in the direction of the forces, whose lengths are equal (in some units) to the magnitudes of the forces, then the resultant of these two forces is represented by the line which forms the diagonal of the parallelogram determined by the given lines.

Such a diagram, called in physics the *parallelogram of forces*, determines the way in which two forces combine. The same diagram is then used to define (physically) the *sum* of two vectors.

While the above description of vectors in physical terms is quite satisfactory for the use that is made of them in elementary physics, it leaves much to be desired mathematically. In particular, it has been found desirable to generalize the idea of a vector to situations in which it is impossible to give an accurate definition of what is meant by "direction." For this reason we would like to give a mathematical definition of a vector, which can then be used without reference to physical intuition.

To a mathematician, the only really satisfactory way to introduce vectors is by the axiomatic method, since only in this manner can he make the broad generalizations, which have been found so useful. This method of introduction corresponds exactly to what is frequently called an "operational definition"; that is, vectors would be defined only in terms of how they behave. A set of postulates would be given and a vector would be anything that satisfied these postulates.

Here, however, we will begin in a more modest manner and merely try to define something which corresponds to the physical description of a vector. At a later stage we may then return to obtain the abstract definition. The above physical description will be held in mind throughout. The mathematical development will be motivated by this physical description.

Let us consider then what is required. The physical description asks for a quantity with both direction and magnitude. We may take our clue from the arrows that physicists use to represent vectors and observe that a directed line segment satisfies our requirements. There is still a difficulty, however. Two directed line segments with the same directions and lengths may be distinct, yet they would represent the same vector. This could be taken care of by using only directed line segments with initial points at the orgin, but it is convenient to be able to associate vectors with arbitrary directed line segments. All we need to do is find a property of a directed line segment which determines its direction and magnitude but which is independent of translation. The set of direction numbers of the directed line segment satisfy this requirement.

Definition 3–9. A *vector* is a triple of numbers. Vectors will be denoted by boldface letters. The vector $\mathbf{0} = [0, 0, 0]$ is called the *zero vector*. The three numbers a_1, a_2, and a_3 are called the *components* of $\mathbf{A}$. Given a vector $\mathbf{A} = [a_1, a_2, a_3]$, the quantity

$$|\mathbf{A}| = [a_1^2 + a_2^2 + a_3^2]^{1/2}$$

is called the *magnitude* of $\mathbf{A}$.

In this text, we follow the common practice of indicating vectors by means of boldface type. In handwritten work it is difficult to indicate boldface letters; so some other convention is usually used. Most students find it easiest to indicate a vector by placing an arrow or bar over the letter, but any consistent usage is satisfactory.

Note that by virtue of the above definition, if two vectors differ in any one of their components, they are different. We therefore write $\mathbf{A} = \mathbf{B}$ if and only if the two triples of numbers are identical.

If we compare the definition of a vector with the definition of a point in space, we see that they are identical. How can this be? Surely they must be different? As suprising as it might seem, there is in reality no essential difference. The set of all vectors, as defined here, constitutes a *vector space* which we can identify in a natural manner with our three-dimensional euclidean space. We could make this identification complete and consider only one space, but because of the possible applications, it is useful to have both the three-dimensional space and the vector space as two distinct entities. On the other hand, many of the properties of three-dimensional space can be expressed most easily in terms of vectors, so it would be convenient to be able to make this identification when needed. For these reasons, we will introduce the following conventions.

Convention 3–1. The same triple of numbers may represent either a point or a vector. When it is meant to represent a point, the triple will be enclosed in parentheses,

$$A = (a_1, a_2, a_3).$$

When it is meant to represent a vector, it will be enclosed in brackets,

$$\mathbf{A} = [a_1, a_2, a_3].$$

The same letter in boldface or italic type will be used to represent the same triple of numbers, considered as a vector or a point, respectively.

These conventions identify the vectors as points in space or, perhaps more accurately, as directed line segments with their initial points at the origin. This point of view produces what physicists call "bound vectors." Physicists also found it useful to have "free vectors," which are thought of as directed line segments with arbitrary placement. To accommodate this idea, we introduce a function which associates a vector to each directed line segment. Note that in this definition, although each directed line segment is associated with a unique vector, many different line segments may be associated with a single vector.

Definition 3–10. Let P_1 and P_2 be two given points and let P_1P_2 be the directed line segment from P_1 to P_2. Then the vector $\overrightarrow{P_1P_2}$ is the vector whose components are the direction numbers of the directed line segment P_1P_2.

Thus, for example, the directed line segment AB, where $A = (3, 5, 2)$ and $B = (-1, 6, 5)$ has associated with it the vector $\overrightarrow{AB} = [-4, 1, 3]$.

In most of our work with vectors, we will find ourselves treating directed line segments as though they were vectors. Much of the time the difference is not really important. But remember, a directed line segment is *not* a vector. A vector is really a property of a directed line segment. The vector determines the direction and length of the directed line segment but not its placement in space.

PROBLEMS

1. Let the point A have coordinates (a_1, a_2, a_3) and suppose that the vector

$$\overrightarrow{AP} = [b_1, b_2, b_3].$$

What are the coordinates of the point P?

2. If the weight in Fig. 3–8 is 100 grams and the two supporting strings make an angle of 90° with each other, find the force exerted by each string in terms of the angle between that string and the vertical.

3. Let A and B be two points of space and suppose that under a translation they are translated to A' and B' respectively. Prove that

$$\overrightarrow{AB} = \overrightarrow{A'B'}.$$

3–4 THE ALGEBRAIC OPERATIONS ON VECTORS

As mentioned in the previous section, it is found useful to have an operation which changes the magnitude of a vector without altering its direction. This operation, called scalar multiplication, is easily found from the comparison of directed line segments of different lengths which are on the same ray.

Definition 3–11. Real numbers are called *scalars*. Given a vector $\mathbf{A} = [a_1, a_2, a_3]$ and a real number (scalar) t, the scalar multiple of $\mathbf{A}$ by t is

$$t\mathbf{A} = [ta_1, ta_2, ta_3].$$

Geometrically, scalar multiplication can be thought of as multiplying the length of the vector (directed line segment) by the number t. Note that if a directed line segment has nonzero length and is represented by a vector $\mathbf{A}$, then its length is $|\mathbf{A}|$ (which is a scalar) and the vector $\mathbf{A}/|\mathbf{A}|$ has length one. The components of $\mathbf{A}/|\mathbf{A}|$ are the direction cosines of the directed line segment.

From Problem 1 of the last section, we see that vector addition in geometric terms corresponds exactly to the addition of vectors by components. Thus we have

Definition 3–12. Given two vectors $\mathbf{A} = [a_1, a_2, a_3]$ and $\mathbf{B} = [b_1, b_2, b_3]$, the *sum* of these two vectors is the vector

$$\mathbf{A} + \mathbf{B} = [a_1 + b_1, a_2 + b_2, a_3 + b_3].$$

Another way of expressing the parallelogram law is to make use of directed line segments. Letting O represent the origin and letting A and P be points such that $\overrightarrow{OA} = \mathbf{A}$ and $\overrightarrow{AP} = \mathbf{B}$, we have

$$\mathbf{A} + \mathbf{B} = \overrightarrow{OA} + \overrightarrow{AP} = \overrightarrow{OP}.$$

Figure 3–9 illustrates these relationships. It should also help the student to see how componentwise addition gives the sum of the two vectors.

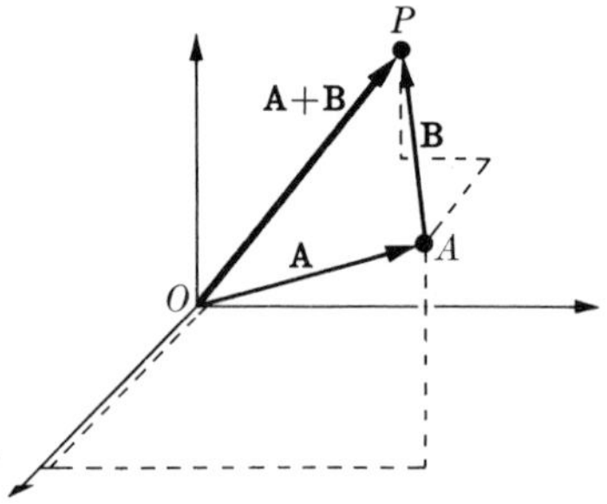

FIGURE 3–9

A special case of a scalar multiple of a vector is worth noting. Given any vector $\mathbf{A} = [a_1, a_2, a_3]$, the vector $(-1)\mathbf{A} = [-a_1, -a_2, -a_3]$ is such that the sum of it and the vector $\mathbf{A}$ is exactly the zero vector. It is useful to have a special notation for this vector and other negative forms.

Definition 3–13. Given any vectors $\mathbf{A}$ and $\mathbf{B}$, we shall use the following notational conventions:

$$-\mathbf{A} = (-1)\mathbf{A},$$
$$\mathbf{A} - \mathbf{B} = \mathbf{A} + (-\mathbf{B}).$$

The expression $\mathbf{A} - \mathbf{B}$ is called the difference between the two vectors and has a special geometric interpretation. In Fig. 3–10(a) we see the parallelogram with sides $\mathbf{A}$ and $-\mathbf{B}$ (dashed). The sum $\mathbf{A} + (-\mathbf{B})$ is then the dashed diagonal which is parallel and equal in length to the solid diagonal. Therefore, the difference $\mathbf{A} - \mathbf{B}$ is exactly the vector $\overrightarrow{BA}$, where B and A are the points associated with the vectors $\mathbf{B}$ and $\mathbf{A}$ respectively (see Fig. 3–10b).

Although this geometric interpretation of the difference of two vectors seems to be purely intuitive, we can actually prove that it is valid (in terms of the definitions which have been given).

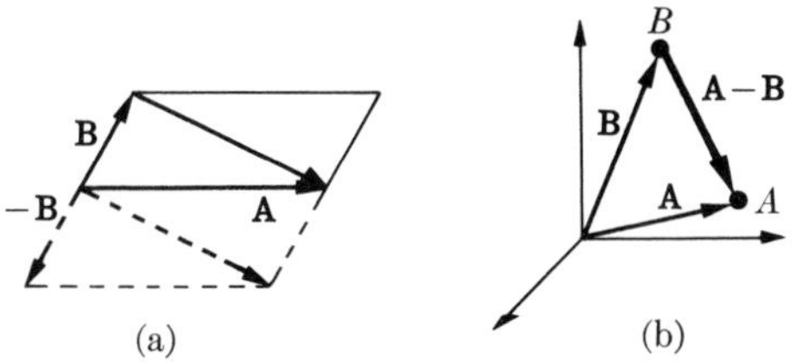

FIGURE 3–10

Theorem 3–2. Let A, B, and C be three points. Then

$$\overrightarrow{AB} + \overrightarrow{BC} = \overrightarrow{AC} \tag{3–5}$$

and

$$\overrightarrow{AB} = \overrightarrow{CB} - \overrightarrow{CA}. \tag{3–6}$$

Proof: Let $A = (a_1, a_2, a_3)$, $B = (b_1, b_2, b_3)$, and $C = (c_1, c_2, c_3)$. Then

$$\overrightarrow{AB} = [b_1 - a_1, b_2 - a_2, b_3 - a_3],$$
$$\overrightarrow{BC} = [c_1 - b_1, c_2 - b_2, c_3 - b_3],$$

and

$$\overrightarrow{AC} = [c_1 - a_1, c_2 - a_2, c_3 - a_3].$$

It is then clear from Definition 3–12 that Eq. (3–5) is true.

To prove Eq. (3–6), we could proceed in the same way, or merely observe that $\overrightarrow{AC} = -\overrightarrow{CA}$, and hence that

$$\begin{aligned}\overrightarrow{CB} - \overrightarrow{CA} &= \overrightarrow{CB} + \overrightarrow{AC}\\ &= \overrightarrow{AC} + \overrightarrow{CB}\\ &= \overrightarrow{AB},\end{aligned}$$

where the last step follows from (3–5), which we have already proved. In the middle step we made use of the commutativity of vector addition, which we have not proved, but which follows immediately from Definition 3–12.

An important fact to note is that by virtue of Definition 3–10, we have the representation of a directed line segment in the following form:

$$\overrightarrow{AB} = \mathbf{B} - \mathbf{A}. \tag{3–7}$$

This result can also be viewed as a special case of (3–6) when we realize that Convention (3–1) and Definition 3–10 can be thought of as saying that $\mathbf{A} = \overrightarrow{OA}$, and $\mathbf{B} = \overrightarrow{OB}$, where O is the origin.

In our informal discussions, we introduced scalar multiplication so as to change the magnitude of a vector while leaving its direction unchanged. That is, the new vector is parallel to the old. We would now like to make formal definitions which will allow us to speak of parallel line segments and vectors.

Definition 3–14. Two directed line segments are called *parallel* if and only if they have the same set of direction cosines. Two vectors are called *collinear* if and only if one is a scalar multiple of the other, and are called *parallel* if and only if one is a nonnegative scalar multiple of the other.

The definition of parallelism made here differs from that made in most elementary courses. Two directed line segments which would ordinarily be called parallel may not be called parallel according to this definition. For example, if we have $A = (1, 1, 1)$, $B = (1, 0, 2)$, and $C = (2, 1, 3)$, then $\overrightarrow{OA} = \overrightarrow{BC}$ and the directed line segments OA and BC are parallel, but the directed line segments OA and CB are not called parallel. In order to be called parallel, two directed line segments must have the same, not opposite, directions.

The above definition is consistent. That is, two directed line segments AB and CD are parallel if and only if the associated vectors $\overrightarrow{AB}$ and $\overrightarrow{CD}$ are parallel. The notion of collinearity does not fit well with thinking of vectors as arbitrarily located directed line segments. It is, however, geometrically evident when we think of vectors as directed line segments whose initial points are at the origin. Two line segments (not directed) are parallel if and only if the associated vectors are collinear.

The zero vector, the vector which has zero for all its components, occupies a peculiar position with regard to this definition. The way we have stated the definition, the zero vector is parallel (and collinear) to any vector. We could have avoided this by using nonzero and positive scalar multiples in the above definition, but it will turn out to be convenient to have the definitions in the form actually given. Remember that parallel vectors (disregarding the zero vector) have the same direction, while collinear vectors have the same or opposite directions.

Now let us observe the algebraic laws satisfied by vector addition and scalar multiplication. There are many such laws, but we choose the following set for emphasis:

Theorem 3–3. Vector addition satisfies the following properties:

P1. For any vectors **A** and **B**

$$\mathbf{A} + \mathbf{B} = \mathbf{B} + \mathbf{A}.$$

P2. For any vectors **A**, **B**, and **C**

$$\mathbf{A} + (\mathbf{B} + \mathbf{C}) = (\mathbf{A} + \mathbf{B}) + \mathbf{C}.$$

P3. There exists a vector **0** such that for any vector **A**

$$\mathbf{A} + \mathbf{0} = \mathbf{A}.$$

P4. For any vector **A** there exists a vector $-\mathbf{A}$ such that

$$\mathbf{A} + (-\mathbf{A}) = \mathbf{0}.$$

These properties are (in view of the definitions we have given) fairly self-evident. The proofs are easy and can be left as problems for the student. The student will recognize these as properties of addition in the real number system. Since they are the same properties, they are referred to by the same names. That is, P1 is called the *commutative property for addition of vectors*, P2 is called the *associative property for addition of vectors*, P3 is *the existence of the identity*, and P4 is *the existence of inverses.*

The student who has heard of a *group* will see that Theorem 3–2 can be rephrased more simply as: *The set of vectors forms a commutative group with respect to addition.* If you have never heard of this concept, you need not worry about it. Merely realizing that this particular set of properties occurs often enough to deserve a special name will be enough at this point.

When we introduce scalar multiplication we obtain further properties of the set of vectors. Note that if we try to verify properties similar to those held by the real number system, we find immediate differences. For example, the scalar multiple of a vector is an indicated product of completely different entities. It is up to us to define what we mean by the indicated product in either order. We obviously wish to define them to be the same regardless of order. In other words, the commutative law holds by definition. We can, however, obtain a close equivalent to the associative property; and the distributive property also applies. In fact, since there are two distinct types of addition (addition of scalars and addition of vectors), there are two distributive properties.

Theorem 3–4. The algebraic operations on vectors have the following properties:

P5. For any vector **A** and any scalars s and t,

$$(st)\mathbf{A} = s(t\mathbf{A}).$$

P6. For any vector **A** and any scalars s and t,

$$(s + t)\mathbf{A} = s\mathbf{A} + t\mathbf{A}.$$

P7. For any vectors **A** and **B** and any scalar t,

$$t(\mathbf{A} + \mathbf{B}) = t\mathbf{A} + t\mathbf{B}.$$

P8. For any vector **A**,

$$1 \cdot \mathbf{A} = \mathbf{A}.$$

The four properties listed here are again very simple to verify. Property 8 may seem too trivial to mention, but it is included for a specific reason. It so happens that the properties P1 through P8 listed in the above two theorems are sufficient to characterize an algebraic system of considerable mathematical importance—a *vector space* or, as it is sometimes called, a *linear space* over the real numbers. This is a set of elements, called vectors, together with the real numbers and two operations, vector addition and scalar multiplication, satisfying the above eight properties (which would then be called postulates). The eighth property becomes quite important, allowing the complete algebra of vectors to be developed.

There are many different types of vector spaces satisfying the above eight properties, but the system of vectors that we have developed requires only one additional property to characterize it completely. The remaining property concerns linear dependence and will be discussed in a later section.

At this stage, the student need not worry about how additional algebraic properties of vectors could be proved from those listed above, but should merely use the properties as needed. Any doubts can usually be resolved by reference to the definitions.

To illustrate some of the concepts introduced in this section, let us give a proof, using vector methods, of the thoerem:

The diagonals of a quadrilateral bisect each other if and only if the quadrilateral is a parallelogram.

Proof: Suppose that A, B, C, and D are the vertices of a quadrilateral with diagonals AC and BD. Let M_1 and M_2 be the midpoints of AC and BD, respectively. Then

$$\begin{aligned}\mathbf{M}_1 &= \overrightarrow{OM}_1 = \overrightarrow{OA} + \overrightarrow{AM}_1 \\ &= \mathbf{A} + \tfrac{1}{2}\overrightarrow{AC} \\ &= \mathbf{A} + \tfrac{1}{2}(\mathbf{C} - \mathbf{A}) \\ &= \tfrac{1}{2}(\mathbf{A} + \mathbf{C})\end{aligned}$$

(see also Problem 2). Similarly,

$$\mathbf{M}_2 = \tfrac{1}{2}(\mathbf{B} + \mathbf{D}).$$

We observe that the diagonals of the quadrilateral bisect each other if and only if $M_1 = M_2$, or equivalently $\mathbf{M}_1 = \mathbf{M}_2$.

The theorem we are trying to prove is an "if and only if" proposition. This means that there are two separate results to be proved. First, let us prove that if the quadrilateral is a parallelogram, then the diagonals bisect each other.

The condition that $ABCD$ be a parallelogram can be restated in the form $\overrightarrow{AB} = \overrightarrow{DC}$ (the opposite sides are parallel—make a sketch). Hence $\mathbf{B} - \mathbf{A} = \mathbf{C} - \mathbf{D}$, or $\mathbf{B} = \mathbf{A} + \mathbf{C} - \mathbf{D}$. Substituting this into the above formula for $\mathbf{M}_2$, we find

$$\begin{aligned}\mathbf{M}_2 &= \tfrac{1}{2}(\mathbf{B} + \mathbf{D}) \\ &= \tfrac{1}{2}(\mathbf{A} + \mathbf{C} - \mathbf{D} + \mathbf{D}) \\ &= \tfrac{1}{2}(\mathbf{A} + \mathbf{C}) \\ &= \mathbf{M}_1.\end{aligned}$$

Therefore, we conclude that the diagonals bisect one another.

Next, we prove the other half of the theorem: if the diagonals bisect each other, then the quadrilateral is a parallelogram.

The assumption that the diagonals bisect each other is equivalent to $\mathbf{M}_1 = \mathbf{M}_2$, or $\mathbf{A} + \mathbf{C} = \mathbf{B} + \mathbf{D}$. This equation implies that

$$\mathbf{A} - \mathbf{B} = \mathbf{D} - \mathbf{C},$$

or

$$\overrightarrow{BA} = \overrightarrow{CD},$$

which tells us that the quadrilateral is a parallelogram.

Exactly what has been proved here? This theorem was proved to be true in the particular model of euclidean space which we have been constructing. Its truth depends on the concepts of length and parallelism which we have *defined*. Similarly, if we use these methods to prove other geometric facts, let us remember that the proof is really only valid in the "vector space" model of euclidean space. It so happens that this model is an accurate representation of euclidean space, but proof of this will not be given here.

PROBLEMS

1. Let O (the origin), P_1, P_2, P_3, and P_4 be points in three-dimensional space. What algebraic condition on the vectors $\overrightarrow{OP_1}$, $\overrightarrow{P_1P_2}$, $\overrightarrow{P_2P_3}$, and $\overrightarrow{P_3P_4}$ is necessary and sufficient for the point P_4 to coincide with the origin?

2. Let **A** and **B** be any two distinct vectors. For any real t between 0 and 1, let $\mathbf{P} = (1 - t)\mathbf{A} + t\mathbf{B}$. Where is the point P in relation to the points A and B? [*Hint:* See Definition 3–10 and compare with Theorem 3–1.]

3. Verify the properties listed in Theorems 3–3 and 3–4.

4. Define the vectors $\mathbf{e}_1 = [1, 0, 0]$, $\mathbf{e}_2 = [0, 1, 0]$, and $\mathbf{e}_3 = [0, 0, 1]$. Find scalars u, v, and w such that

$$u\mathbf{e}_1 + v\mathbf{e}_2 + w\mathbf{e}_3 = \mathbf{A},$$

where

(a) $\mathbf{A} = [7, 3, -4]$, (b) $\mathbf{A} = [1, 0, \frac{7}{2}]$,
(c) $\mathbf{A} = [0, 0, 0]$, (d) $\mathbf{A} = [a_1, a_2, a_3]$.

5. Find u, v, and w to satisfy the same conditions as those of Problem 4 if $\mathbf{e}_1 = [1, 1, 0]$, $\mathbf{e}_2 = [1, -1, 1]$, and $\mathbf{e}_3 = [-1, 1, 2]$.

6. Can you find u, v, and w such that

$$u\mathbf{e}_1 + v\mathbf{e}_2 + w\mathbf{e}_3 = [1, 0, 0],$$

if

(a) $\mathbf{e}_1 = [1, 1, 0]$, $\mathbf{e}_2 = [1, -1, 1]$, $\mathbf{e}_3 = [2, 0, 1]$,
(b) $\mathbf{e}_1 = [0, 0, 1]$, $\mathbf{e}_2 = [0, 1, 1]$, $\mathbf{e}_3 = [0, -1, 2]$?

If not, why not?

7. For each part of Problem 6, find u, v, and w not all zero such that

$$u\mathbf{e}_1 + v\mathbf{e}_2 + w\mathbf{e}_3 = \mathbf{0}.$$

8. For each of the following vectors, find a vector **B** with the same direction but magnitude 1.

(a) $\mathbf{A} = [3, -6, 2]$ (b) $\mathbf{A} = [1, 1, 1]$
(c) $\mathbf{A} = [12, 0, -5]$ (d) $\mathbf{A} = [3, 5, 7]$.

9. Which of the following systems satisfy all eight of the properties P1 through P8, and hence are vector spaces? If a system does not satisfy all the properties, which fail to hold (in general)?

(a) The set of all n-tuples of real numbers $\mathbf{A} = [a_1, a_2, \ldots, a_n]$ with vector addition defined by

$$[a_1, a_2, \ldots, a_n] + [b_1, b_2, \ldots, b_n] = [a_1 + b_1, a_2 + b_2, \ldots, a_n + b_n],$$

and scalar multiplication defined by

$$t[a_1, a_2, \ldots, a_n] = [ta_1, ta_2, \ldots, ta_n].$$

(b) The set of all ordered pairs of real numbers $\mathbf{A} = [a_1, a_2]$ with vector addition defined by

$$[a_1, a_2] + [b_1, b_2] = [a_1 + b_1, a_2 + b_2],$$

and scalar multiplication defined by

$$t[a_1, a_2] = [ta_1, 0].$$

(c) The set of all real-valued functions f defined for all x, $0 \leq x \leq 1$, with vector addition defined by $f + g$ being the function whose value at x is $f(x) + g(x)$, and scalar multiplication defined by tf being the function whose value at x is $tf(x)$.

10. Let A and B be two points in space. How are $\overrightarrow{AB}$ and $\overrightarrow{BA}$ related?

11. Let A, B, C, and D be any four distinct points in space.

(a) Show that

$$\overrightarrow{AD} = \overrightarrow{AB} + \overrightarrow{BC} + \overrightarrow{CD}.$$

(b) Let E, F, G, and H be the midpoints of the line segments AB, BC, CD, and DA respectively. Show that

$$\overrightarrow{EF} = \tfrac{1}{2}\overrightarrow{AB} + \tfrac{1}{2}\overrightarrow{BC}$$
$$\overrightarrow{HG} = \tfrac{1}{2}\overrightarrow{AD} + \tfrac{1}{2}\overrightarrow{DC}.$$

(c) Show that $\overrightarrow{EF} = \overrightarrow{HG}$. Express this as a geometrical theorem.

12. Let A, B, and C be any three distinct points in space. Let D be the midpoint of the line segment BC. Then AD is a median of the triangle ABC.

(a) Find $\overrightarrow{AD}$ in terms of the vectors $\mathbf{A}$, $\mathbf{B}$, and $\mathbf{C}$.
(b) Find $\mathbf{A} + \tfrac{2}{3}\overrightarrow{AD}$ in terms of $\mathbf{A}$, $\mathbf{B}$, and $\mathbf{C}$.
(c) What would happen if the roles of A, B, and C were interchanged in the above? What theorem has been proved? Compare with Problem 8 of Section 3–2.

Using vector methods, prove each of the following theorems.

13. The line segment joining the midpoints of two sides of a triangle is parallel to, and one-half the length of, the third side.

14. The line segment joining the midpoints of the nonparallel sides of a trapezoid is parallel to the bases and equal to half the sum of their lengths.

15. The line segments joining the midpoints of opposite sides of any quadrilateral bisect each other.

16. The midpoints of two opposite sides of any quadrilateral and the midpoints of the diagonals are the vertices of a parallelogram.

17. The two lines from a vertex of a parallelogram to the midpoints of the opposite sides trisect the diagonal that they cross.

3–5 PROJECTIONS AND THE DOT PRODUCT

Let L be a given line and AB a given directed line segment in three-dimensional space. We wish to make an intuitive definition of the projection of AB onto L. To do this, erect planes perpendicular to L through A and B and let these planes cut L at points A' and B' as in Fig. 3–11. We will call the directed line segment $A'B'$ *the projection of* AB *onto the line* L.

In many texts, particularly those in engineering, it is common to find the projection defined as the *length* of the segment $A'B'$ described above rather than the segment itself. We will find it more useful, however, to consider the projection as a vector rather than as a scalar.

It is the vector properties of the directed line segment $A'B'$ that we are really interested in. Note that if we use another line which is parallel to L in Fig. 3–11, the resulting projection will be a different directed line segment, but the associated vector will be the same.

Similarly, suppose that we have another directed line segment, CD, which is parallel to and of the same length as AB, that is $\overrightarrow{CD} = \overrightarrow{AB}$; then we see that the projection of CD onto L will be a directed line segment $C'D'$ such that $\overrightarrow{C'D'} = \overrightarrow{A'B'}$. This can be seen easily by observing that the two planes through C and D will be the same distance apart as the planes through A and B. From this, it follows that the vector $\overrightarrow{A'B'}$ is determined by the vector $\overrightarrow{AB}$. For this reason, we will say that the projection of the vector $\overrightarrow{AB}$ is the vector $\overrightarrow{A'B'}$.

Observe that there is no difficulty here in having two different things being called a projection. The projection of a directed line segment is a directed line segment, while the projection of a vector is a vector.

Given a vector and a line, we find the projection of the vector onto the line by drawing a directed line segment with that vector, finding the projection of that directed line segment, and converting the resulting directed line segment into a vector. Since the result depends only on the direction of the line L, we might as well assume that the desired line L passes through the origin. Thus given a vector $\mathbf{A}$, the obvious directed line segment to associate with $\mathbf{A}$ is OA. The projection of this onto L will then be OA', and we denote the projection of **A** onto L by

$$\text{Proj}_L(\mathbf{A}) = \overrightarrow{OA'}.$$

When we use this notation, the line L is understood. To be completely correct, we should indicate the line in our notation, but this would be rather cumbersome for our purposes.

We now wish to investigate (intuitively) some of the properties of this projection function in order to learn what the appropriate formal definition should be. For these intuitive purposes, it is clearly sufficient to think in terms of directed line segments.

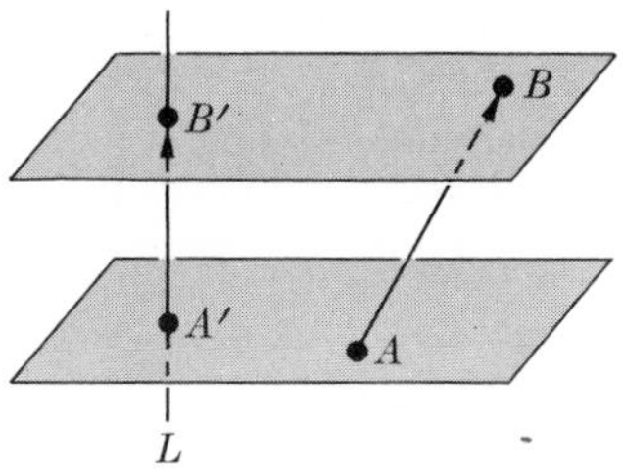

FIGURE 3–11

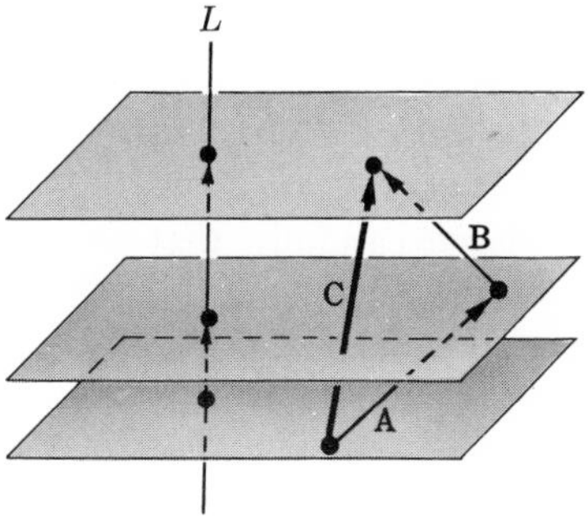

FIGURE 3–12

Let us see what the projection of the sum of two vectors is. Let $\mathbf{C} = \mathbf{A} + \mathbf{B}$ and suppose we project **C** onto a line L.

Observe Fig. 3–12. Here we see the vector **C** as the sum of **A** and **B**, and three planes drawn through the appropriate points. It is then clear that

$$\text{Proj}(\mathbf{A} + \mathbf{B}) = \text{Proj}(\mathbf{A}) + \text{Proj}(\mathbf{B}).$$

We also observe that for a fixed line L, the projection of t times **A** is t times the projection of **A**, as is easily seen by observing the similar triangles formed when **A** is drawn as a directed line segment with its initial point on L (see Fig. 3–13). Thus, having fixed L, we can write for any vectors **A** and **B**, and for any scalars s and t, the following relation:

$$\text{Proj}(s\mathbf{A} + t\mathbf{B}) = s \cdot \text{Proj}(\mathbf{A}) + t \cdot \text{Proj}(\mathbf{B}), \tag{3–8}$$

which is usually called *the linearity property of the projection.*

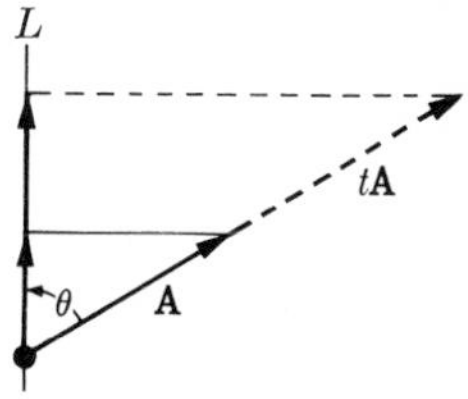

FIGURE 3–13

It is the direction of the line L which is important in determining the projection. For a given line L, all projections onto this line will be collinear; that is, they will all be scalar multiples of some one nonzero vector which determines the direction of L. Suppose that **B** is a nonzero vector on the line (i.e. that there are two points P and Q on the line such that $\overrightarrow{PQ} = \mathbf{B}$). This vector **B** will then determine a sense of direction on L. Think of the vectors **A** and **B** as directed line segments drawn from the same point and let θ be the angle between these two (Fig. 3-13 again). Then clearly,

$$\text{Proj}\ (\mathbf{A}) = |\mathbf{A}|(\cos\theta)\mathbf{e}, \tag{3-9}$$

where $\mathbf{e}$ is a vector of unit length parallel to **B**. That is, $\mathbf{e} = \mathbf{B}/|\mathbf{B}|$, and so

$$\text{Proj}\ (\mathbf{A}) = |\mathbf{A}|(\cos\theta)\,\frac{\mathbf{B}}{|\mathbf{B}|}\cdot \tag{3-10}$$

Observe carefully that this result is independent of which vector **B** is taken on the line L. If $\mathbf{B}'$ is another nonzero vector, parallel to **B**, that is, a positive scalar multiple of **B**, then

$$\frac{\mathbf{B}'}{|\mathbf{B}'|} = \frac{\mathbf{B}}{|\mathbf{B}|}\cdot$$

If, however, $\mathbf{B}''$ is some negative multiple of **B** (hence is collinear but not parallel), then

$$\frac{\mathbf{B}''}{|\mathbf{B}''|} = -\frac{\mathbf{B}}{|\mathbf{B}|},$$

but the angle θ'' between **A** and $\mathbf{B}''$ will be changed by π from θ. Hence $\cos\theta'' = -\cos\theta$ and the net result is that

$$\text{Proj}\ (\mathbf{A}) = \frac{|\mathbf{A}|(\cos\theta)\mathbf{B}}{|\mathbf{B}|} = \frac{|\mathbf{A}|(\cos\theta'')\mathbf{B}''}{|\mathbf{B}''|}\cdot$$

Let $\mathbf{A} = [a_1, a_2, a_3]$ be a given vector and let $\mathbf{B} = [b_1, b_2, b_3]$ be a nonzero vector which determines the direction of a line L. We wish to find the projection of **A** onto L. We will do this with the help of the linearity property (3-8), breaking **A** up into the sum of three vectors, each in the direction of one of the coordinate axes.

Definition 3-15. The *unit coordinate vectors* are the vectors

$$\mathbf{e}_1 = [1, 0, 0], \qquad \mathbf{e}_2 = [0, 1, 0], \qquad \text{and} \qquad \mathbf{e}_3 = [0, 0, 1].$$

With this definition, we can write

$$\mathbf{A} = a_1\mathbf{e}_1 + a_2\mathbf{e}_2 + a_3\mathbf{e}_3$$

(see Fig. 3–14). This could also be written in compact form by using the summation symbol

$$\mathbf{A} = \sum_{i=1}^{3} a_i\mathbf{e}_i.$$

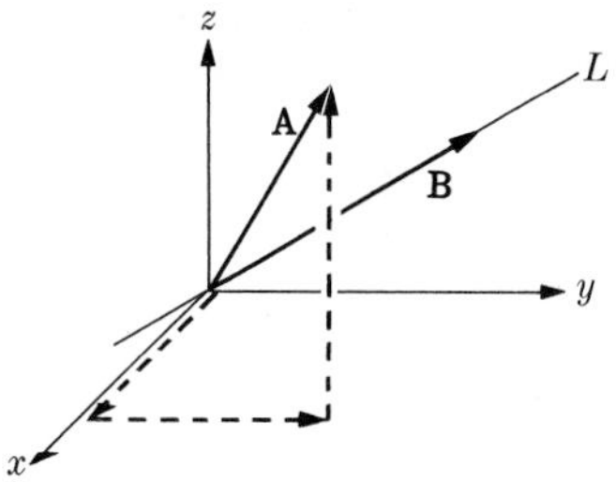

FIGURE 3–14

Now we need the projections of the three unit vectors. From (3–9), the projection of $\mathbf{e}_1$ in the direction of $\mathbf{B}$ is $|\mathbf{e}_1|(\cos\alpha)\mathbf{e} = (\cos\alpha)\mathbf{e}$, where $\mathbf{e} = \mathbf{B}/|\mathbf{B}|$ and α is the angle between the x-axis ($\mathbf{e}_1$) and the vector $\mathbf{B}$. However, $\cos\alpha$ is exactly the first direction cosine of $\mathbf{B}$, or $\cos\alpha = b_1/|\mathbf{B}|$. In exactly the same way the projections of $\mathbf{e}_2$ and $\mathbf{e}_3$ can be seen to be $(b_2/|\mathbf{B}|)\mathbf{e}$ and $(b_3/|\mathbf{B}|)\mathbf{e}$ respectively.

Therefore, using the linearity property, we find that the projection of $\mathbf{A}$ onto L is

$$\begin{aligned}\text{Proj}\,(\mathbf{A}) &= \text{Proj}\,(a_1\mathbf{e}_1 + a_2\mathbf{e}_2 + a_3\mathbf{e}_3)\\ &= a_1\,\text{Proj}\,(\mathbf{e}_1) + a_2\,\text{Proj}\,(\mathbf{e}_2) + a_3\,\text{Proj}\,(\mathbf{e}_3)\\ &= \frac{a_1b_1}{|\mathbf{B}|}\,\mathbf{e} + \frac{a_2b_2}{|\mathbf{B}|}\,\mathbf{e} + \frac{a_3b_3}{|\mathbf{B}|}\,\mathbf{e}\\ &= (a_1b_1 + a_2b_2 + a_3b_3)\,\frac{\mathbf{e}}{|\mathbf{B}|}\\ &= (a_1b_1 + a_2b_2 + a_3b_3)\,\frac{\mathbf{B}}{|\mathbf{B}|^2}\,.\end{aligned}$$

On the other hand, if θ is the angle between $\mathbf{A}$ and $\mathbf{B}$, this same projection is given, according to (3–9), by

$$\text{Proj}\,(\mathbf{A}) = |\mathbf{A}|(\cos\theta)\mathbf{e} = |\mathbf{A}|(\cos\theta)\,\frac{\mathbf{B}}{|\mathbf{B}|}\,.$$

Comparing these two results, we find the interesting relation

$$|\mathbf{A}|\,|\mathbf{B}|\cos\theta = a_1b_1 + a_2b_2 + a_3b_3, \tag{3–11}$$

or, using the summation notation, we have

$$|\mathbf{A}|\,|\mathbf{B}|\cos\theta = \sum_{i=1}^{3} a_ib_i.$$

All of this discussion has been based on our understanding of the geometry of three-dimensional space. We want our algebraic development to correspond to the familiar geometry of space. We do this by seeing that our definitions correspond to the above results. In particular, we would like to have a simple symbol which would represent the combination of two vectors which appears on the right-hand side of (3–11). This then, is our motivation for the following definitions.

Definition 3–16. Given two vectors $\mathbf{A} = [a_1, a_2, a_3]$ and $\mathbf{B} = [b_1, b_2, b_3]$, the *dot product* of these two vectors is

$$\mathbf{A} \cdot \mathbf{B} = a_1b_1 + a_2b_2 + a_3b_3.$$

The *projection* of $\mathbf{A}$ onto a line L whose direction is determined by a vector $\mathbf{B} \neq 0$ is

$$\text{Proj}\ (\mathbf{A}) = \frac{(\mathbf{A} \cdot \mathbf{B})\mathbf{B}}{|\mathbf{B}|^2}.$$

The *cosine of the angle* between the two vectors is defined to be

$$\cos\theta = \frac{\mathbf{A} \cdot \mathbf{B}}{|\mathbf{A}|\ |\mathbf{B}|},$$

provided $\mathbf{A} \neq \mathbf{0}$ and $\mathbf{B} \neq \mathbf{0}$. In particular, the two vectors $\mathbf{A}$ and $\mathbf{B}$ are called *orthogonal* (or *perpendicular*) if and only if $\mathbf{A} \cdot \mathbf{B} = 0$.

Several remarks about this definition are in order. First, the quantity *defined* to be the *cosine of the angle between the vectors* has not been proved to be the actual cosine of a real angle. In order to know this, we would have to know that the quantity so defined always is between -1 and $+1$ or, what amounts to the same thing, that for any two vectors $\mathbf{A}$ and $\mathbf{B}$

$$|\mathbf{A} \cdot \mathbf{B}| \leq |\mathbf{A}| \cdot |\mathbf{B}|.$$

This happens to be true, as will be proved in the next section, so that we can use the above definition to define the angle between two vectors. The orthogonality condition then corresponds correctly to our usual ideas of orthogonality.

A second observation is that according to the above definition, the zero vector, $\mathbf{0}$, is orthogonal to *every* vector. While this may seem unusual, it turns out to be a useful convention and so we will use it.

Finally, the unit vectors $\mathbf{e}_1$, $\mathbf{e}_2$, and $\mathbf{e}_3$, defined on p. 108, are mutally orthogonal according to this definition. Since we have been basing our algebraic development on the geometric picture of mutually orthogonal coordinate axes, this fits in with our picture.

The use of the name *dot product* for the type of product defined above is based only on the way we write the product. Other names for this concept are *inner product* and *scalar product.* The expression "inner product" is probably the most suitable mathematically, but we will find that the term "dot product" will serve our purposes. It is essential to give the full name, however. In a later section we will define a different type of product, which we will call the *cross product,* and with two types of product it is necessary to specify which is being used.

As examples of the use of these concepts, let us suppose that $\mathbf{A} = [1, -4, 8]$, $\mathbf{B} = [-7, 6, 6]$, and $\mathbf{C} = [-4, 15, 8]$, and find

(1) $\mathbf{A} \cdot \mathbf{B}$;
(2) The cosines of the angles between **A** and **B** and between **A** and **C**;
(3) The projections of **B** and **C** onto the line whose direction is determined by **A**.

We solve these problems as follows:

(1)
$$\begin{aligned}\mathbf{A} \cdot \mathbf{B} &= [1, -4, 8] \cdot [-7, 6, 6] \\ &= -7 - 24 + 48 \\ &= 17.\end{aligned}$$

(2) Let θ be the angle between **A** and **B**. Then

$$\cos\theta = \frac{\mathbf{A} \cdot \mathbf{B}}{|\mathbf{A}|\,|\mathbf{B}|} = \frac{17}{[121]^{1/2}[121]^{1/2}} = \frac{17}{121}.$$

Let ϕ be the angle between **A** and **C**. Then

$$\cos\phi = \frac{\mathbf{A} \cdot \mathbf{C}}{|\mathbf{A}|\,|\mathbf{C}|} = \frac{-4 - 60 + 64}{11[305]^{1/2}} = 0.$$

So **A** and **C** are orthogonal.

(3)
$$\text{Proj}\,(\mathbf{B}) = \frac{(\mathbf{B} \cdot \mathbf{A})\mathbf{A}}{|\mathbf{A}|^2} = \frac{17}{121}\,\mathbf{A} = \left[\frac{17}{121}, \frac{-68}{121}, \frac{136}{121}\right].$$

$$\text{Proj}\,(\mathbf{C}) = \frac{(\mathbf{C} \cdot \mathbf{A})\mathbf{A}}{|\mathbf{A}|^2} = \frac{0}{121}\,\mathbf{A} = \mathbf{0}.$$

Let us now state the fundamental algebraic properties of the dot product.

Theorem 3–5. The dot product of vectors is such that for any vectors **A**, **B**, and **C**, and any scalar s, the following properties are satisfied:

P1. $\mathbf{A} \cdot \mathbf{B} = \mathbf{B} \cdot \mathbf{A}$.

P2. $\mathbf{A} \cdot (\mathbf{B} + \mathbf{C}) = \mathbf{A} \cdot \mathbf{B} + \mathbf{A} \cdot \mathbf{C}$.

P3. $s(\mathbf{A} \cdot \mathbf{B}) = (s\mathbf{A}) \cdot \mathbf{B} = \mathbf{A} \cdot (s\mathbf{B})$.

P4. $\mathbf{A} \cdot \mathbf{A} = |\mathbf{A}|^2 \geq 0$ for every **A**, and $\mathbf{A} \cdot \mathbf{A} = 0$ if and only if $\mathbf{A} = \mathbf{0}$.

Again, the proofs of these facts are almost trivial and can be left to the reader. Note that the first three can be summarized by the observation that as far as vector addition, scalar multiplication, and the dot product go, the ordinary rules of algebra apply. However, there is one rule which is definitely missing—the cancellation law. Suppose we have

$$\mathbf{A} \cdot \mathbf{B} = \mathbf{A} \cdot \mathbf{C},$$

and $\mathbf{A} \neq \mathbf{0}$. Then we cannot conclude that $\mathbf{B} = \mathbf{C}$. We can say that $\mathbf{A} \cdot \mathbf{B} - \mathbf{A} \cdot \mathbf{C} = 0$, and hence using P2, that

$$\mathbf{A} \cdot (\mathbf{B} - \mathbf{C}) = 0.*$$

But from this, all we can conclude is that $\mathbf{B} - \mathbf{C}$ is orthogonal to $\mathbf{A}$, which need not imply $\mathbf{B} = \mathbf{C}$. For example, if $\mathbf{A} = \mathbf{e}_1 = [1, 0, 0]$, $\mathbf{B} = [1, 2, 1]$, and $\mathbf{C} = [1, 1, -2]$, the student can easily verify that $\mathbf{A} \cdot \mathbf{B} = \mathbf{A} \cdot \mathbf{C}$, but clearly $\mathbf{B} \neq \mathbf{C}$.

The properties listed in this theorem are again standard properties which have been found valuable in much more general situations. In fact, they appear as the postulates which must be satisfied by the inner product in a special mathematical structure of great importance, an *inner product space.* At some time in his career, the student will probably hear of a *Hilbert Space.* A real Hilbert space is nothing more than a vector space with an inner product which satisfies the postulates mentioned in this and the last section.

The first property, P1, which is obviously a commutative law, is called the *symmetric property* of the dot product. Property P2, clearly a form of the distributive law, and property P3, which appears to be some form of an associative law, are together referred to as the *bilinearity property* of the dot product. This is best explained by observing that if we consider the vector $\mathbf{A}$ fixed, then for any vectors $\mathbf{B}$ and $\mathbf{C}$ and any scalars s and t,

$$\mathbf{A} \cdot (s\mathbf{B} + t\mathbf{C}) = s(\mathbf{A} \cdot \mathbf{B}) + t(\mathbf{A} \cdot \mathbf{C}),$$

which is exactly the linearity property mentioned in connection with projections. The word "bilinear" is used because this property also holds with respect to the first factor in the dot product.

The property P4 is usually described by saying that the inner product is *positive definite.* It is called *positive* because $\mathbf{A} \cdot \mathbf{A} \geq 0$ for every $\mathbf{A}$, and *definite* because this inner product is zero only when $\mathbf{A} = \mathbf{0}$.

---

* Note that this argument makes implicit use of P3, with $s = -1$, in order to obtain the distributive law for the difference of two vectors.

The properties of the dot product given in these theorems can be generalized in obvious ways. For example, using the properties of vector addition and the distributive law of P2, we can generalize the distributive law to the product of the sum of a set of vectors with the sum of another set. Thus, for example,

$$(\mathbf{A}_1 + \mathbf{A}_2 + \mathbf{A}_3) \cdot (\mathbf{B}_1 + \mathbf{B}_2) = \mathbf{A}_1 \cdot \mathbf{B}_1 + \mathbf{A}_1 \cdot \mathbf{B}_2 + \mathbf{A}_2 \cdot \mathbf{B}_1 + \mathbf{A}_2 \cdot \mathbf{B}_2 + \mathbf{A}_3 \cdot \mathbf{B}_1 + \mathbf{A}_3 \cdot \mathbf{B}_2. \tag{3–12}$$

This same result can be written more concisely by using the summation notation. Equation (3–12) is equivalent to

$$\left(\sum_{i=1}^{3} \mathbf{A}_i\right) \cdot \left(\sum_{j=1}^{2} \mathbf{B}_j\right) = \sum_{i=1}^{3} \sum_{j=1}^{2} \mathbf{A}_i \cdot \mathbf{B}_j. \tag{3–13}$$

The student may not be familiar with the double summation shown on the right-hand side of this equation. This may be interpreted as follows:

$$\begin{aligned}\sum_{i=1}^{3} \sum_{j=1}^{2} \mathbf{A}_i \cdot \mathbf{B}_j &= \sum_{i=1}^{3} \left(\sum_{j=1}^{2} \mathbf{A}_i \cdot \mathbf{B}_j\right) \\ &= \sum_{i=1}^{3} (\mathbf{A}_i \cdot \mathbf{B}_1 + \mathbf{A}_i \cdot \mathbf{B}_2) \\ &= \mathbf{A}_1 \cdot \mathbf{B}_1 + \mathbf{A}_1 \cdot \mathbf{B}_2 + \mathbf{A}_2 \cdot \mathbf{B}_1 \\ &\qquad + \mathbf{A}_2 \cdot \mathbf{B}_2 + \mathbf{A}_3 \cdot \mathbf{B}_1 + \mathbf{A}_3 \cdot \mathbf{B}_2.\end{aligned}$$

PROBLEMS

1. Let $\mathbf{B}$ be a nonzero vector which defines the direction of a line L. Prove that the projection of $\mathbf{A}$ onto L is given by

$$\text{Proj}\ (\mathbf{A}) = (\mathbf{A} \cdot \mathbf{e})\mathbf{e},$$

where $\mathbf{e} = \mathbf{B}/|\mathbf{B}|$.

2. Find the projection of the vector $\mathbf{A} = [7, 1, -4]$ onto the lines determined by the vectors

(a) $\mathbf{B} = [2, 6, 3]$
(b) $\mathbf{B} = [2, 2, -1]$
(c) $\mathbf{B} = [-2, -2, 1]$
(d) $\mathbf{B} = [7, 1, -3]$
(e) $\mathbf{B} = [-7, -1, 3]$

3. Find the projections of the vector $\mathbf{A} = [2, -4, 3]$ onto the lines determined by the vectors

(a) $\mathbf{B} = [1, 0, -3]$
(b) $\mathbf{B} = [2, 2, -1]$
(c) $\mathbf{B} = [-3, 3, 6]$
(d) $\mathbf{B} = [-8, 16, -12]$
(e) $\mathbf{B} = [2, -4, 0]$

4. What are the projections of $\mathbf{A} = [a_1, a_2, a_3]$ onto the coordinate axes?

5. Find the cosines of the angles between the vector $\mathbf{A} = [3, -2, -6]$ and the vectors $\mathbf{B}$, where

   (a) $\mathbf{B} = [4, -1, 8]$ (b) $\mathbf{B} = [4, 7, -4]$ (c) $\mathbf{B} = [12, 4, 3]$

6. Find the angle between the vector $\mathbf{A} = [2, -1, 2]$ and the vector $\mathbf{B}$ if

   (a) $\mathbf{B} = [-1, 2, 2]$ (b) $\mathbf{B} = [-6, 3, -6]$ (c) $\mathbf{B} = [0, 1, -1]$.

7. Find some nonzero vector $\mathbf{B}$ orthogonal to $\mathbf{A} = [1, 2, 5]$.

8. Find a vector $\mathbf{C}$ orthogonal to both $\mathbf{A} = [1, 2, 5]$ and $\mathbf{B} = [2, 0, -1]$.

9. Prove Theorem 3–5. Note that the proof here is to be purely algebraic, depending only on Definition 3–16.

10. Prove that the four properties of Theorem 3–5 hold for the vector space of Problem 9(a), Section 4, if the inner product is defined as

$$\mathbf{A} \cdot \mathbf{B} = a_1 b_1 + a_2 b_2 + \cdots + a_n b_n.$$

11. The *law of cosines* can be stated as follows: if three sides of a triangle are of lengths $|\mathbf{A}|$, $|\mathbf{B}|$, and $|\mathbf{C}|$, and if the angle opposite the side of length $|\mathbf{C}|$ is θ, then $|\mathbf{C}|^2 = |\mathbf{A}|^2 + |\mathbf{B}|^2 - 2|\mathbf{A}| \cdot |\mathbf{B}| \cos \theta$ (see Fig. 3–15).

   (a) Assume the law of cosines, let $\mathbf{A} = [a_1, a_2, a_3]$, $\mathbf{B} = [b_1, b_2, b_3]$, and suppose that the point O in Fig. 3–15 is the origin. Find $\mathbf{C}$ and use the above formula to compute $|\mathbf{A}|\ |\mathbf{B}| \cos \theta$.

   (b) Assume the properties of Theorem 3–5 and compute $|\mathbf{C}|^2 = |\mathbf{A} - \mathbf{B}|^2$. Compare with the law of cosines.

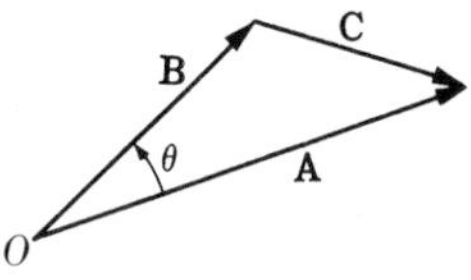

FIGURE 3–15

Remark: Parts (a) and (b) of this problem together show that the law of cosines is equivalent to the formula $\mathbf{A} \cdot \mathbf{B} = |\mathbf{A}|\ |\mathbf{B}| \cos \theta$ (granting the algebraic properties of the inner product).

3–6 THE TRIANGLE INEQUALITY

In Problem 11 of the last section, it was shown that the formula $\mathbf{A} \cdot \mathbf{B} = |\mathbf{A}|\ |\mathbf{B}| \cos \theta$ is equivalent to the law of cosines. In this section we will prove the inequality

$$|\mathbf{A} \cdot \mathbf{B}| \leq |\mathbf{A}|\ |\mathbf{B}|,$$

which was needed in the last section to justify the definition of the cosine of the angle between two vectors, and we shall show that this inequality is essentially equivalent to the familiar geometric fact that the length of one side of a triangle is less than the sum of the lengths of the other two sides.

The above inequality is very important in many different situations. In general vector spaces it is called the *Cauchy-Schwarz inequality*.

Theorem 3–6. (*The Cauchy-Schwarz Inequality.*) Given any two vectors $\mathbf{A}$ and $\mathbf{B}$,

$$|\mathbf{A} \cdot \mathbf{B}| \leq |\mathbf{A}|\,|\mathbf{B}|. \tag{3–14}$$

Proof: Observe carefully that in the following proof we make use of only those properties of vectors given in Theorems 3–3, 3–4, and 3–5.

Let t be any scalar. Then we may compute

$$\begin{aligned} |t\mathbf{A} + \mathbf{B}|^2 &= (t\mathbf{A} + \mathbf{B}) \cdot (t\mathbf{A} + \mathbf{B}) \\ &= t^2(\mathbf{A} \cdot \mathbf{A}) + 2t(\mathbf{A} \cdot \mathbf{B}) + (\mathbf{B} \cdot \mathbf{B}) \\ &= t^2|\mathbf{A}|^2 + 2t(\mathbf{A} \cdot \mathbf{B}) + |\mathbf{B}|^2. \end{aligned} \tag{3–15}$$

The right-hand member of this equation is a quadratic in t except when the length of $\mathbf{A}$ is zero.

Suppose that $|\mathbf{A}| = 0$, then $\mathbf{A} = \mathbf{0}$ and hence $\mathbf{A} \cdot \mathbf{B} = 0$. It then follows that inequality (3–14) is true (with equality holding in this case).

If $|\mathbf{A}| \neq 0$, then we have a proper quadratic expression in (3–15). We may complete the square in this expression. Doing so gives us

$$\begin{aligned} |t\mathbf{A} + \mathbf{B}|^2 &= t^2|\mathbf{A}|^2 + 2t(\mathbf{A} \cdot \mathbf{B}) + \frac{(\mathbf{A} \cdot \mathbf{B})^2}{|\mathbf{A}|^2} + |\mathbf{B}|^2 - \frac{(\mathbf{A} \cdot \mathbf{B})^2}{|\mathbf{A}|^2} \\ &= \left[t|\mathbf{A}| + \frac{(\mathbf{A} \cdot \mathbf{B})}{|\mathbf{A}|}\right]^2 + \frac{1}{|\mathbf{A}|^2}\,[|\mathbf{A}|^2|\mathbf{B}|^2 - (\mathbf{A} \cdot \mathbf{B})^2]. \end{aligned}$$

The left-hand side of this equation is nonnegative for any t. Hence this must also be true of the right-hand side. In particular, the smallest possible value of the right-hand side must be greater than or equal to zero. However, the right-hand side is the sum of two terms, one of which is squared. It will take on its smallest possible value when the squared term is zero, that is, when $t = -(\mathbf{A} \cdot \mathbf{B})/|\mathbf{A}|^2$. We thus conclude that

$$\frac{1}{|\mathbf{A}|^2}\,[|\mathbf{A}|^2|\mathbf{B}|^2 - (\mathbf{A} \cdot \mathbf{B})^2] \geq 0,$$

or, since $|\mathbf{A}|^2 > 0$,

$$(\mathbf{A} \cdot \mathbf{B})^2 \leq |\mathbf{A}|^2\,|\mathbf{B}|^2,$$

which is equivalent to the Cauchy-Schwarz inequality.

If the student feels that the above proof depends upon a trick, he is correct. While most proofs that he has seen earlier were probably fairly obvious, it might not be clear how a proof such as this might be discovered.

The reason for this is that there is no easy method for finding such proofs. One must discover the special device (or trick) that makes the proof possible. Once one has seen such a proof, however, he should be able to make use of the same trick in other proofs.

Now let us consider the sum of two vectors, $\mathbf{A} + \mathbf{B}$. If we draw a picture showing the physical realization of this vector sum (Fig. 3-16) and use the fact that the sum of the lengths of two sides of a triangle is greater than the length of the third side, we have

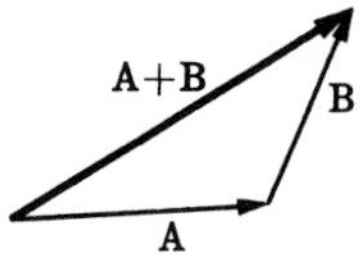

FIGURE 3-16

$$|\mathbf{A} + \mathbf{B}| \leq |\mathbf{A}| + |\mathbf{B}|. \tag{3-16}$$

This inequality, for obvious reasons, is called *the triangle inequality.* The most interesting point is that we do not have to assume its truth or depend on the geometric discussion given here. We can prove this inequality using only the algebraic properties of vectors.

Theorem 3-7. (*The triangle inequality.*) For any two vectors **A** and **B**,

$$|\mathbf{A} + \mathbf{B}| \leq |\mathbf{A}| + |\mathbf{B}|.$$

Proof: Let us compute the square of the left-hand member of this inequality. This is

$$\begin{aligned}|\mathbf{A} + \mathbf{B}|^2 &= (\mathbf{A} + \mathbf{B}) \cdot (\mathbf{A} + \mathbf{B}) \\ &= |\mathbf{A}|^2 + 2\mathbf{A} \cdot \mathbf{B} + |\mathbf{B}|^2.\end{aligned}$$

From the Cauchy-Schwarz inequality, $\mathbf{A} \cdot \mathbf{B} \leq |\mathbf{A}|\,|\mathbf{B}|$, and hence

$$\begin{aligned}|\mathbf{A} + \mathbf{B}|^2 &\leq |\mathbf{A}|^2 + 2|\mathbf{A}|\,|\mathbf{B}| + |\mathbf{B}|^2 \\ &= (|\mathbf{A}| + |\mathbf{B}|)^2.\end{aligned}$$

This last inequality implies the triangle inequality.

An important thing to note about the work in this section is the use of the fact that $|\mathbf{R}|^2 = \mathbf{R} \cdot \mathbf{R}$ to find the length of a vector which is given as the sum of two or more vectors. Let us give a few other examples of the use of this fact.

Theorem 3-8.

$$|\mathbf{A} + \mathbf{B}|^2 = |\mathbf{A}|^2 + |\mathbf{B}|^2$$

if and only if **A** and **B** are orthogonal.

Proof: We compute (exactly as above)

$$|\mathbf{A} + \mathbf{B}|^2 = |\mathbf{A}|^2 + 2(\mathbf{A} \cdot \mathbf{B}) + |\mathbf{A}|^2.$$

The conclusion of the theorem then follows immediately upon application of Definition 3–16.

This same algebraic device can be used to give vector proofs of theorems involving the lengths of segments (and sometimes also theorems involving angles). For example, let us prove the following:

The medians to the equal sides of an isosceles triangle are equal in length.

Proof: Let A, B, and C be the vertices of the triangle and suppose that $|AB| = |AC|$. The midpoints of the equal sides are given by $\frac{1}{2}(\mathbf{A} + \mathbf{B})$ and $\frac{1}{2}(\mathbf{A} + \mathbf{C})$, and so the lengths of the medians are $|\frac{1}{2}(\mathbf{A} + \mathbf{B}) - \mathbf{C}|$ and $|\frac{1}{2}(\mathbf{A} + \mathbf{C}) - \mathbf{B}|$. To prove these two equal we compute

$$\begin{aligned}|\tfrac{1}{2}(\mathbf{A} + \mathbf{B}) - \mathbf{C}|^2 - |\tfrac{1}{2}(\mathbf{A} + \mathbf{C}) - \mathbf{B}|^2 &= [\tfrac{1}{4}|\mathbf{A}|^2 + \tfrac{1}{4}|\mathbf{B}|^2 + |\mathbf{C}|^2 \\ &\quad + \tfrac{1}{2}\mathbf{A}\cdot\mathbf{B} - \mathbf{A}\cdot\mathbf{C} - \mathbf{B}\cdot\mathbf{C}] \\ &\quad - [\tfrac{1}{4}|\mathbf{A}|^2 + \tfrac{1}{4}|\mathbf{C}|^2 + |\mathbf{B}|^2 \\ &\quad + \tfrac{1}{2}\mathbf{A}\cdot\mathbf{C} - \mathbf{A}\cdot\mathbf{B} - \mathbf{B}\cdot\mathbf{C}] \\ &= \tfrac{3}{4}|\mathbf{C}|^2 - \tfrac{3}{4}|\mathbf{B}|^2 + \tfrac{3}{2}\mathbf{A}\cdot\mathbf{B} - \tfrac{3}{2}\mathbf{A}\cdot\mathbf{C} \\ &= \tfrac{3}{4}[|\mathbf{C}|^2 - |\mathbf{B}|^2 + 2\mathbf{A}\cdot\mathbf{B} - 2\mathbf{A}\cdot\mathbf{C}].\end{aligned}$$

However, by the assumption of the equal length of the two sides we have

$$\begin{aligned}0 &= |\mathbf{C} - \mathbf{A}|^2 - |\mathbf{B} - \mathbf{A}|^2 \\ &= |\mathbf{C}|^2 - 2\mathbf{A}\cdot\mathbf{C} + |\mathbf{A}|^2 - |\mathbf{B}|^2 + 2\mathbf{A}\cdot\mathbf{B} - |\mathbf{A}|^2 \\ &= |\mathbf{C}|^2 - |\mathbf{B}|^2 + 2\mathbf{A}\cdot\mathbf{B} - 2\mathbf{A}\cdot\mathbf{C}.\end{aligned}$$

Putting this into the above equation then proves the theorem.

We remark that this proof could have been simplified by proper choice of notation, but this proof is offered to show how the result can be obtained even if no special care is taken. In the proof of the next theorem we show how one can choose the notation so as to simplify the computations. Let us prove:

The diagonals of a rhombus intersect at right angles.

Proof: Let A be a vertex of the rhombus and let $\mathbf{R}$ and $\mathbf{S}$ be the vectors associated with the two directed line segments forming the sides of the rhombus meeting at A. Then three of the vertices are given by $\mathbf{A}$, $\mathbf{A} + \mathbf{R}$, and $\mathbf{A} + \mathbf{S}$.

Since a rhombus is a parallelogram, the fourth vertex is given by $\mathbf{A} + \mathbf{R} + \mathbf{S}$. The sides of a rhombus are all equal. This tells us that $|\mathbf{R}| = |\mathbf{S}|$.

The vectors giving the diagonals are

$$\mathbf{D}_1 = (\mathbf{A} + \mathbf{R} + \mathbf{S}) - \mathbf{A} = \mathbf{R} + \mathbf{S}$$

and

$$\mathbf{D}_2 = (\mathbf{A} + \mathbf{R}) - (\mathbf{A} + \mathbf{S}) = \mathbf{R} - \mathbf{S}.$$

To show that these two diagonals are orthogonal, we compute

$$\begin{aligned} \mathbf{D}_1 \cdot \mathbf{D}_2 &= (\mathbf{R} + \mathbf{S}) \cdot (\mathbf{R} - \mathbf{S}) \\ &= |\mathbf{R}|^2 - |\mathbf{S}|^2 \\ &= 0, \end{aligned}$$

which proves the theorem.

The reader should also observe how these computations can be simplified even further by letting the point A be the origin. He should then go back to the previous theorem and see how the calculations would be simplified if the vertex A of the triangle were at the origin.

PROBLEMS

1. Assume that the triangle inequality is true. By comparing the expansion of $|\mathbf{A} + \mathbf{B}|^2$ and $(|\mathbf{A}| + |\mathbf{B}|)^2$, prove the Cauchy-Schwarz inequality.

2. Write the Cauchy-Schwarz inequality in terms of the components of the vectors involved.

3. Verify that the Cauchy-Schwarz inequality holds for the vector space of Problem 9(a) of Section 3–4. Write this out in terms of components.

4. Show that equality can hold in the Cauchy-Schwarz inequality only if the two vectors are collinear.

5. Under what circumstances can equality hold in the triangle inequality? These circumstances can be determined by observing when equality holds in the proof.

6. Write the triangle inequality in terms of components.

7. Let $\mathbf{A} = x\mathbf{e}_1, \mathbf{B} = y\mathbf{e}_1$ where $\mathbf{e}_1 = [1, 0, 0]$. What are $|\mathbf{A}|$, $|\mathbf{B}|$, and $|\mathbf{A}+\mathbf{B}|$? What does the triangle inequality reduce to?

8. Let O be the center of a circle, let A and B be the endpoints of a diameter of the circle, and let C be any other point on the circle. Set $\overrightarrow{OA} = \mathbf{R}$ and $\overrightarrow{OC} = \mathbf{P}$. What are $\overrightarrow{OB}$, $\overrightarrow{AC}$, and $\overrightarrow{BC}$ in terms of $\mathbf{R}$ and $\mathbf{P}$? Prove that AC and BC are orthogonal.

Using vector methods, prove the following theorems:

9. If the diagonals of a parallelogram are orthogonal, then the parallelogram is a rhombus.

10. The midpoint of the hypotenuse of a right triangle is equidistant from the three vertices.

11. If the diagonals of a parallelogram are equal in length, then the parallelogram is a rectangle.

12. The line segments joining the midpoints of consecutive sides of a rhombus form a rectangle.

13. The line segments joining the midpoints of consecutive sides of a rectangle form a rhombus.

14. The sum of the squares of the distances from a point P to two opposite vertices of a rectangle is equal to the sum of the squares of the distances from P to the other two vertices.

15. State and prove the converse of Problem 14.

16. Use Theorem 3–16 to prove the Pythagorean theorem and its converse.

17. Prove that the sum of the squares of the lengths of the diagonals of a parallelogram is equal to the sums of the squares of the four sides. Is the converse true?

4

Planes and Lines

4–1 PLANES

In his *Elements*, Euclid attempted to define planes. By our present day standards his definition leaves much to be desired, but then, it is not easy to give a truly adequate definition. For example, if pressed, the student might try to define a plane as follows: *A plane is a set of points with the property that if any two points are in it, then the entire straight line through these two points is in it.*

Leaving aside for the moment any questions about the existence of the line, there is still a great deal wrong with this attempted definition. Once again, the student should attempt to find the difficulty for himself before reading further.

There are many ways in which we could proceed to give a definition for a plane, but we wish to choose one which can be generalized easily and which leads to useful results in higher dimensions. At the same time, we wish to have a definition which is both rigorous and easy to work with. The definition attempted above, for example, is inadequate because the entire space or a straight line satisfies it. We therefore will not attempt to patch up this definition, but will start fresh.

The fundamental property we will use is that there exists a unique plane through a given point, perpendicular to a given line. The student may notice that this property has been used in the geometric discussions in earlier sections. It therefore is only right that we make this our defining property.

Definition 4–1. Let P_0 be a given point in space and let $\mathbf{A}$ be a given nonzero vector. Then by the *plane* through P_0 *orthogonal* to $\mathbf{A}$ we mean the set of points $P = (x, y, z)$,

$$M = \{P \mid (\overrightarrow{P_0P}) \cdot \mathbf{A} = 0\}.$$

Note that according to our conventions, $\overrightarrow{P_0P} = \mathbf{P} - \mathbf{P}_0$. Thus if $P_0 = (x_0, y_0, z_0)$ and $\mathbf{A} = [a, b, c]$, then $\overrightarrow{P_0P} = [x - x_0, y - y_0, z - z_0]$

and $(\overrightarrow{P_0P}) \cdot \mathbf{A} = a(x - x_0) + b(y - y_0) + c(z - z_0)$, so the point (x, y, z) is on the plane if and only if

$$a(x - x_0) + b(y - y_0) + c(z - z_0) = 0. \tag{4-1}$$

If this equation is multiplied out, and we set $d = -ax_0 - by_0 - cz_0$, then we have the equation

$$ax + by + cz + d = 0, \tag{4-2}$$

which must be satisfied by the coordinates of the points of the plane. This last equation has the form of a general linear equation. It is called the cartesian form of the equation of the plane.

Suppose, on the other hand, that we are given a linear equation $ax + by + cz + d = 0$, not all three of a, b, and c being zero. For example, suppose $a \neq 0$. Set $x_0 = -d/a$, $y_0 = 0$, and $z_0 = 0$. Then this equation is equivalent to the equation $a(x - x_0) + b(y - y_0) + c(z - z_0) = 0$, and hence is equivalent to $(\overrightarrow{P_0P}) \cdot \mathbf{A} = 0$ when $P_0 = (x_0, y_0, z_0)$, $P = (x, y, z)$, and $\mathbf{A} = [a, b, c]$. That is, the set of all points (x, y, z) whose coordinates satisfy a nontrivial linear equation constitutes a plane. (A nontrivial linear equation is a linear equation in which not all of the coefficients of the variables are zero.) These facts are important enough to warrant their collection into a theorem.

Theorem 4–1. The coordinates of all points on a plane satisfy a nontrivial linear equation. Conversely, the set of all points whose coordinates satisfy a nontrivial linear equation constitutes a plane.

Let us try to make clear exactly what we mean by saying that a vector is orthogonal to a plane. This idea is expressed in Definition 4–1, but needs to be made precise.

Definition 4–2. A vector $\mathbf{R}$ is *parallel* to a plane M if and only if there exist points P_1 and P_2 in M such that $\overrightarrow{P_1P_2} = \mathbf{R}$.

Definition 4–3. A vector which is orthogonal to every vector parallel to a plane M is said to be *orthogonal* to M.

These definitions should be clear enough. In order for the terminology of Definition 4–1 to correspond to these definitions, we must have the following theorem:

Theorem 4–2. Let M be the plane through P_0, orthogonal to $\mathbf{A}$, as in Definition 4–1. Then $\mathbf{A}$ is orthogonal to M in the sense of Definition 4–3.

Proof: Let P_1 and P_2 be any two points of M. From Definition 4–1 we have

$$\mathbf{A} \cdot (\overrightarrow{P_0P_1}) = \mathbf{A} \cdot (\mathbf{P}_1 - \mathbf{P}_0) = 0,$$
$$\mathbf{A} \cdot (\overrightarrow{P_0P_2}) = \mathbf{A} \cdot (\mathbf{P}_2 - \mathbf{P}_0) = 0.$$

However, then

$$\begin{aligned}\mathbf{A} \cdot (\overrightarrow{P_1P_2}) &= \mathbf{A} \cdot (\mathbf{P}_2 - \mathbf{P}_1)\\ &= \mathbf{A} \cdot [(\mathbf{P}_2 - \mathbf{P}_0) - (\mathbf{P}_1 - \mathbf{P}_0)]\\ &= \mathbf{A} \cdot (\mathbf{P}_2 - \mathbf{P}_0) - \mathbf{A} \cdot (\mathbf{P}_1 - \mathbf{P}_0)\\ &= 0,\end{aligned}$$

which proves the theorem.

There is essentially only one vector orthogonal to a given plane. That is, any two vectors orthogonal to the same plane must be collinear. We can obtain this result more easily at a later stage, but since it seems to be relevant at this point, let us prove it here.

Theorem 4–3. Let M be the plane through P_0 orthogonal to $\mathbf{A}$. If $\mathbf{B}$ is orthogonal to M, then $\mathbf{A}$ and $\mathbf{B}$ are collinear.

Proof: The vector $\mathbf{A} \neq \mathbf{0}$. If $\mathbf{A} = [a_1, a_2, a_3]$, then one of the three components is not zero. Let us suppose for definiteness that $a_1 \neq 0$. The proof would be similar in other cases. Let

$$t = \frac{b_1}{a_1} \cdot$$

Now $P = (x, y, z)$ is a point of the plane if and only if

$$a_1(x - x_0) + a_2(y - y_0) + a_3(z - z_0) = 0. \qquad (4\text{–}3)$$

Multiplying this equation by t, we have, since $ta_1 = b_1$,

$$b_1(x - x_0) + ta_2(y - y_0) + ta_3(z - z_0) = 0. \qquad (4\text{–}4)$$

However, if $\mathbf{B}$ is orthogonal to the plane, it must be orthogonal to $\mathbf{P} - \mathbf{P}_0$, and hence

$$b_1(x - x_0) + b_2(y - y_0) + b_3(z - z_0) = 0.$$

Subtracting (4–4) from this, we see that for any point P on the plane,

$$(b_2 - ta_2)(y - y_0) + (b_3 - ta_3)(z - z_0) = 0. \qquad (4\text{–}5)$$

We now make use of this relation by choosing particular points on the plane. First, set

$$x = x_0 - \frac{a_2}{a_1}, \qquad y = y_0 + 1, \qquad z = z_0. \tag{4-6}$$

Substituting these values into Eq. (4-3), we see that the point (x, y, z) is on the plane. When these values are put into (4-5), however, we find $b_2 = ta_2$.

In the same way, if we set

$$x = x_0 - \frac{a_3}{a_1}, \qquad y = y_0, \qquad z = z_0 + 1, \tag{4-7}$$

we again have a point on the plane, and Eq. (4-5) gives us $b_3 = ta_3$. We therefore have shown

$$b_1 = ta_1, \qquad b_2 = ta_2, \qquad b_3 = ta_3, \tag{4-8}$$

or $\mathbf{B} = t\mathbf{A}$, which proves the theorem.

Theorems 4-2 and 4-3 together show that, exclusive of scalar multiples, there is only one vector orthogonal to a given plane. Suppose, on the other hand, that two nonzero vectors **A** and **B** are collinear and that a point P_0 is given. Are the planes through P_0 orthogonal to **A** and **B** the same? The answer is, of course, yes.

Theorem 4-4. If **A** and **B** are nonzero collinear vectors and if P_0 is a fixed point, then the plane through P_0 orthogonal to **A** is identical to the plane through P_0 orthogonal to **B**.

Proof: Let $\mathbf{B} = k\mathbf{A}$, where $k \neq 0$ (why is this possible?). Let

$$M_1 = \{P \mid \mathbf{A} \cdot (\mathbf{P} - \mathbf{P}_0) = 0\},$$

and

$$\begin{aligned} M_2 &= \{P \mid \mathbf{B} \cdot (\mathbf{P} - \mathbf{P}_0) = 0\} \\ &= \{P \mid k\mathbf{A} \cdot (\mathbf{P} - \mathbf{P}_0) = 0\}. \end{aligned}$$

However, since $k \neq 0$, the expression in the last line can be zero if and only if $\mathbf{A} \cdot (\mathbf{P} - \mathbf{P}_0) = 0$, and hence we can conclude that $M_1 = M_2$.

The equation, in vector form, of the plane through a point P_0 orthogonal to a given vector **A** is

$$\mathbf{A} \cdot (\mathbf{P} - \mathbf{P}_0) = 0.$$

By making use of the algebraic properties of the dot product, this can also be written in the form

$$\mathbf{A} \cdot \mathbf{P} - \mathbf{A} \cdot \mathbf{P}_0 = 0, \tag{4-9}$$

or equivalently, in the form

$$\mathbf{A} \cdot \mathbf{P} = \mathbf{A} \cdot \mathbf{P}_0.$$

This last form is quite easy to remember, since it is obvious that $P = P_0$ satisfies this equation. Form (4-9), however, corresponds exactly to (4-2), since if $\mathbf{A} = [a, b, c]$ and $P = (x, y, z)$, then

$$\mathbf{A} \cdot \mathbf{P} = ax + by + cz,$$

while $\mathbf{A} \cdot \mathbf{P}_0$ is a constant which can be identified with $-d$, d being the constant in (4-2).

Suppose, for example, that we wish to find the cartesian equation of the plane through $P_0 = (1, 2, 3)$ orthogonal to $\mathbf{A} = [3, -4, 1]$. We have

$$\mathbf{A} \cdot \mathbf{P} = 3x - 4y + z,$$

while

$$\mathbf{A} \cdot \mathbf{P}_0 = 3 - 8 + 3 = -2,$$

and hence the desired equation is

$$3x - 4y + z + 2 = 0.$$

Conversely, if we are given an equation such as

$$2x + y - 3z - 5 = 0,$$

we recognize it as the equation of a plane orthogonal to $\mathbf{A} = [2, 1, -3]$. But what point does it pass through? All we need do is to find any P_0 whose coordinates satisfy the given equation. In this case, a simple choice is $P_0 = (0, 5, 0)$. This equation is, therefore, the equation of the plane through $(0, 5, 0)$ orthogonal to $[2, 1, -3]$, and is equivalent to

$$[2, 1, -3] \cdot ([x, y, z] - [0, 5, 0]) = 0.$$

PROBLEMS

1. Let M be the plane, as defined above, through the point P_0 orthogonal to the vector $\mathbf{A}$. Let P_1 be another point in M and let M_1 be the plane through P_1 orthogonal to $\mathbf{A}$. Prove that $M = M_1$. (Recall that in order to show that two sets are the same we must show that any point in the first is also in the second, and any point in the second is also in the first.)

2. Find the equation, in standard form $ax + by + cz + d = 0$ of the plane through the point P_0 orthogonal to $\mathbf{A}$ if
   (a) $P_0 = (1, 3, -2)$, $\mathbf{A} = [1, 2, 7]$
   (b) $P_0 = (\frac{1}{2}, 0, -1)$, $\mathbf{A} = [2, 2, -1]$
   (c) $P_0 = (2, 1, 0)$, $\mathbf{A} = [0, 0, 1]$
   (d) $P_0 = (1, 1, 1)$, $\mathbf{A} = [1, 0, 0]$

3. Find the equation, in standard form, for the plane through P_0 orthogonal to $\mathbf{A}$ for each of the following. Find the point at which the resulting plane cuts the z-axis.
   (a) $P_0 = (1, 2, 3)$, $\mathbf{A} = [5, 1, 1]$
   (b) $P_0 = (0, 1, 0)$, $\mathbf{A} = [1, 1, -1]$
   (c) $P_0 = (5, -5, 0)$, $\mathbf{A} = [1, 1, 2]$
   (d) $P_0 = (1, 10, 1)$, $\mathbf{A} = [-5, 1, -4]$

4. For each of the following equations, give a point P_0 and a vector $\mathbf{A}$ such that the equation is that of a plane through P_0 orthogonal to $\mathbf{A}$:
   (a) $3x - 2y + z + 5 = 0$
   (b) $x + y + 1 = 0$
   (c) $2x + y + 4z = 0$
   (d) $-x - 2y - 3z + 6 = 0$

5. By assuming an equation of the form $ax + by + cz + d = 0$, and treating a, b, c, and d as unknowns, find the equation of the plane containing the three points $(1, 0, 2)$, $(2, 1, 1)$, and $(-1, -3, 3)$. How is it that we can solve for four unknowns, with only three equations being given by these three requirements?

6. Let M be a plane through the origin. A vector $\mathbf{X} = [x_1, x_2, x_3]$ is in the plane M if and only if the point $X = (x_1, x_2, x_3)$ is in the plane. Let P_0 be any point in space and set $N = \{P \mid \overrightarrow{P_0P} \in M\}$. What is N? Prove your answer.

7. Let $\mathbf{B} = [b_1, b_2, b_3]$ and $\mathbf{C} = [c_1, c_2, c_3]$ be two nonzero vectors which are not collinear. Suppose the vector $\mathbf{A} = [a_1, a_2, a_3]$ is orthogonal to both $\mathbf{B}$ and $\mathbf{C}$ (and $\mathbf{A} \neq \mathbf{0}$). Prove that for any real s and t, $s\mathbf{B} + t\mathbf{C}$ lies in the plane through the origin orthogonal to $\mathbf{A}$.

8. Verify the details of the proof of Theorem 4–3 by showing that the points given by (4–6) and (4–7) are on the plane and that (4–8) follows.

9. At what points does the plane

$$ax + by + cz + d = 0$$

cut the three coordinate axes? Use these formulas to make a sketch showing the location of the planes for each part of Problem 3. Draw the triangular section of the plane determined by these three points. What happens in (*b*)?

10. (a) What is the equation of the sphere with center $(1, 0, 12)$ which passes through the point $(3, 5, -2)$?
(b) Find the equation of the plane through the point $(3, 5, -2)$ which is tangent to the sphere of part (*a*). [*Hint:* What line segment through this point would be orthogonal to the plane?]

4-2 THE CROSS PRODUCT

A number of problems in the preceding sections could be reduced to finding a vector orthogonal to two given vectors. In particular, Problem 5 of the last section is simplified if we could find such a vector.

Suppose two vectors $\mathbf{A} = [a_1, a_2, a_3]$ and $\mathbf{B} = [b_1, b_2, b_3]$ are given, and we wish to find a vector $\mathbf{X} = [x, y, z]$ simultaneously orthogonal to both, that is, to find an $\mathbf{X}$ satisfying $\mathbf{A} \cdot \mathbf{X} = 0$ and $\mathbf{B} \cdot \mathbf{X} = 0$, or

$$a_1x + a_2y + a_3z = 0,$$
$$b_1x + b_2y + b_3z = 0.$$

We wish to solve this pair of equations for the three unknowns x, y, and z. The solution obviously cannot be unique (think geometrically; if any nonzero vector $\mathbf{X}$ satisfies the requirement, then so does any vector collinear with $\mathbf{X}$), but we will be satisfied to obtain any nonzero vector solution.

In trying to solve this pair of equations we must be cautious. We cannot divide through by any of the a_i or b_i, since some may be zero. Therefore, if we try to eliminate one of the unknowns, say z, we must do so by multiplying the first equation by b_3 and the second by a_3 and subtracting. This gives us

$$(a_1b_3 - a_3b_1)x + (a_2b_3 - a_3b_2)y = 0.$$

This equation can be satisfied (we cannot divide!) if we set

$$x = (a_2b_3 - a_3b_2),$$
$$y = -(a_1b_3 - a_3b_1).$$

We can put these two values into our original equations. After some simplification, this gives

$$a_3a_2b_1 - a_3a_1b_2 + a_3z = 0,$$
$$b_3a_2b_1 - b_3a_1b_2 + b_3z = 0.$$

It can be seen that these are both satisfied if

$$z = a_1b_2 - a_2b_1.$$

These three values thus yield us a somewhat arbitrary solution to our problem. We give this solution a special name.

Definition 4–4. Given two vectors $\mathbf{A} = [a_1, a_2, a_3]$ and $\mathbf{B} = [b_1, b_2, b_3]$, the *cross product* of these two vectors is defined to be the vector

$$\mathbf{A} \times \mathbf{B} = [(a_2b_3 - a_3b_2), -(a_1b_3 - a_3b_1), (a_1b_2 - a_2b_1)]. \tag{4–10}$$

A useful mnemonic which is helpful in remembering the form of the cross product is the representation as a formal determinant:

$$\mathbf{A} \times \mathbf{B} = \begin{vmatrix} \mathbf{e}_1 & \mathbf{e}_2 & \mathbf{e}_3 \\ a_1 & a_2 & a_3 \\ b_1 & b_2 & b_3 \end{vmatrix}.$$

Expansion of this determinant by the cofactors of the top row gives a representation of $\mathbf{A} \times \mathbf{B}$.

Thus, for example, to find $[-1, 3, 2] \times [5, 1, -1]$ we write

$$\begin{aligned} \begin{vmatrix} \mathbf{e}_1 & \mathbf{e}_2 & \mathbf{e}_3 \\ -1 & 3 & 2 \\ 5 & 1 & -1 \end{vmatrix} &= \mathbf{e}_1 \begin{vmatrix} 3 & 2 \\ 1 & -1 \end{vmatrix} - \mathbf{e}_2 \begin{vmatrix} -1 & 2 \\ 5 & -1 \end{vmatrix} + \mathbf{e}_3 \begin{vmatrix} -1 & 3 \\ 5 & 1 \end{vmatrix} \\ &= -5\mathbf{e}_1 + 9\mathbf{e}_2 - 16\mathbf{e}_3 \\ &= [-5, 9, -16]. \end{aligned}$$

After a bit of practice the reader should find it possible to write down the final vector directly after writing the second vector below the first:

$$\begin{matrix} [-1, & 3, & 2], \\ [\ \ 5, & 1, & -1], \end{matrix}$$

and visualizing the appropriate cofactors (don't forget the negative sign on the second cofactor). When this is done, the student should always check that the dot product of the original vectors and this result is zero.

Geometrically, it is evident that there are exactly two vectors of a given magnitude orthogonal to a given pair of noncollinear vectors, $\mathbf{A}$ and $\mathbf{B}$. If $\mathbf{A}$ and $\mathbf{B}$ are thought of as directed line segments from the same point, then they determine a plane through that point and there are two vectors of magnitude 1, say, orthogonal to that plane, one pointing to each side of the plane.

Suppose $\mathbf{A}$ and $\mathbf{B}$, contained in a plane M, are not collinear, and are represented as directed line segments from a common point. If we measure the angle from $\mathbf{A}$ to $\mathbf{B}$ *counterclockwise* in the plane M, we will get an angle less than π looking at the plane from one side, and an angle greater than π looking at it from the other side. *The vector* $\mathbf{A} \times \mathbf{B}$ *points toward the side of the plane from which this angle is less than* π.

Another way of expressing this result is in terms of the *right-hand rule.* If the right hand is held as in Fig. 3–2(e), with the thumb pointing in the direction of the vector **A** and the first finger pointing in the direction of **B** (or as close to the direction of **B** as the joints will allow), then the middle finger will point in the direction of $\mathbf{A} \times \mathbf{B}$.

The proof of this would be tedious, and will not be given here. The student may use this fact without question, however.

In (4–10) we have defined a unique vector obtained from two given vectors, that is, an algebraic product of a new type. Again, we are interested in the algebraic laws that are satisfied. Here we find some surprises. First, let us think of the commutative law. Interchanging **A** and **B** in the above definition amounts to interchanging the small a's and small b's. Note that if this is done, the two terms in each component of the definition of $\mathbf{A} \times \mathbf{B}$ are interchanged. But these two terms have opposite signs. *Thus the commutative law does not hold in general.* In fact, we actually have an anticommutative law:

$$\mathbf{A} \times \mathbf{B} = -(\mathbf{B} \times \mathbf{A}).$$

Note how this result is connected with the physical picture described above. Interchanging the roles of the vectors reverses the direction of the cross product.

The next general property to investigate is the associative law. Here again we find that the law fails in general. For, setting as usual $\mathbf{e}_1 = [1, 0, 0]$, $\mathbf{e}_2 = [0, 1, 0]$, and $\mathbf{e}_3 = [0, 0, 1]$, we find $\mathbf{e}_1 \times \mathbf{e}_2 = \mathbf{e}_3$, $\mathbf{e}_2 \times \mathbf{e}_3 = \mathbf{e}_1$, and $\mathbf{e}_2 \times \mathbf{e}_2 = \mathbf{0}$. Hence

$$\mathbf{e}_2 \times (\mathbf{e}_2 \times \mathbf{e}_3) = \mathbf{e}_2 \times \mathbf{e}_1 = -\mathbf{e}_3,$$
$$(\mathbf{e}_2 \times \mathbf{e}_2) \times \mathbf{e}_3 = \mathbf{0} \times \mathbf{e}_3 = \mathbf{0}.$$

The failure of these laws to hold means that care must be exercised in algebraic manipulations involving the cross product.

The associative and commutative laws do hold when we mix the scalar multiple and the cross product. This property, which is usually called the homogeneity property, is easily verified in the form $t(\mathbf{A} \times \mathbf{B}) = (t\mathbf{A}) \times \mathbf{B} = \mathbf{A} \times (t\mathbf{B})$. This follows from the observation that in the definition of $\mathbf{A} \times \mathbf{B}$, each term in each component contains exactly one component of **A** as a factor, so if each component of **A**, say, is multiplied by t, a single factor of t appears in each component of $\mathbf{A} \times \mathbf{B}$. Similarly, each term of each component of $\mathbf{A} \times \mathbf{B}$ contains exactly one component of **B** as a factor, and hence $\mathbf{A} \times (t\mathbf{B}) = t(\mathbf{A} \times \mathbf{B})$.

We will postpone discussion of the behavior of combinations of the dot and cross products and turn to the distributive law. Looking at the definition of $\mathbf{A} \times \mathbf{B}$, we see that each component is linear in the components of $\mathbf{B}$. Hence $\mathbf{A} \times (\mathbf{B} + \mathbf{C}) = \mathbf{A} \times \mathbf{B} + \mathbf{A} \times \mathbf{C}$. Similarly, we could show that the distributive law holds in the other order, or we can use the anticommutative law to obtain the same result.

The above analysis can be summarized in the following theorem:

Theorem 4–5. The cross product is a binary operation between vectors which is neither commutative nor associative, but which satisfies the following algebraic laws.

(1) Anticommutativity:

$$\mathbf{A} \times \mathbf{B} = -(\mathbf{B} \times \mathbf{A}).$$

(2) Bilinearity:

$$\begin{aligned} (t\mathbf{A}) \times \mathbf{B} = \mathbf{A} \times (t\mathbf{B}) &= t(\mathbf{A} \times \mathbf{B}), \\ \mathbf{A} \times (\mathbf{B} + \mathbf{C}) &= \mathbf{A} \times \mathbf{B} + \mathbf{A} \times \mathbf{C}, \\ (\mathbf{B} + \mathbf{C}) \times \mathbf{A} &= \mathbf{B} \times \mathbf{A} + \mathbf{C} \times \mathbf{A}. \end{aligned}$$

The bilinearity property of the cross product is essentially a distributive property. It can also be extended to the cross product of sums of vectors. For example,

$$\left(\sum_{i=1}^{n} \mathbf{A}_i\right) \times \left(\sum_{j=1}^{m} \mathbf{B}_j\right) = \sum_{i=1}^{n} \sum_{j=1}^{m} \mathbf{A}_i \times \mathbf{B}_j.$$

Similarly, the first part of the bilinearity property could also be combined with this same result (see Problem 11).

Next we wish to examine the combinations of three vectors involving the cross and dot products. Given two vectors $\mathbf{B}$ and $\mathbf{C}$, $\mathbf{B} \times \mathbf{C}$ is also a vector. Hence we can consider the dot product of this vector and a third vector $\mathbf{A}$. This particular combination, $\mathbf{A} \cdot (\mathbf{B} \times \mathbf{C})$, occurs frequently enough to deserve a special name.

Definition 4–5. Given three vectors $\mathbf{A}$, $\mathbf{B}$, and $\mathbf{C}$, the *scalar triple product* of these three vectors, in this order, is $\mathbf{A} \cdot \mathbf{B} \times \mathbf{C}$.

Note that in this definition, the parentheses have been left off $\mathbf{B} \times \mathbf{C}$. This can be done since there is no way in which the result could be misunderstood. Since the cross product is defined only between two vectors, we could not take the dot product first.

If we let $\mathbf{A} = [a_1, a_2, a_3]$, $\mathbf{B} = [b_1, b_2, b_3]$, and $\mathbf{C} = [c_1, c_2, c_3]$, then it is easily verified from the definitions that

$$\mathbf{A} \cdot \mathbf{B} \times \mathbf{C} = a_1b_2c_3 + a_2b_3c_1 + a_3b_1c_2 - a_3b_2c_1 - a_1b_3c_2 - a_2b_1c_3. \tag{4-11}$$

This is easily seen by noting that

$$\begin{aligned}
\mathbf{A} \cdot \mathbf{B} \times \mathbf{C} &= \mathbf{A} \cdot \begin{vmatrix} \mathbf{e}_1 & \mathbf{e}_2 & \mathbf{e}_3 \\ b_1 & b_2 & b_3 \\ c_1 & c_2 & c_3 \end{vmatrix} \\
&= \mathbf{A} \cdot \left[\mathbf{e}_1 \begin{vmatrix} b_2 & b_3 \\ c_2 & c_3 \end{vmatrix} - \mathbf{e}_2 \begin{vmatrix} b_1 & b_3 \\ c_1 & c_3 \end{vmatrix} + \mathbf{e}_3 \begin{vmatrix} b_1 & b_2 \\ c_1 & c_2 \end{vmatrix} \right] \\
&= a_1 \begin{vmatrix} b_2 & b_3 \\ c_2 & c_3 \end{vmatrix} - a_2 \begin{vmatrix} b_1 & b_3 \\ c_1 & c_3 \end{vmatrix} + a_3 \begin{vmatrix} b_1 & b_2 \\ c_1 & c_2 \end{vmatrix} \\
&= \begin{vmatrix} a_1 & a_2 & a_3 \\ b_1 & b_2 & b_3 \\ c_1 & c_2 & c_3 \end{vmatrix},
\end{aligned} \tag{4-12}$$

which is itself a useful result.

We can obtain the expansion of $\mathbf{C} \cdot \mathbf{A} \times \mathbf{B}$ by replacing each a by c, each b by a, and each c by b in (4-11). It is easily seen that if we do so, this expression is unaltered. The three terms with the positive sign interchange cyclically, and so do the three with the negative sign. In other words,

$$\mathbf{A} \cdot \mathbf{B} \times \mathbf{C} = \mathbf{C} \cdot \mathbf{A} \times \mathbf{B}.$$

This can also be put in the form

$$\mathbf{A} \cdot \mathbf{B} \times \mathbf{C} = \mathbf{A} \times \mathbf{B} \cdot \mathbf{C},$$

which is easily remembered as the fact that the dot and cross can be interchanged without altering the scalar triple product.

As a consequence of this and the anticommutative law, $\mathbf{B} \times \mathbf{C} = -\mathbf{C} \times \mathbf{B}$, we can evaluate any of the six possible scalar triple products by using $\mathbf{A}$, $\mathbf{B}$, and $\mathbf{C}$ in various orders. Another simple consequence is that $\mathbf{A} \cdot \mathbf{B} \times \mathbf{C}$ is zero if any two of the three vectors are identical. This follows since the cross product of any vector and itself is zero. If two vectors are collinear, the same result must follow, since a scalar multiple can be factored out of the product. We therefore have:

Theorem 4–6. The scalar triple product is unchanged upon interchange of the dot and cross product,

$$\mathbf{A} \times \mathbf{B} \cdot \mathbf{C} = \mathbf{A} \cdot \mathbf{B} \times \mathbf{C}.$$

The value of the scalar triple product is zero if any two of the three vectors are collinear.

By the way in which it was constructed, *the cross product of two vectors is orthogonal to both the original vectors.* But what if the two vectors are collinear? There is no single direction orthogonal to both of them. What happens to the cross product? The answer is contained in

Theorem 4–7. $\mathbf{A} \times \mathbf{B} = \mathbf{0}$ if and only if $\mathbf{A}$ and $\mathbf{B}$ are collinear.

Proof: Suppose that $\mathbf{A} \times \mathbf{B} = \mathbf{0}$. Now, if $\mathbf{A} = \mathbf{0}$, then $\mathbf{A}$ and $\mathbf{B}$ are automatically collinear; so suppose that $\mathbf{A} \neq \mathbf{0}$. Then at least one component of $\mathbf{A}$ is nonzero. Let us suppose that $a_1 \neq 0$ (the proof would be similar if one of the other components were taken to be nonzero).

Let $t = b_1/a_1$. Then

$$b_1 = ta_1.$$

The fact that $\mathbf{A} \times \mathbf{B} = \mathbf{0}$ means that all three components are zero, and hence

$$a_2b_3 - a_3b_2 = 0,$$
$$a_1b_3 - a_3b_1 = 0,$$

and

$$a_1b_2 - a_2b_1 = 0.$$

From the last of these, we have

$$b_2 = \frac{b_1}{a_1}a_2 = ta_2.$$

From the second of the relations, we have

$$b_3 = \frac{b_1}{a_1}a_3 = ta_3.$$

Thus we have proved

$$\begin{aligned} \mathbf{B} &= [b_1, b_2, b_3] = [ta_1, ta_2, ta_3] \\ &= t\mathbf{A}, \end{aligned}$$

which proves the first half of the theorem.

The proof of the other half of the theorem will be left to the student (see Problem 2 at the end of this section).

Let us illustrate the use of the cross product in the solution of a problem. We wish to find the equation of the plane passing through the points $A = (1, 0, 2)$, $B = (2, 2, -1)$, and $C = (1, 1, 0)$. This plane must be orthogonal to a vector which is in turn orthogonal to both of the vectors $\overrightarrow{AC} = [0, 1, -2]$ and $\overrightarrow{BC} = [-1, -1, 1]$. Thus, a vector orthogonal to the plane is

$$\overrightarrow{AC} \times \overrightarrow{BC} = [-1, 2, 1].$$

Therefore the equation of the desired plane is

$$[-1, 2, 1] \cdot [x, y, z] - [-1, 2, 1] \cdot [1, 1, 0] = 0,$$

or

$$-x + 2y + z - 1 = 0.$$

PROBLEMS

1. Find $\mathbf{A} \times \mathbf{B}$, given that
   (a) $\mathbf{A} = [1, 3, 1]$, $\mathbf{B} = [7, 2, -1]$
   (b) $\mathbf{A} = [0, 1, 1]$, $\mathbf{B} = [1, 0, 1]$
   (c) $\mathbf{A} = [1, -2, 3]$, $\mathbf{B} = [-3, 2, -1]$
   (d) $\mathbf{A} = [5, 2, -1]$, $\mathbf{B} = [4, -7, 2]$
   (e) $\mathbf{A} = [1, 1, 1]$, $\mathbf{B} = [-1, -1, 1]$

2. Prove that $\mathbf{A} \times \mathbf{B} = \mathbf{0}$, given that $\mathbf{A}$ and $\mathbf{B}$ are collinear.

3. By actually computing the vectors involved, prove that $t(\mathbf{A} \times \mathbf{B}) = (t\mathbf{A}) \times \mathbf{B} = \mathbf{A} \times (t\mathbf{B})$.

4. By actually computing the vectors involved, prove that $\mathbf{A} \times (\mathbf{B} + \mathbf{C}) = \mathbf{A} \times \mathbf{B} + \mathbf{A} \times \mathbf{C}$.

5. Prepare a multiplication table for the cross products of the vectors $\mathbf{e}_1$, $\mathbf{e}_2$, and $\mathbf{e}_3$.

6. There are twelve possible scalar triple products which can be written down using $\mathbf{A}$, $\mathbf{B}$, and $\mathbf{C}$. Write down each of these and, using the two operations discussed at the end of this section, obtain its value in terms of $\mathbf{A} \cdot \mathbf{B} \times \mathbf{C}$.

7. Find the equations of the planes containing the three given points:
   (a) $(1, -2, 5)$, $(0, -5, -1)$, $(-3, 5, 0)$
   (b) $(5, 0, 1)$, $(2, 3, 1)$, $(0, -5, 3)$
   (c) $(2, 5, 3)$, $(0, 1, 1)$, $(-1, 3, 0)$
   (d) $(1, -4, 1)$, $(0, -2, 0)$, $(-2, 2, -2)$

8. Find the equation of the plane containing the points $(1, 0, 1)$ and $(3, 1, 2)$ and parallel to $\mathbf{B} = [1, -1, 2]$.

9. Find a nonzero vector parallel to the plane $3x + y - z - 2 = 0$ and orthogonal to $\mathbf{B} = [1, 0, 2]$.

10. Find a nonzero vector simultaneously parallel to both of the planes $x + 2y - z + 1 = 0$ and $2x - y + z + 9 = 0$.

11. Verify that

$$\left(\sum_{i=1}^{3} a_i\mathbf{e}_i\right) \times \left(\sum_{j=1}^{3} b_j\mathbf{e}_j\right) = \sum_{i=1}^{3}\sum_{j=1}^{3} a_ib_j\mathbf{e}_i \times \mathbf{e}_j.$$

4–3 DISTANCE FORMULAS

Let A and Q be given points and let $\mathbf{B}$ be a given nonzero vector. We wish to find the distance from Q to the plane through A orthogonal to $\mathbf{B}$. Our knowledge of euclidean geometry tells us that this distance would be the distance between the point Q and the point P on the plane which is such that the vector $\overrightarrow{QP}$ is collinear with $\mathbf{B}$ (and hence orthogonal to the plane). This vector is the projection of $\overrightarrow{QA}$ on the line with the direction $\mathbf{B}$. This gives us, from Definition 3–16,

$$\overrightarrow{QP} = \frac{(\overrightarrow{QA} \cdot \mathbf{B})}{|\mathbf{B}|^2}\mathbf{B},$$

and the required distance is (Fig. 4–1)

$$|\overrightarrow{QP}| = \frac{|\overrightarrow{QA} \cdot \mathbf{B}|}{|\mathbf{B}|}.$$

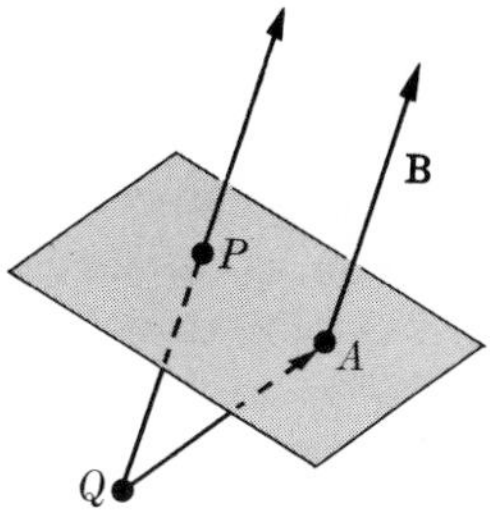

FIGURE 4–1

We should, however, verify this solution, using the algebraic properties we have assumed. First, let us see that the point P is indeed on the plane. From the definition of a plane, this is true if and only if $\overrightarrow{AP} \cdot \mathbf{B} = (\overrightarrow{QP} - \overrightarrow{QA}) \cdot \mathbf{B} = 0$. But using the value given above for $\overrightarrow{QP}$, we have

$$\begin{aligned}(\overrightarrow{QP} - \overrightarrow{QA}) \cdot \mathbf{B} &= \frac{(\overrightarrow{QA} \cdot \mathbf{B})}{|\mathbf{B}|^2}(\mathbf{B} \cdot \mathbf{B}) - (\overrightarrow{QA} \cdot \mathbf{B}) \\ &= (\overrightarrow{QA} \cdot \mathbf{B}) - (\overrightarrow{QA} \cdot \mathbf{B}) \\ &= 0.\end{aligned}$$

Next, we verify that the point P is the closest point of the plane to Q. Suppose X is any other point on the plane. Since this plane is also the plane through P orthogonal to $\mathbf{B}$, we must have $\overrightarrow{PX}$ orthogonal to $\mathbf{B}$. But then $\overrightarrow{PX}$ must also be orthogonal to $\overrightarrow{QP}$, since $\overrightarrow{QP}$ and $\mathbf{B}$ are collinear. We must then have

$$|\overrightarrow{QX}|^2 = |\overrightarrow{QP} + \overrightarrow{PX}|^2 = |\overrightarrow{QP}|^2 + |\overrightarrow{PX}|^2$$

from Theorem 3–8. From this, we can conclude that $|\overrightarrow{QX}|$ is always greater than or equal to $|\overrightarrow{QP}|$, with equality holding only when $X = P$. We have thus proved

Theorem 4–8. Given points A and Q and a nonzero vector $\mathbf{B}$, the point on the plane through A orthogonal to $\mathbf{B}$ which is closest to Q is P, where

$$\mathbf{P} = \frac{(\overrightarrow{QA} \cdot \mathbf{B})}{|\mathbf{B}|^2}\mathbf{B} + \mathbf{Q},$$

and the distance from Q to the plane is

$$|\overrightarrow{QP}| = \frac{|\overrightarrow{QA} \cdot \mathbf{B}|}{|\mathbf{B}|}. \tag{4–14}$$

Rather than trying to memorize these formulas, many students find it easier to remember only the formula for projections, and redevelop (4–13) or (4–14) as needed, by thinking of Fig. 4–1. Note how (4–14) is related to the formula given in Definition 3–16 for the cosine of the angle between two vectors. If θ is the angle between $\overrightarrow{QA}$ and $\overrightarrow{QP}$ (or equivalently between $\overrightarrow{QA}$ and $\mathbf{B}$), then from Fig. 4–1 we would have

$$|\overrightarrow{QP}| = |\overrightarrow{QA}|\,|\cos\theta|.$$

But from Definition 3–16,

$$|\cos\theta| = \frac{|\overrightarrow{QA} \cdot \mathbf{B}|}{|\overrightarrow{QA}|\,|\mathbf{B}|}.$$

An immediate consequence of these two equations is (4–14).

Suppose the given plane has the equation $ax + by + cz + d = 0$, and we wish to find the distance from this plane to the point $Q = (x_1, y_1, z_1)$. To use the above formula, we need a point of the plane. Let $A = (x_0, y_0, z_0)$ be such a point. Then we must have $ax_0 + by_0 + cz_0 = -d$. The formula in Theorem 4–8 then gives the distance from Q to the plane as

$$\frac{|[x_0 - x_1, y_0 - y_1, z_0 - z_1] \cdot [a, b, c]|}{(a^2 + b^2 + c^2)^{1/2}}$$
$$= \frac{|ax_0 + by_0 + cz_0 - (ax_1 + by_1 + cz_1)|}{(a^2 + b^2 + c^2)^{1/2}} = \frac{|ax_1 + by_1 + cz_1 + d|}{(a^2 + b^2 + c^2)^{1/2}}.$$

Theorem 4–9. The distance from the point (x_1, y_1, z_1) to the plane having equation $ax + by + cz + d = 0$ is

$$\frac{|ax_1 + by_1 + cz_1 + d|}{(a^2 + b^2 + c^2)^{1/2}}. \tag{4–15}$$

The reader should note the simplification of this formula when the normal vector $[a, b, c]$ is taken to be of length one and also what the formula reduces to when the distance from the origin to the plane is calculated.

Let us see an example of the use of the formulas developed above. Consider the plane M with equation

$$5x - 14y + 2z + 9 = 0$$

and the point $Q = (-2, 15, -7)$. We wish to find the distance from Q to the plane and the point on the plane which is closest to Q.

It is easy to find the distance from Q to M by the use of formula (4–15). This formula gives us the distance

$$\delta = \frac{|-10 - 210 - 14 + 9|}{(25 + 196 + 4)^{1/2}} = \frac{225}{15} = 15.$$

We can use (4–13) to find the point P on M which is closest to Q. For this formula we need a point A on M, however. We choose one arbitrarily to satisfy the given equation. For example, we let $A = (1, 1, 0)$. Then $\overrightarrow{QA} = [3, -14, 7]$, and hence

$$\begin{aligned}\mathbf{P} &= \frac{[3, -14, 7] \cdot [5, -14, 2]}{15^2}[5, -14, 2] + [-2, 15, -7]\\ &= \frac{225}{15^2}[5, -14, 2] + [-2, 15, -7]\\ &= [3, 1, -5].\end{aligned}$$

A plane which is parallel to the z-axis has an equation which contains no z-term. This can also be thought of as the equation of a line in the xy-plane (the line formed by the intersection with the xy-plane). Consideration of the above formulas in these terms leads to the following conclusion:

Theorem 4–10. The distance from a point (x_1, y_1) of the xy-plane to a line $ax + by + d = 0$ is

$$\frac{|ax_1 + by_1 + d|}{(a^2 + b^2)^{1/2}}.$$

Further discussion of this result can be found in the problems at the end of this section.

One final formula which can be included at this time is for the determination of the angle between two planes. When two planes intersect we may choose a point on the line of intersection and measure the angle formed between two lines, one in each plane, from this point. It can easily be seen that no matter how the planes are situated, the resulting angle can fall anywhere between 0 and π, inclusive. The two limiting cases result when both lines are chosen to be along the line of intersection. In order to specify the angle of intersection between two planes, we must decide which of these many possible angles to measure. Reference to geometric intuition tells us that we should choose to measure the angle between the two lines which are orthogonal to the line of intersection.

It could actually be shown that this pair of lines has a stronger property. Indeed, if we fix a line in one plane and let the line in the other plane vary, we will find that we get many angles, but one of them will be a minimum. If we then let the first line vary, this minimum will change, but for some angle it will be a maximum. The maximum value of the minimum turns out to be the angle between the two lines orthogonal to the line of intersection, exactly the angle we choose to call the angle between the two planes.

Since we do not have these lines given to us, but we do know the vectors orthogonal to the two planes, we choose to define the angle between the planes as the angle between the orthogonal vectors. This corresponds to the familiar geometric fact that two angles whose sides are respectively orthogonal are equal. However, each plane has two distinct orthogonal vectors of a given length (one the negative of the other). There are therefore two possible angles (between 0 and π). They are related by the fact that their cosines are negatives of each other. Hence one of them is between $\pi/2$ and π, and the other is between 0 and $\pi/2$. We will choose the smaller of the two angles to call the angle between the two planes.

Definition 4–6. Let M_1 and M_2 be two planes and let $\mathbf{B}_1$ and $\mathbf{B}_2$ be nonzero vectors orthogonal to M_1 and M_2 respectively. Then the cosine of the angle between M_1 and M_2 is

$$\frac{|\mathbf{B}_1 \cdot \mathbf{B}_2|}{|\mathbf{B}_1|\,|\mathbf{B}_2|}.$$

For example, the cosine of the angle between the planes with equations

$$3x - 6y + 6z - 5 = 0$$

and

$$6x + 9y - 2z + 3 = 0$$

is

$$\frac{|18 - 54 - 12|}{9 \cdot 11} = \frac{16}{33}.$$

PROBLEMS

1. Find the distance from the given point to the given plane:
   (a) $(1, 3, 1)$, $3x + 7y - 5z + 3 = 0$
   (b) $(2, 1, -5)$, $2x - y + 2z + 1 = 0$
   (c) $(1, 1, 0)$, $3x + 4z + 2 = 0$
   (d) $(2, 0, 3)$, $6x + 2y + 3z = 0$

2. In the distance formula of Theorem 4–10, the absolute value of the numerator is taken. What is the meaning of the sign of this quantity? Consider this question in connection with the direction of the normal vector $[a, b, c]$.

3. Let M be the plane with equation $ax + by + cz + d = 0$. Let P be the point on M which is closest to $Q = (x_1, y_1, z_1)$. Show that

$$\mathbf{P} = [x_1, y_1, z_1] - \frac{ax_1 + by_1 + cz_1 + d}{a^2 + b^2 + c^2}[a, b, c].$$

4. For each part of Problem 1, find the point on the given plane which is closest to the given point.

5. If two numbers a and b are such that $a^2 + b^2 = 1$, then there exists an angle α such that $a = \cos\alpha$, $b = \sin\alpha$. Show that the equation of any straight line in the plane can be brought into the form

$$x\cos\alpha + y\sin\alpha + p = 0.$$

   For an equation in this form, what is the geometric meaning of α and p? [*Hint:* Use Theorem 4–10.] This is called the normal form of the equation of a line.

6. Find the cosine of the angle between the following pairs of planes:
   (a) $3x - 2y + z - 5 = 0$, $2x + 3y - z + 1 = 0$
   (b) $7x - z + 1 = 0$, $x + y - 1 = 0$
   (c) $y + z = 0$, $x - y = 0$
   (d) $x - y + z + 1 = 0$, $2x - 2y + 2z - 3 = 0$
   (e) $3x + 5y - 2z - 5 = 0$, $2x + 2y + 8z + 7 = 0$

7. What does formula (4–13) become if $|\mathbf{B}| = 1$? For an arbitrary $\mathbf{B}$, set $\mathbf{e} = \mathbf{B}/|\mathbf{B}|$ and state (4–13) and (4–14) in terms of $\mathbf{e}$.

8. What is the equation of the sphere with center $(3, -9, -15)$ which is tangent to the plane

$$4x - 7y - 4z + 27 = 0?$$

   [*Hint:* What is the radius of the required sphere?]

9. Find the distance from the point $(3, 5, 3)$ to the plane passing through the three points $(2, -5, -1)$, $(-3, 1, 1)$, and $(0, 2, 9)$ by first finding the equation of the plane.

10. Let A, B, C, and Q be four noncollinear points in space and let $\overrightarrow{AB} = \mathbf{R}$, $\overrightarrow{AC} = \mathbf{S}$, and $\overrightarrow{AQ} = \mathbf{T}$. Prove that the distance from Q to the plane passing through A, B, and C is

$$\frac{|\mathbf{T} \cdot \mathbf{R} \times \mathbf{S}|}{|\mathbf{R} \times \mathbf{S}|}.$$

11. Let A_1 and A_2 be two distinct points and let $\overrightarrow{A_1A_2} = \mathbf{B}$. Let M_1 and M_2 be the planes through A_1 and A_2 respectively, each orthogonal to $\mathbf{B}$. Let Q be any point in M_2. Prove that the distance from Q to M_1 is $|\mathbf{B}|$.

Remark: This proves that two distinct planes orthogonal to the same vector have no points in common (i.e. they are parallel).

4-4 THE STRAIGHT LINE

We now turn to a discussion of straight lines. Definition 3-8 can be rewritten in the following way:

Definition 4-7. Given a point P_0 and a nonzero vector $\mathbf{A}$ the *straight line* determined by this point and this vector is

$$L = \{X \mid \overrightarrow{P_0X} = t\mathbf{A},\ t \text{ any real number}\}.$$

If we use the representation of a point X as a vector $\mathbf{X}$, this definition can be written in the form

$$\mathbf{X} = \mathbf{P}_0 + t\mathbf{A}; \tag{4-17}$$

the same definition in terms of the components would give

$$\begin{aligned} x &= x_0 + ta, \\ y &= y_0 + tb, \\ z &= z_0 + tc, \end{aligned} \tag{4-18}$$

where $P_0 = (x_0, y_0, z_0)$ and $\mathbf{A} = [a, b, c]$. These three forms are completely equivalent, and any one of them can be used as the situation requires.

What is defined here is a set of points constituting the straight line. However, there is a natural direction associated with this line, namely the direction on the line induced by the parameter t. The line can actually be thought of as a coordinate line with t as the coordinate. We will use the notion of a direction on this line, induced by the parameter t, without further comment whenever needed.

Any of the three forms given above for the determination of the coordinates of a point on the line is called the *parametric form of the equation of a line*. Any desired information about the line can be found from its parametric equation. In many textbooks on analytic geometry, the standard form of a line is given by the *symmetric equations*. These are of limited utility, however, since for many lines special conventions must be introduced to give the symmetric equations a meaning. (A discussion of the symmetric equations will not be given here, but will be found in the problems at the end of this section.) For short, we will call (4–17) an *equation of the line*, and (4–18) *equations of the line*.

What are equations of the line through $P_0 = (1, 1, 0)$ with the direction $\mathbf{A} = [1, -2, 1]$? From (4–17) we have in this case the equation

$$\mathbf{X} = [x, y, z] = [1, 1, 0] + t[1, -2, 1],$$

or equivalently,

$$\mathbf{X} = [1 + t, 1 - 2t, t].$$

This last form can also be thought of as

$$(x, y, z) = (1 + t, 1 - 2t, t),$$

which is a condensed method for writing the three equations of the form (4–18).

Is the point $(5, -7, 5)$ on this line? No, since the only possible way of getting the first coordinate of the point on the line to be equal to 5 is to put $t = 4$. This gives us the point $(5, -7, 4)$ rather than the point $(5, -7, 5)$.

At what point does this line cross the plane $y = 3$? To have $y = 3$, we see that we must have $1 - 2t = 3$, or $t = -1$. This then gives the point $(0, 3, -1)$.

At what point does the line cross the plane whose equation is

$$5x + 6y + z + 1 = 0?$$

Substituting the coordinates of a general point into this equation, we find that we must have

$$5(1 + t) + 6(1 - 2t) + t + 1 = 0,$$

or

$$12 - 6t = 0.$$

This is satisfied by $t = 2$, giving the point $(3, -3, 2)$.

The first question we raise is about the uniqueness of a straight line. The definition is given in terms of a point on a line and a vector which defines the direction of the line. We are interested in showing that the line remains the same if we substitute another point on the line and another vector collinear with the given vector.

Theorem 4-11. Let a point P_1 be on the line L determined by the point P_0 and the vector $\mathbf{A}$. Let $\mathbf{B} \neq \mathbf{0}$ be collinear with $\mathbf{A}$. Then the line determined by P_1 and $\mathbf{B}$ is identical to L.

Proof: We have $L = \{X \mid \mathbf{X} = \mathbf{P}_0 + t\mathbf{A}\}$. Set $M = \{X \mid \mathbf{X} = \mathbf{P}_1 + s\mathbf{B}\}$. Here we use a different parameter, s, to avoid confusion in discussing the points in these two sets. We are given that P_1 is on the line L; hence there exists a t_0 such that

$$\mathbf{P}_1 = \mathbf{P}_0 + t_0\mathbf{A}.$$

Likewise, since $\mathbf{B}$ is collinear with $\mathbf{A}$, there exists a nonzero constant k such that $\mathbf{B} = k\mathbf{A}$. (Why must $k \neq 0$?)

Suppose $X \in M$. Then there is a real s such that

$$\begin{aligned} \mathbf{X} &= \mathbf{P}_1 + s\mathbf{B} \\ &= (\mathbf{P}_0 + t_0\mathbf{A}) + sk\mathbf{A} \\ &= \mathbf{P}_0 + (t_0 + sk)\mathbf{A} \\ &= \mathbf{P}_0 + t\mathbf{A}, \end{aligned}$$

where we set $t = t_0 + sk$. This shows that if $X \in M$, then $X \in L$. Conversely, if $X \in L$, then we have

$$\begin{aligned} \mathbf{X} &= \mathbf{P}_0 + t\mathbf{A} \\ &= \mathbf{P}_0 + t_0\mathbf{A} + (t - t_0)\mathbf{A} \\ &= \mathbf{P}_1 + s\mathbf{B}, \end{aligned}$$

where $s = (t - t_0)/k$. This then completes the proof and shows that $L = M$.

A line is determined by a point and a vector, but there are also many other conditions which determine a line. This gives rise to problems of how to obtain the parametric equations of a line when it is determined by conditions other than the standard ones.

As a first example, we observe that two points determine a line, and that if we are given two points $P_1 = (x_1, y_1, z_1)$ and $P_2 = (x_2, y_2, z_2)$, we can easily find the line determined by these two points. Either of the two points will serve as a point on the line, and so we only need to find a vector with the required direction. Clearly such a vector is $\overrightarrow{P_1P_2} = \mathbf{P}_2 - \mathbf{P}_1$.

Therefore, a parametric equation of the line determined by the points P_1 and P_2 is

$$\mathbf{X} = \mathbf{P}_1 + t(\mathbf{P}_2 - \mathbf{P}_1),$$

or

$$\mathbf{X} = (1 - t)\mathbf{P}_1 + t\mathbf{P}_2. \tag{4–19}$$

This is the form we used to define directed line segments in an earlier section and could have been used in this section.

As an example of this, let us find an equation of the line through the points (1, 0, 2) and (3, 1, 5). Here, a vector giving the direction of the line is $[3, 1, 5] - [1, 0, 2] = [2, 1, 3]$, and so a vector parametric equation for the line is

$$\mathbf{X} = [1, 0, 2] + t[2, 1, 3].$$

A second way in which a line can be determined is by a point and the requirement that it be orthogonal to two given vectors. If the two given vectors are **A** and **B**, then clearly the vector $\mathbf{A} \times \mathbf{B}$ is the desired vector determining the direction of the line. Thus, the line through a point P_0 orthogonal to the vectors **A** and **B** is given by the equation

$$\mathbf{X} = \mathbf{P}_0 + t(\mathbf{A} \times \mathbf{B}). \tag{4–20}$$

If we are given two nonparallel planes, they determine a line, their line of intersection. Finding a vector giving the direction of this line is easy. It is merely the cross product of the two orthogonal vectors of the planes. (Why?) The only problem is to find a point on the line. This can be done by taking the equations of the two planes, eliminating one of the unknowns and assigning any convenient value to one of the remaining unknowns. This procedure can be illustrated best by an example. Suppose we are asked for an equation of the line of intersection of the two planes with equations

$$3x - y + 2z - 7 = 0,$$
$$x + y - 5z + 5 = 0.$$

The orthogonal vectors are $[3, -1, 2]$ and $[1, 1, -5]$. A direction vector for the line is therefore $[3, -1, 2] \times [1, 1, -5] = [3, 17, 4]$. Eliminating y between the equations gives

$$4x - 3z - 2 = 0.$$

Setting $z = 2$ in this equation gives $4x = 8$, or $x = 2$. Putting these values back into the second equation yields $2 + y - 10 + 5 = 0$, or $y = 3$. So a point on the line is (2, 3, 2). Hence a parametric equation of the desired line is

$$[x, y, z] = [2, 3, 2] + t[3, 17, 4].$$

Other conditions could be given which would serve to determine a line, but those listed above are the main ones which appear in practice. Other sets of conditions appear only rarely.

When two equations represent the same plane, it is easy to recognize the fact since this can happen only when one equation is a nonzero multiple of the other. The situation is not so simple in the case of the parametric equations of lines. For example, two of the lines

$$\begin{aligned} L_1&: \mathbf{X} = [1, -5, 3] + t[6, 8, -4], \\ L_2&: \mathbf{X} = [6, 0, 5] + t[-3, 4, 2], \\ L_3&: \mathbf{X} = [7, -3, -1] + t[-3, -4, 2], \\ L_4&: \mathbf{X} = [4, -7, 1] + t[9, 12, -6], \end{aligned}$$

are actually identical. But which two?

In order to be identical, it is first necessary that two lines have collinear direction vectors. On this basis we can eliminate line L_2 from consideration. It is not parallel to any of the others. The remaining three lines are all parallel, however. Two will be identical if and only if they have a point in common. We check this by seeing whether the "initial point" of one line is on another.

We first check whether $(7, -3, -1)$ is on L_1. To have $x = 7$ in L_1, we must have $t = 1$. This gives the point $(7, 3, -1)$, and we conclude that this point is not on the line.

Next we see whether $(4, -7, 1)$ is on L_1. To have $x = 4$ we must have $t = \frac{1}{2}$, giving the point $(4, -1, 1)$ on L_1. Therefore L_1 and L_4 cannot be identical.

Finally, we verify that the remaining two lines, L_3 and L_4, are identical by noting that $t = 1$ in L_3 gives the point $(4, -7, 1)$, which is on the line L_4.

PROBLEMS

1. Give parametric equations of the lines joining the pairs of points listed below.
   (a) $(1, 2, 7)$ and $(-3, 1, 1)$
   (b) $(3, 1, 0)$ and $(5, -2, 7)$
   (c) $(11, 12, 13)$ and $(2, 1, -1)$
   (d) $(1, 1, 1)$ and $(3, 1, -1)$
   (e) $(0, 1, 2)$ and $(0, 1, 3)$
   (f) $(1, -1, 1)$ and $(0, -1, 0)$

2. Find parametric equations of the lines of intersection of the pairs of planes listed.
   (a) $3x - 2y + z - 5 = 0,\ 2x + 3y - z + 1 = 0$
   (b) $7x - z + 1 = 0,\ x + y - 1 = 0$
   (c) $y + z = 0,\ x - y = 0$
   (d) $x - y + z + 1 = 0,\ 2x - 2y + z - 3 = 0$
   (e) $3x + 5y - 2z - 5 = 0,\ 2x + 2y + 8z + 7 = 0$
   (f) $x + 1 = 0,\ x + y + z = 0$

3. For each (or a selected number) of the lines in Problem 1 (and/or 2), find the value of the parameter and the coordinates of the points at which the line cuts the three coordinate planes (that is, the planes with equations $x = 0$, $y = 0$, and $z = 0$).

4. What is an equation of the line joining the points $(x_1, y_1, 0)$ and $(x_2, 0, z_2)$? At what point does this line cut the plane $x = 0$?

5. The line of intersection of the plane through P_0 orthogonal to $\mathbf{A}$ and the plane through P_0 orthogonal to $\mathbf{B}$ is given by $\mathbf{X} = \mathbf{P}_0 + t(\mathbf{A} \times \mathbf{B})$ according to the result of the text. (Assume $\mathbf{A}$ and $\mathbf{B}$ are not collinear.) Prove that every point on this line is common to both planes.

6. For the line $\mathbf{X} = \mathbf{P}_0 + t\mathbf{A}$, show that the parameter t is, in general, determined by any of the three coordinates of a point on the line in the form:

$$t = \frac{(x - x_0)}{a} = \frac{(y - y_0)}{b} = \frac{(z - z_0)}{c}$$

The three expressions on the right-hand side can be set equal in pairs, giving the equations of three planes. Identify these planes (a sketch will help). The form

$$\frac{x - x_0}{a} = \frac{y - y_0}{b} = \frac{z - z_0}{c}$$

is called the symmetric form of the equations of the line. Under what conditions can this form be considered valid?

7. For each of the following, find the value of the parameter and the coordinates of the point at which the given line cuts the given plane.
(a) $\mathbf{X} = [1, 3, -2] + t[1, -2, 3]; \quad 3x + 2y + z - 1 = 0$
(b) $\mathbf{X} = [0, 1, -1] + t[1, 5, -2]; \quad 7x - y + z + 2 = 0$
(c) $\mathbf{X} = [5, 8, 1] + t[1, 0, 8]; \quad 2x - 2y - z - 5 = 0$
(d) $\mathbf{X} = [3, 0, 5] + t[1, 1, -1]; \quad 5x + z = 0$

8. At what points does the line

$$\mathbf{X} = [1, 3, -12] + t[1, 0, 5]$$

cut the sphere

$$(x - 6)^2 + (y + 1)^2 + z^2 = 81?$$

9. Find equations for the line through $(1, -1, 2)$ which is orthogonal to the plane $3x - 2y + z - 5 = 0$.

10. Find equations for the line through $(-1, 5, 0)$, orthogonal to the line $\mathbf{X} = [1, 1, 2] + t[-1, 3, 0]$, and parallel to the plane $x + y - 4z + 2 = 0$.

11. If the given pair of lines intersect, find the point of intersection.
   (a) $\mathbf{X} = [1, 5, 4] + t[2, 1, -7]; \quad \mathbf{X} = [14, -2, 5] + t[3, -3, 5]$
   (b) $\mathbf{X} = [1, 2, 0] + t[5, 0, 7]; \quad \mathbf{X} = [0, 0, 8] + t[-8, 4, 2]$
   (c) $\mathbf{X} = [3, 4, 5] + t[1, -1, -2]; \quad \mathbf{X} = [9, -8, 3] + t[-1, 4, -3]$
   (d) $\mathbf{X} = [5, 1, -5] + t[2, 1, 5]; \quad \mathbf{X} = [1, -1, -14] + t[1, 3, -1]$

12. For parts (*a*) and (*b*) of Problem 11, find equations of the lines orthogonal to the given pair of lines and passing through the point of intersection.

13. The angle between a line and a plane is defined to be $(\pi/2) - \phi$, where ϕ is the angle between the line and the vector orthogonal to the plane (choosing the angle between 0 and $\pi/2$). Find the cosines of the angles between the line and the plane in each of the four parts of Problem 7.

1, 5, 4
14, −2, 5

(25 + 8), −(5 − 64), (1 × −2)
33, 59, −2

2, 1, −7
3, −3, 5

1 × 5 − (−7 × −3), −[(2 × 5) − (−7 × 3)]
5 − 21
16,

5

Vectors as Coordinate Systems

5–1 SOME VECTOR IDENTITIES

Let us consider the triple cross product $\mathbf{A} \times (\mathbf{B} \times \mathbf{C})$. As was commented earlier, the parentheses are necessary here since the cross product is not associative. This combination clearly represents a vector orthogonal to $\mathbf{A}$ and to $\mathbf{B} \times \mathbf{C}$. A vector orthogonal to $\mathbf{B} \times \mathbf{C}$ must lie in the plane (through the origin) determined by $\mathbf{B}$ and $\mathbf{C}$ and, as will be shown in the next section, must therefore be a linear combination of $\mathbf{B}$ and $\mathbf{C}$. If we write $\mathbf{A} \times (\mathbf{B} \times \mathbf{C}) = u\mathbf{B} + v\mathbf{C}$, then

$$\begin{aligned} \mathbf{A} \cdot [u\mathbf{B} + v\mathbf{C}] &= u(\mathbf{A} \cdot \mathbf{B}) + v(\mathbf{A} \cdot \mathbf{C}) \\ &= \mathbf{A} \cdot [\mathbf{A} \times (\mathbf{B} \times \mathbf{C})] \\ &= 0. \end{aligned}$$

This last follows since $\mathbf{A} \cdot [\mathbf{A} \times (\mathbf{B} \times \mathbf{C})]$ is the scalar triple product of three vectors, two of which are identical. As a consequence of this calculation, we can conclude that $u = k(\mathbf{A} \cdot \mathbf{C})$ and $v = -k(\mathbf{A} \cdot \mathbf{B})$ for some scalar k. An actual example shows that $k = 1$, but an attempt to prove that k is a constant independent of $\mathbf{A}$, $\mathbf{B}$, and $\mathbf{C}$ would be very difficult. The required argument is quite deep and involves the concept of continuity. It would be very difficult to give a rigorous proof along these lines at this stage.

The actual identity which we wish to prove is stated in the following theorem.

Theorem 5–1. For any vectors $\mathbf{A}$, $\mathbf{B}$, and $\mathbf{C}$,

$$\mathbf{A} \times (\mathbf{B} \times \mathbf{C}) = (\mathbf{A} \cdot \mathbf{C})\mathbf{B} - (\mathbf{A} \cdot \mathbf{B})\mathbf{C}. \tag{5–1}$$

We will use this in obtaining all the other identities of this section and so would like to have a complete proof of it. A direct proof by calculating each side in terms of components is possible but extremely tedious. Instead, we will offer two proofs, which, while still long, are shorter than direct computation.

First proof: Let $\mathbf{A} = a_1\mathbf{e}_1 + a_2\mathbf{e}_2 + a_3\mathbf{e}_3, \mathbf{B} = b_1\mathbf{e}_1 + b_2\mathbf{e}_2 + b_3\mathbf{e}_3$, and $\mathbf{C} = c_1\mathbf{e}_1 + c_2\mathbf{e}_2 + c_3\mathbf{e}_3$. Then

$$\mathbf{B} \times \mathbf{C} = (b_2c_3 - b_3c_2)\mathbf{e}_1 + (b_3c_1 - b_1c_3)\mathbf{e}_2 + (b_1c_2 - b_2c_1)\mathbf{e}_3,$$

and

$$\mathbf{A} \times (\mathbf{B} \times \mathbf{C}) = a_1\mathbf{e}_1 \times (\mathbf{B} \times \mathbf{C}) + a_2\mathbf{e}_2 \times (\mathbf{B} \times \mathbf{C}) + a_3\mathbf{e}_3 \times (\mathbf{B} \times \mathbf{C})$$

by the linearity of the cross product. Let us investigate the first term of this expansion. Using $\mathbf{e}_1 \times \mathbf{e}_1 = \mathbf{0}$, $\mathbf{e}_1 \times \mathbf{e}_2 = \mathbf{e}_3$, $\mathbf{e}_1 \times \mathbf{e}_3 = -\mathbf{e}_2$, and the linearity of the cross product, we have

$$\begin{aligned} a_1\mathbf{e}_1 \times (\mathbf{B} \times \mathbf{C}) &= a_1(b_3c_1 - b_1c_3)\mathbf{e}_3 - a_1(b_1c_2 - b_2c_1)\mathbf{e}_2 \\ &= a_1c_1b_2\mathbf{e}_2 + a_1c_1b_3\mathbf{e}_3 - a_1b_1c_2\mathbf{e}_2 - a_1b_1c_3\mathbf{e}_3 \\ &= a_1c_1b_1\mathbf{e}_1 + a_1c_1b_2\mathbf{e}_2 + a_1c_1b_3\mathbf{e}_3 - a_1b_1c_1\mathbf{e}_1 - \\ &\qquad a_1b_1c_2\mathbf{e}_2 - a_1b_1c_3\mathbf{e}_3 \\ &= a_1c_1\mathbf{B} - a_1b_1\mathbf{C}. \end{aligned}$$

Here, in the next to last step, we added and subtracted the term $a_1b_1c_1\mathbf{e}_1$. In the same way we could show that

$$\begin{aligned} a_2\mathbf{e}_2 \times (\mathbf{B} \times \mathbf{C}) &= a_2c_2\mathbf{B} - a_2b_2\mathbf{C}, \\ a_3\mathbf{e}_3 \times (\mathbf{B} \times \mathbf{C}) &= a_3c_3\mathbf{B} - a_3b_3\mathbf{C}. \end{aligned}$$

Adding these three results together would give (5–1).

Second proof: Let us first look at the unit vectors. Since the cross product of two collinear vectors is zero,

$$\mathbf{e}_i \times (\mathbf{e}_j \times \mathbf{e}_k) = \mathbf{0} \quad \text{if} \quad j = k.$$

On the other hand, if $j \neq k$, then $\mathbf{e}_j \times \mathbf{e}_k$ is collinear with the third unit vector, and hence

$$\mathbf{e}_i \times (\mathbf{e}_j \times \mathbf{e}_k) = \mathbf{0} \quad \text{if} \quad j \neq k \quad \text{and} \quad i \neq j \quad \text{or} \quad k.$$

With the help of the right-hand rule it is easy to verify that

$$\begin{aligned} \mathbf{e}_i \times (\mathbf{e}_j \times \mathbf{e}_k) &= -\mathbf{e}_k \quad && \text{if} \quad i = j \quad \text{and} \quad j \neq k, \\ &= \mathbf{e}_j \quad && \text{if} \quad i = k \quad \text{and} \quad j \neq k. \end{aligned}$$

Looking at these four cases, we verify that for any i, j, and k,

$$\mathbf{e}_i \times (\mathbf{e}_j \times \mathbf{e}_k) = (\mathbf{e}_i \cdot \mathbf{e}_k)\mathbf{e}_j - (\mathbf{e}_i \cdot \mathbf{e}_j)\mathbf{e}_k,$$

that is, (5–1) holds if **A**, **B**, and **C** are the unit vectors.

To save writing, we will make use of the summation notation and write

$$\mathbf{A} = \sum_{i=1}^{3} a_i\mathbf{e}_i, \qquad \mathbf{B} = \sum_{j=1}^{3} b_j\mathbf{e}_j, \qquad \mathbf{C} = \sum_{k=1}^{3} c_k\mathbf{e}_k.$$

Then from the linearity of the cross product, we have

$$\mathbf{B} \times \mathbf{C} = \sum_{j=1}^{3} \sum_{k=1}^{3} b_j c_k \mathbf{e}_j \times \mathbf{e}_k$$

and

$$\mathbf{A} \times (\mathbf{B} \times \mathbf{C}) = \sum_{i=1}^{3} \sum_{j=1}^{3} \sum_{k=1}^{3} a_i b_j c_k \mathbf{e}_i \times (\mathbf{e}_j \times \mathbf{e}_k).$$

The multiple summation symbols indicate that we are to take the sums over all three indices, giving a total of 27 terms. But then

$$\mathbf{A} \times (\mathbf{B} \times \mathbf{C}) = \sum_{i=1}^{3} \sum_{j=1}^{3} \sum_{k=1}^{3} a_i b_j c_k (\mathbf{e}_i \cdot \mathbf{e}_k)\mathbf{e}_j - \sum_{i=1}^{3} \sum_{j=1}^{3} \sum_{k=1}^{3} a_i b_j c_k (\mathbf{e}_i \cdot \mathbf{e}_j)\mathbf{e}_k.$$

In the first of these summations $\mathbf{e}_i \cdot \mathbf{e}_k = 0$ except when $i = k$; hence for any fixed j, the nine terms with that value of j reduce to three, and are in fact

$$(\mathbf{A} \cdot \mathbf{C})b_j\mathbf{e}_j.$$

Summing these over j gives $(\mathbf{A} \cdot \mathbf{C})\mathbf{B}$. Similarly, the second summation is identified as $-(\mathbf{A} \cdot \mathbf{B})\mathbf{C}$, and the proof of (5–1) has again been obtained.

From (5–1) and the anticommutative property of the cross product, we can obtain the similar identity:

Theorem 5–2. For any vectors **A**, **B**, and **C**,

$$(\mathbf{A} \times \mathbf{B}) \times \mathbf{C} = (\mathbf{A} \cdot \mathbf{C})\mathbf{B} - (\mathbf{B} \cdot \mathbf{C})\mathbf{A}. \tag{5–2}$$

Also, from (5–1) and (5–2) we can prove the following theorem.

Theorem 5–3. For any vectors **A**, **B**, **C**, and **D**,

$$(\mathbf{A}\times\mathbf{B})\times(\mathbf{C}\times\mathbf{D}) = (\mathbf{A}\cdot\mathbf{B}\times\mathbf{D})\mathbf{C} - (\mathbf{A}\cdot\mathbf{B}\times\mathbf{C})\mathbf{D}, \tag{5–3}$$

and

$$(\mathbf{A}\times\mathbf{B})\times(\mathbf{C}\times\mathbf{D}) = (\mathbf{A}\cdot\mathbf{C}\times\mathbf{D})\mathbf{B} - (\mathbf{B}\cdot\mathbf{C}\times\mathbf{D})\mathbf{A}. \tag{5–4}$$

Proof: We prove (5–3) by considering $(\mathbf{A}\times\mathbf{B})$ on the left-hand side as a single vector and using (5–1) on this combination. The properties of the scalar triple product then suffice to complete the proof.

The proof of (5–4) is found similarly by using (5–2) considering $(\mathbf{C}\times\mathbf{D})$, as a single vector.

The right-hand sides of (5–3) and (5–4) represent the same vector. Setting these two expressions equal and doing some rearranging, we find

Theorem 5–4. For any vectors **A**, **B**, **C**, and **D**,

$$(\mathbf{B}\cdot\mathbf{C}\times\mathbf{D})\mathbf{A} - (\mathbf{A}\cdot\mathbf{C}\times\mathbf{D})\mathbf{B} + (\mathbf{A}\cdot\mathbf{B}\times\mathbf{D})\mathbf{C} - (\mathbf{A}\cdot\mathbf{B}\times\mathbf{C})\mathbf{D} = \mathbf{0}. \tag{5–5}$$

Note that the scalar triple products which appear in this result contain the three vectors not being multiplied and that the three vectors appear in their natural order in every case.

Next, we prove an extremely important pair of relations:

Theorem 5–5. For any vectors **A**, **B**, **C**, and **D**,

$$(\mathbf{A}\times\mathbf{B})\cdot(\mathbf{C}\times\mathbf{D}) = (\mathbf{A}\cdot\mathbf{C})(\mathbf{B}\cdot\mathbf{D}) - (\mathbf{B}\cdot\mathbf{C})(\mathbf{A}\cdot\mathbf{D}), \tag{5–6}$$

and

$$|\mathbf{A}\times\mathbf{B}|^2 = |\mathbf{A}|^2|\mathbf{B}|^2 - (\mathbf{A}\cdot\mathbf{B})^2. \tag{5–7}$$

Formula (5–7) is known as *Lagrange's Identity* and (5–6) is usually called the *Extended Lagrange Identity.*

Proof: We prove (5–6) by considering the left-hand member as a scalar triple product and using (5–1) in the following manner:

$$\begin{aligned}(\mathbf{A}\times\mathbf{B})\cdot(\mathbf{C}\times\mathbf{D}) &= \mathbf{A}\cdot[\mathbf{B}\times(\mathbf{C}\times\mathbf{D})]\\ &= \mathbf{A}\cdot[(\mathbf{B}\cdot\mathbf{D})\mathbf{C} - (\mathbf{B}\cdot\mathbf{C})\mathbf{D}]\\ &= (\mathbf{A}\cdot\mathbf{C})(\mathbf{B}\cdot\mathbf{D}) - (\mathbf{B}\cdot\mathbf{C})(\mathbf{A}\cdot\mathbf{D}).\end{aligned}$$

Formula (5–7) is a special case of (5–6), obtained by setting $\mathbf{C} = \mathbf{A}$ and $\mathbf{D} = \mathbf{B}$.

Lagrange's identity Eq. (5–7) has a special geometric significance. If we let θ be the angle between the vectors **A** and **B**, we have $\mathbf{A}\cdot\mathbf{B} = |\mathbf{A}||\mathbf{B}|\cos\theta$.

If we put this into (5–7), we have

$$\begin{aligned}|\mathbf{A} \times \mathbf{B}|^2 &= |\mathbf{A}|^2|\mathbf{B}|^2 - |\mathbf{A}|^2|\mathbf{B}|^2 \cos^2 \theta \\ &= |\mathbf{A}|^2|\mathbf{B}|^2[1 - \cos^2 \theta] \\ &= |\mathbf{A}|^2|\mathbf{B}|^2 \sin^2 \theta.\end{aligned}$$

Taking the square root of this expression shows that

$$|\mathbf{A} \times \mathbf{B}| = |\mathbf{A}||\mathbf{B}| \sin \theta, \tag{5–8}$$

a formula which is similar to the relation found for the dot product. We of course take $\sin \theta$ as nonnegative in this formula. This is equivalent to using only angles between 0 and π.

The importance of formula (5–8) is indicated by the fact that many texts on vector analysis have used this equation to define the cross product. That is, $\mathbf{A} \times \mathbf{B}$ would be defined as a vector orthogonal to both $\mathbf{A}$ and $\mathbf{B}$, with a direction as given by the right-hand rule, and with a magnitude given by (5–8). Such a definition is, however, very difficult to work with. Proving such a fundamental fact as the linearity of the cross product would already cause trouble.

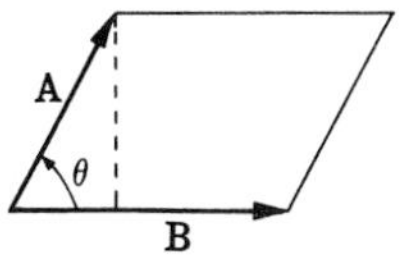

FIGURE 5–1

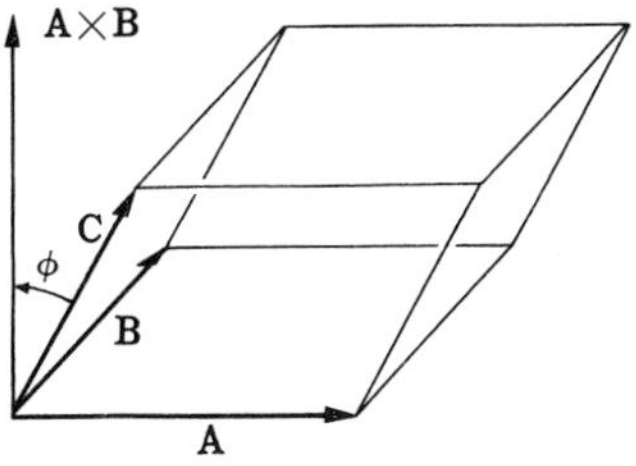

FIGURE 5–2

Consider now the parallelogram determined by the pair of vectors $\mathbf{A}$ and $\mathbf{B}$ (Fig. 5–1). If θ is the angle between the vectors $\mathbf{A}$ and $\mathbf{B}$, then taking $|\mathbf{B}|$ as the length of the base of the parallelogram, we find that the length of the altitude is $|\mathbf{A}| \sin \theta$. Hence the area of this parallelogram is $|\mathbf{A}||\mathbf{B}| \sin \theta = |\mathbf{A} \times \mathbf{B}|$. This can also be interpreted as saying that the vector $\mathbf{A} \times \mathbf{B}$ has a direction orthogonal to the plane of $\mathbf{A}$ and $\mathbf{B}$ and a magnitude equal to the area of the plane parallelogram with sides $\mathbf{A}$ and $\mathbf{B}$.

If we now add a third vector $\mathbf{C}$, we see that

$$(\mathbf{A} \times \mathbf{B}) \cdot \mathbf{C} = |\mathbf{A} \times \mathbf{B}||\mathbf{C}| \cos \phi,$$

where ϕ is the angle between $\mathbf{A} \times \mathbf{B}$ and $\mathbf{C}$. But $|\mathbf{C}| \cos \phi$ is exactly the length of the projection of $\mathbf{C}$ onto the line with direction $\mathbf{A} \times \mathbf{B}$, and hence is the altitude of the parallelepiped with sides **A**, **B**, and **C** (Fig. 5–2). That is, we see that the scalar triple product $\mathbf{A} \times \mathbf{B} \cdot \mathbf{C}$ has a magnitude equal to the volume of this parallelepiped. The sign of the scalar triple product is positive or negative as the triple of vectors forms a right-handed or left-handed set. That is, if the angle between $\mathbf{A} \times \mathbf{B}$ and **C** lies in the range 0 to $\pi/2$, then $\mathbf{A} \times \mathbf{B} \cdot \mathbf{C}$ is positive.

PROBLEMS

1. Prove (5–2) from (5–1).
2. Prove (5–3) from (5–1).
3. Prove (5–4) from (5–2).
4. Let $\mathbf{A} = [1, 2, 5]$, $\mathbf{B} = [-1, -5, 2]$, $\mathbf{C} = [1, 3, 2]$, $\mathbf{D} = [1, 1, -1]$.
   (a) Calculate directly the right-hand and left-hand members of (5–1). Which side is easier to calculate?
   (b) Do the same for (5–3).
   (c) Do the same for (5–6).
5. Show that

$$|\mathbf{A} \times \mathbf{B}|^2 + (\mathbf{A} \cdot \mathbf{B})^2 = |\mathbf{A}|^2|\mathbf{B}|^2,$$

   and prove:
   (a) $\mathbf{A} \times \mathbf{B} = \mathbf{0}$ if and only if $|\mathbf{A} \cdot \mathbf{B}| = |\mathbf{A}| \cdot |\mathbf{B}|$,
   (b) $\mathbf{A} \cdot \mathbf{B} = 0$ if and only if $|\mathbf{A} \times \mathbf{B}| = |\mathbf{A}| \cdot |\mathbf{B}|$.
6. Calculate the area of the parallelogram determined by:
   (a) **A** and **B** in Problem 4
   (b) **A** and **C** in Problem 4
   (c) **B** and **C** in Problem 4
7. Calculate the volume of the parallelepiped determined by **A**, **B**, and **C** of Problem 4.
8. Show that if A, B, and C are three points in space, then the area of the triangle with these three points as vertices is

$$\tfrac{1}{2}|\overrightarrow{AB} \times \overrightarrow{AC}|.$$

9. Show that if A, B, C, and D are four points in space, then the volume of the tetrahedron with these four points as vertices is

$$\tfrac{1}{3}|\overrightarrow{AB} \cdot \overrightarrow{AC} \times \overrightarrow{AD}|.$$

10. Let $A = (1, 3, 7)$, $B = (2, 5, 1)$, $C = (1, 1, 5)$, and $D = (-2, 3, 2)$.
    (a) Find the area of the triangle ABC.
    (b) Find the area of the triangle ABD.
    (c) Find the volume of the tetrahedron $ABCD$.

11. Let (a_1, a_2) and (b_1, b_2) be two points of the plane. Show that the area of the parallelogram which has vertices at the origin and these two points is the absolute value of

$$\begin{vmatrix} a_1 & a_2 \\ b_1 & b_2 \end{vmatrix}.$$

12. Find a formula for the volume of the parallelopiped determined by the four vertices, O (the origin), A, B, and C, in terms of the coordinates of A, B, and C. (See formula 4–12.)

13. From the results of Problems 11 and 12, can you give a condition on the coordinates of the points so that
(a) two points in the plane are on the same line through the origin,
or
(b) three points in space are on the same plane through the origin?

14. Let **A** and **B** be two nonzero vectors. Discuss the problem of finding a vector **X** such that

$$\mathbf{A} \times \mathbf{X} = \mathbf{B}.$$

Find all solutions of this equation if any exist. [*Hint:* What is the direction of the cross product of two vectors? What if **B** is not orthogonal to **A**? If **B** is orthogonal to **A**, **X** must be orthogonal to **B**. Try writing $\mathbf{X} = \mathbf{U} \times \mathbf{B}$. What conditions must **U** satisfy?]

15. Show that there are five different ways in which parentheses can be introduced into the product $\mathbf{A} \times \mathbf{B} \times \mathbf{A} \times \mathbf{B}$ to make it well defined. Using the formulas of this section, simplify each product and show that four of them are always the same.

16. Using the formulas of this section, simplify each of the following expressions.
(a) $\mathbf{A} \times (\mathbf{A} \times \mathbf{B})$
(b) $\mathbf{A} \times (\mathbf{A} \times (\mathbf{A} \times \mathbf{B}))$
(c) $\mathbf{A} \times (\mathbf{A} \times (\mathbf{A} \times (\mathbf{A} \times \mathbf{B})))$
(d) $\mathbf{A} \times (\mathbf{A} \times (\mathbf{A} \times (\mathbf{A} \times (\mathbf{A} \times \mathbf{B}))))$
(e) $\mathbf{A} \times (\mathbf{A} \times (\mathbf{A} \times (\mathbf{A} \times (\mathbf{A} \times (\mathbf{A} \times \mathbf{B})))))$
(f) What would the general formula be?

17. Using (5–8), prove the law of sines for a triangle by vector methods.

18. Find a condition on the vectors **A**, **B**, **C**, and **D** which will guarantee that the plane through the origin, A, and B will be orthogonal to the plane through the origin, C, and D.

19. Prove each of the following:
(a) $(\mathbf{A} \times \mathbf{B}) \cdot (\mathbf{B} \times \mathbf{C}) \times (\mathbf{C} \times \mathbf{A}) = (\mathbf{A} \cdot \mathbf{B} \times \mathbf{C})^2$
(b) $(\mathbf{A} \times \mathbf{B}) \times (\mathbf{A} \times \mathbf{C}) = (\mathbf{A} \cdot \mathbf{B} \times \mathbf{C})\mathbf{A}$
(c) $(((\mathbf{A} \times \mathbf{B}) \times \mathbf{A}) \times (\mathbf{A} \times \mathbf{B})) \cdot ((\mathbf{A} \times \mathbf{B}) \times \mathbf{A}) = 0$
(d) $|\mathbf{A} \times (\mathbf{A} \times \mathbf{B})|^2 = |\mathbf{A}|^4|\mathbf{B}|^2 - |\mathbf{A}|^2(\mathbf{A} \cdot \mathbf{B})^2$
(e) $\mathbf{A} \times (\mathbf{B} \times \mathbf{C}) + \mathbf{B} \times (\mathbf{C} \times \mathbf{A}) + \mathbf{C} \times (\mathbf{A} \times \mathbf{B}) = 0$
(f) $(\mathbf{A} \times \mathbf{B}) \cdot (\mathbf{C} \times \mathbf{D}) + (\mathbf{A} \times \mathbf{D}) \cdot (\mathbf{B} \times \mathbf{C}) = (\mathbf{A} \times \mathbf{C}) \cdot (\mathbf{B} \times \mathbf{D})$

20. Let $\mathbf{A}_1$, $\mathbf{A}_2$, and $\mathbf{A}_3$ be three given vectors. Define $\mathbf{B}_1 = \mathbf{A}_2 \times \mathbf{A}_3$, $\mathbf{B}_2 = \mathbf{A}_3 \times \mathbf{A}_1$, $\mathbf{B}_3 = \mathbf{A}_1 \times \mathbf{A}_2$. Prove that $\mathbf{A}_i \cdot \mathbf{B}_j = 0$ for all $i \neq j$. Can you interpret this geometrically?

5–2 COLLINEAR AND COPLANAR VECTORS

We said that two vectors are collinear if and only if one is a scalar multiple of the other. We have used several intuitive properties of collinearity in our discussions of previous sections. In this section we would like to organize and prove these properties more carefully. The first thing we are interested in is the connection between the cross and dot products and collinearity. This connection is given by the following theorem:

Theorem 5–6. Two vectors $\mathbf{A}$ and $\mathbf{B}$ are collinear if and only if either $\mathbf{A} \times \mathbf{B} = \mathbf{0}$ or $|\mathbf{A} \cdot \mathbf{B}| = |\mathbf{A}||\mathbf{B}|$.

Proof: Formula (5–7) of the last section shows that the two conditions of the theorem are equivalent (see also Problem 5 of that section). Therefore, we see that this result has already been proved in Theorem 4–7. We will, however, offer another proof here, which is somewhat simpler than the proof given in Theorem 4–7.

Half of the theorem is immediately obvious, for if $\mathbf{A}$ and $\mathbf{B}$ are collinear, then there is some t such that $\mathbf{A} = t\mathbf{B}$, and

$$\mathbf{A} \times \mathbf{B} = t\mathbf{B} \times \mathbf{B} = t\mathbf{0} = \mathbf{0}.$$

The other half of the proof is similar to the proof of the Cauchy-Schwarz inequality. Suppose that $|\mathbf{A} \cdot \mathbf{B}| = |\mathbf{A}||\mathbf{B}|$. Further, let us suppose that $\mathbf{A} \neq \mathbf{0}$ (if $\mathbf{A} = \mathbf{0}$, then $\mathbf{A}$ and $\mathbf{B}$ are trivially collinear). Set $t = \pm|\mathbf{B}|/|\mathbf{A}|$, choosing the same sign as $(\mathbf{A} \cdot \mathbf{B})$ so that

$$t(\mathbf{A} \cdot \mathbf{B}) = |t||\mathbf{A} \cdot \mathbf{B}| = \frac{|\mathbf{B}|}{|\mathbf{A}|}|\mathbf{A}||\mathbf{B}| = |\mathbf{B}|^2.$$

Then, just as in the proof of the Cauchy-Schwarz inequality, we find

$$\begin{aligned} |t\mathbf{A} - \mathbf{B}|^2 &= t^2|\mathbf{A}|^2 - 2t(\mathbf{A} \cdot \mathbf{B}) + |\mathbf{B}|^2 \\ &= |\mathbf{B}|^2 - 2|\mathbf{B}|^2 + |\mathbf{B}|^2 = 0. \end{aligned}$$

Hence we can conclude that $\mathbf{B} = t\mathbf{A}$, thus proving the theorem.

As a consequence of this result, we can prove the following theorem, which states a fact that we have already been using in our informal discussion. It is, in effect, the converse of the statement that $\mathbf{A} \times \mathbf{B}$ is orthogonal to both $\mathbf{A}$ and $\mathbf{B}$.

Theorem 5–7. If $\mathbf{C}$ is orthogonal to both $\mathbf{A}$ and $\mathbf{B}$, then $\mathbf{C}$ is collinear with $\mathbf{A} \times \mathbf{B}$.

Proof: If $\mathbf{C}$ is orthogonal to both $\mathbf{A}$ and $\mathbf{B}$, then $\mathbf{C} \cdot \mathbf{A} = 0$ and $\mathbf{C} \cdot \mathbf{B} = 0$. But then, using (5–1), we can compute

$$\begin{aligned} \mathbf{C} \times (\mathbf{A} \times \mathbf{B}) &= (\mathbf{C} \cdot \mathbf{B})\mathbf{A} - (\mathbf{C} \cdot \mathbf{A})\mathbf{B} \\ &= \mathbf{0}, \end{aligned}$$

and hence we can conclude from Theorem 5–6 that $\mathbf{C}$ is collinear with $\mathbf{A} \times \mathbf{B}$. This result should be compared with Theorems 4–2 and 4–3.

We now turn to a consideration of coplanar vectors. We shall call a collection of vectors coplanar if they are all parallel to the same plane. If we think of a set of vectors as being line segments drawn from the origin, then they are coplanar only if there exists a plane through the origin containing all of them. From our definition of a plane, this will occur only if there is some vector (the orthogonal vector to the plane) orthogonal to all vectors in the plane. Therefore, we use this as our formal definition.

Definition 5–1. A collection of vectors is called *coplanar* if and only if there exists a nonzero vector $\mathbf{N}$ orthogonal to all vectors in the collection.

Directly from this definition we can prove

Theorem 5–8. Two vectors are always coplanar. Three vectors, $\mathbf{A}$, $\mathbf{B}$, and $\mathbf{C}$, are coplanar if and only if $\mathbf{A} \cdot \mathbf{B} \times \mathbf{C} = 0$.

Proof: Let $\mathbf{A}$ and $\mathbf{B}$ be two given vectors. Suppose first that they are not collinear. Then $\mathbf{A} \times \mathbf{B} \neq \mathbf{0}$ (from Theorem 5–6), and the vector $\mathbf{N} = \mathbf{A} \times \mathbf{B}$ will be the required common orthogonal to $\mathbf{A}$ and $\mathbf{B}$.

On the other hand, if $\mathbf{A}$ and $\mathbf{B}$ are collinear and if either is nonzero, then any nonzero vector orthogonal to it will satisfy the requirements. The existence of such a vector is easy to show. If both $\mathbf{A}$ and $\mathbf{B}$ are zero, then any nonzero vector is orthogonal to both.

The remaining part of the theorem requires two proofs, since it is an "if and only if" statement. For the first proof, let us suppose that $\mathbf{A}$, $\mathbf{B}$, and $\mathbf{C}$ are coplanar—that is, that there exists a nonzero vector $\mathbf{N}$ orthogonal to all three. We must then show that $\mathbf{A} \cdot \mathbf{B} \times \mathbf{C} = 0$. However, since $\mathbf{A} \cdot \mathbf{N} = 0$ and $\mathbf{B} \cdot \mathbf{N} = 0$, we find from Theorem 5–7 that $\mathbf{N}$ is collinear with $\mathbf{A} \times \mathbf{B}$. Since $\mathbf{N} \neq \mathbf{0}$, this means that there must exist a scalar t such that $\mathbf{A} \times \mathbf{B} = t\mathbf{N}$. But then we calculate

$$\begin{aligned} \mathbf{A} \cdot \mathbf{B} \times \mathbf{C} &= (\mathbf{A} \times \mathbf{B}) \cdot \mathbf{C} \\ &= t\mathbf{N} \cdot \mathbf{C} \\ &= 0, \end{aligned}$$

because $\mathbf{N}$ was also orthogonal to $\mathbf{C}$.

To prove the last part of the theorem, let us suppose that $\mathbf{A} \cdot \mathbf{B} \times \mathbf{C} = 0$. If $\mathbf{A} \times \mathbf{B} \neq \mathbf{0}$, we can set $\mathbf{N} = \mathbf{A} \times \mathbf{B}$. Then $\mathbf{N} \cdot \mathbf{A} = \mathbf{N} \cdot \mathbf{B} = 0$, and $\mathbf{N} \cdot \mathbf{C} = \mathbf{A} \times \mathbf{B} \cdot \mathbf{C} = 0$, hence $\mathbf{A}$, $\mathbf{B}$, and $\mathbf{C}$ are coplanar. On the other hand, if $\mathbf{A} \times \mathbf{B} = \mathbf{0}$, then $\mathbf{A}$ and $\mathbf{B}$ are collinear. If $\mathbf{A} = \mathbf{B} = \mathbf{0}$, then using the first part of the theorem, we see that $\mathbf{A}$, $\mathbf{B}$, and $\mathbf{C}$ are coplanar. If one of these, say $\mathbf{A}$, is not zero, then $\mathbf{B} = t\mathbf{A}$, and again from the first part of the theorem, $\mathbf{A}$ and $\mathbf{C}$ are coplanar. That is, there exists a nonzero $\mathbf{N}$ such that $\mathbf{N} \cdot \mathbf{A} = \mathbf{N} \cdot \mathbf{C} = 0$. This also implies $\mathbf{N} \cdot \mathbf{B} = t(\mathbf{N} \cdot \mathbf{A}) = 0$, and hence we have proved the theorem.

The last part of this proof is somewhat involved, because there are many separate cases which have to be considered. The reader may find it useful to diagram the proof, seeing how the various cases arise and how they are disposed of. The basic ideas used in the "main" cases are really the important ones.

Theorem 5–9. Let $\mathbf{A}$ and $\mathbf{B}$ be two noncollinear vectors. Then a vector $\mathbf{C}$ is coplanar with $\mathbf{A}$ and $\mathbf{B}$ if and only if there exist scalars s and t such that

$$\mathbf{C} = s\mathbf{A} + t\mathbf{B}. \tag{5-9}$$

Proof: Suppose that $\mathbf{C} = s\mathbf{A} + t\mathbf{B}$. Then

$$\begin{aligned} \mathbf{A} \cdot \mathbf{B} \times \mathbf{C} &= (\mathbf{A} \times \mathbf{B}) \cdot \mathbf{C} \\ &= (\mathbf{A} \times \mathbf{B}) \cdot [s\mathbf{A} + t\mathbf{B}] \\ &= s(\mathbf{A} \times \mathbf{B}) \cdot \mathbf{A} + t(\mathbf{A} \times \mathbf{B}) \cdot \mathbf{B}. \end{aligned}$$

But $\mathbf{A} \times \mathbf{B} \cdot \mathbf{A} = \mathbf{A} \times \mathbf{B} \cdot \mathbf{B} = 0$, and hence we conclude from Theorem 5–8 that $\mathbf{A}$, $\mathbf{B}$, and $\mathbf{C}$ are coplanar.

The other half of the theorem is more difficult. Suppose that $\mathbf{A}$, $\mathbf{B}$, and $\mathbf{C}$ are coplanar. Then $\mathbf{A} \cdot \mathbf{B} \times \mathbf{C} = 0$ (from Theorem 5–8). From the hypothesis that $\mathbf{A}$ and $\mathbf{B}$ are not collinear we have $\mathbf{A} \times \mathbf{B} \neq \mathbf{0}$. Let $\mathbf{D} = \mathbf{A} \times \mathbf{B}$. We now make use of formula (5–5) of the last section. This gives us

$$(\mathbf{B} \cdot \mathbf{C} \times \mathbf{D})\mathbf{A} - (\mathbf{A} \cdot \mathbf{C} \times \mathbf{D})\mathbf{B} + (\mathbf{A} \cdot \mathbf{B} \times \mathbf{D})\mathbf{C} - (\mathbf{A} \cdot \mathbf{B} \times \mathbf{C})\mathbf{D} = \mathbf{0}. \tag{5-10}$$

As we have seen, the coefficient of **D** in this expression is 0. The coefficient of **C** is

$$\begin{aligned}(\mathbf{A} \cdot \mathbf{B} \times \mathbf{D}) &= (\mathbf{A} \times \mathbf{B} \cdot \mathbf{D}) \\ &= (\mathbf{A} \times \mathbf{B}) \cdot (\mathbf{A} \times \mathbf{B}) \\ &= |\mathbf{A} \times \mathbf{B}|^2,\end{aligned}$$

which is nonzero by hypothesis. We can therefore solve (5–10) for **C**. Doing so and replacing **D** by **A** × **B** gives

$$\mathbf{C} = -\frac{(\mathbf{B} \times \mathbf{C}) \cdot (\mathbf{A} \times \mathbf{B})}{|\mathbf{A} \times \mathbf{B}|^2}\mathbf{A} + \frac{(\mathbf{A} \times \mathbf{C}) \cdot (\mathbf{A} \times \mathbf{B})}{|\mathbf{A} \times \mathbf{B}|^2}\mathbf{B}. \qquad (5\text{–}11)$$

This is the expression of the form (5–9) needed to prove the theorem.

The last result can be extended to give us the following important theorem:

Theorem 5–10. If the vectors **A**, **B**, and **C** are not coplanar, then every vector **D** can be written as a linear combination of **A**, **B**, and **C**. That is, for any **D** there exist scalars s, t, and u such that

$$\mathbf{D} = s\mathbf{A} + t\mathbf{B} + u\mathbf{C}. \qquad (5\text{–}12)$$

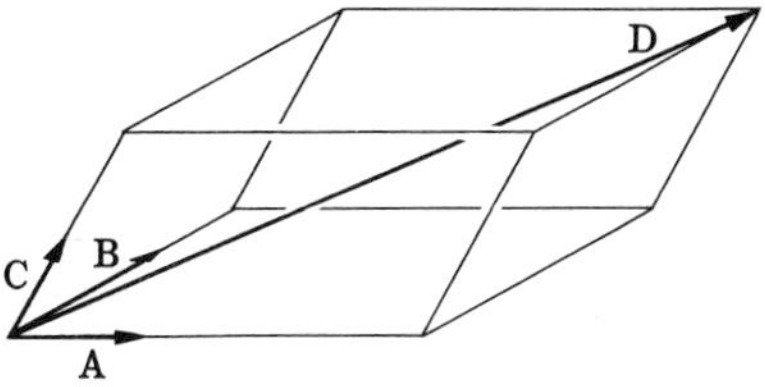

FIGURE 5–3

Proof: For any four vectors, formula (5–10) holds. By the hypothesis that **A**, **B**, and **C** are not coplanar and by Theorem 5–8, $\mathbf{A} \cdot \mathbf{B} \times \mathbf{C} \neq 0$. Hence we can solve (5–10) for **D**, giving

$$\mathbf{D} = \frac{(\mathbf{B} \cdot \mathbf{C} \times \mathbf{D})}{(\mathbf{A} \cdot \mathbf{B} \times \mathbf{C})}\mathbf{A} - \frac{(\mathbf{A} \cdot \mathbf{C} \times \mathbf{D})}{(\mathbf{A} \cdot \mathbf{B} \times \mathbf{C})}\mathbf{B} + \frac{(\mathbf{A} \cdot \mathbf{B} \times \mathbf{D})}{(\mathbf{A} \cdot \mathbf{B} \times \mathbf{C})}\mathbf{C}. \qquad (5\text{–}13)$$

The last theorem tells us that if we are given any three noncoplanar vectors, then every vector can be expressed as a linear combination of these. The geometric meaning of this statement is illustrated in Fig. 5–3. Here, all vectors are represented as directed line segments from the origin. Comparing this sketch with Fig. 3–1, we see that the three vectors **A**, **B**, and **C** can be thought of as determining an oblique system of coordinates. A point D in space can be determined by its **A**, **B**, **C** coordinates, which are (s, t, u) as given by (5–12). We will exploit this point of view further in the next section.

Let us emphasize that the formulas and conclusions of this section have been obtained with the help of the cross product. In a later section we will see what can be done without having to use the cross product.

Formulas (5–11) and (5–13) are easy to use in practice. For example, suppose that

$$\mathbf{A} = [1, -3, 2], \quad \mathbf{B} = [1, -1, -1], \quad \text{and} \quad \mathbf{C} = [-3, -7, 18].$$

We find $\mathbf{A} \times \mathbf{B} = [5, 3, 2]$, and so $\mathbf{A}$ and $\mathbf{B}$ are not collinear. But $\mathbf{A} \cdot \mathbf{B} \times \mathbf{C} = 0$; so the three vectors are coplanar. Computing the coefficients in (5–11) gives us

$$\mathbf{C} = 5\mathbf{A} - 8\mathbf{B},$$

as the reader may easily verify.

Theorems 5–9 and 5–10 seem to have a great deal in common. Adding the remark that if $\mathbf{A} \neq \mathbf{0}$ and $\mathbf{A}$ and $\mathbf{B}$ are collinear, then there is a scalar s such that $\mathbf{B} = s\mathbf{A}$, we see that the following three statements are related:

(i) A single vector $\mathbf{A}$ is nonzero;

(ii) Two vectors $\mathbf{A}$ and $\mathbf{B}$ are noncollinear;

(iii) Three vectors $\mathbf{A}$, $\mathbf{B}$, and $\mathbf{C}$ are noncoplanar.

There is a fundamental property which underlies these three statements. This property has been found to be most important in any attempt to extend the concept of vectors. It is called *linear independence.*

Definition 5–2. A finite collection of vectors $\mathbf{A}_1, \mathbf{A}_2, \ldots, \mathbf{A}_n$ is called *linearly dependent* if and only if there exist scalars λ_i $(i = 1, \ldots, n)$, not all zero, such that

$$\lambda_1\mathbf{A}_1 + \lambda_2\mathbf{A}_2 + \cdots + \lambda_n\mathbf{A}_n = \mathbf{0}. \tag{5–14}$$

A collection of vectors which is not linearly dependent is called *linearly independent.*

Note that in order to prove that a set of vectors is linearly independent, one must show that if (5–14) holds, then $\lambda_1 = \lambda_2 = \cdots = \lambda_n = 0$. The connection of linear independence with the concepts already discussed in this section is contained in the following theorem:

Theorem 5–11.

(1) A single vector $\mathbf{A}$ is linearly dependent if and only if $\mathbf{A} = \mathbf{0}$.
(2) Two vectors, $\mathbf{A}$ and $\mathbf{B}$, are linearly dependent if and only if they are collinear.
(3) Three vectors are linearly dependent if and only if they are coplanar.
(4) Four vectors are always linearly dependent.

Proof: Statement (1) follows obviously from Definition 5–2.

Statement (2) follows easily from the definition of collinearity. For if there exist λ_1 and λ_2 not both zero such that

$$\lambda_1\mathbf{A} + \lambda_2\mathbf{B} = \mathbf{0}, \tag{5–15}$$

then we can solve for one of the two vectors as a scalar multiple of the other, and hence vectors **A** and **B** are collinear. On the other hand, if **A** and **B** are collinear, then one is a scalar multiple of the other. Suppose, for example, that $\mathbf{A} = t\mathbf{B}$. This statement can then be rewritten in the form (5–15),

$$\mathbf{A} + (-t)\mathbf{B} = \mathbf{0}.$$

One of the coefficients is 1, and hence is nonzero.

Statement (3) follows in the same manner with the help of Theorem 5–9.

Similarly, statement (4) follows from Theorem 5–10, provided three of the four vectors are noncoplanar. If, however, some three of the vectors are coplanar, then these three are already linearly dependent. We can, therefore, write (5–14) with not all coefficients zero, using just these three vectors. To write such an expression involving all four vectors, just add the fourth vector with a coefficient of zero. This shows that the four vectors are linearly dependent in any case.

Note that Theorem 5–10 can now be rewritten in the following form:

Theorem 5–12. If **A**, **B**, and **C** are linearly independent, then any vector **D** can be written as a linear combination of **A**, **B**, and **C**.

PROBLEMS

1. Let n vectors, $\mathbf{A}_1, \mathbf{A}_2, \ldots, \mathbf{A}_n$, be given. Let **R** be some nonzero vector. Prove that the vectors $\mathbf{B}_1 = \mathbf{R} \times \mathbf{A}_1$, $\mathbf{B}_2 = \mathbf{R} \times \mathbf{A}_2, \ldots, \mathbf{B}_n = \mathbf{R} \times \mathbf{A}_n$ are coplanar.

2. Prove that if **A** is collinear with $\mathbf{B} \neq \mathbf{0}$ and **B** is collinear with **C**, then **A** is collinear with **C**.

3. Prove that there always exists a nonzero vector orthogonal to a given vector.

4. Use identity (5–5) on the final expression obtained for **C** in formula (5–11). How is this expression simplified if $|\mathbf{A}| = 1$, $|\mathbf{B}| = 1$, and **A** and **B** are orthogonal?

5. Let **A**, **B**, and **C** be three noncoplanar vectors. Show that the representation of a vector **D** as given in (5–12) is unique.

6. Show that a plane is defined by

$$\{\mathbf{X} \mid \mathbf{X} = \mathbf{P}_0 + s\mathbf{A} + t\mathbf{B}, \text{ for all real } s \text{ and } t\},$$

where **A** and **B** are a pair of noncollinear vectors. What is the equation of this plane? (This is called the parametric representation of a plane.)

7. Let $\mathbf{A} = [a_1, a_2, a_3]$, $\mathbf{B} = [b_1, b_2, b_3]$, $\mathbf{C} = [c_1, c_2, c_3]$ and $\mathbf{D} = [d_1, d_2, d_3]$. Show that the system of equations

$$\begin{aligned} a_1x + b_1y + c_1z &= d_1, \\ a_2x + b_2y + c_2z &= d_2, \\ a_3x + b_3y + c_3z &= d_3 \end{aligned}$$

is equivalent to the single vector equation

$$x\mathbf{A} + y\mathbf{B} + z\mathbf{C} = \mathbf{D}.$$

What happens to this equation if we take the dot product of each side with $\mathbf{B} \times \mathbf{C}$? Use this to solve for x. Do the same with $\mathbf{A} \times \mathbf{C}$ and $\mathbf{A} \times \mathbf{B}$. Under what circumstances will a solution exist?

8. Prove that for any vectors **A**, **B**, **C**, and **D**, with $\mathbf{A} \cdot \mathbf{B} \times \mathbf{C} \neq 0$,

$$\mathbf{D} = \frac{(\mathbf{D} \cdot \mathbf{B} \times \mathbf{C})}{(\mathbf{A} \cdot \mathbf{B} \times \mathbf{C})}\mathbf{A} + \frac{(\mathbf{A} \cdot \mathbf{D} \times \mathbf{C})}{(\mathbf{A} \cdot \mathbf{B} \times \mathbf{C})}\mathbf{B} + \frac{(\mathbf{A} \cdot \mathbf{B} \times \mathbf{D})}{(\mathbf{A} \cdot \mathbf{B} \times \mathbf{C})}\mathbf{C}.$$

9. Suppose that **A** and **B** are two noncollinear vectors. Show that if $\mathbf{C} = \mathbf{A} \times \mathbf{B}$, then **A**, **B**, and **C** are noncoplanar.

10. Let **A** and **B** be noncollinear vectors. Rewrite formula (5–13) in terms of **A**, **B**, and **D** alone when $\mathbf{C} = \mathbf{A} \times \mathbf{B}$. Compare with (5–11).

11. For each of the following, prove that the three vectors are coplanar and obtain **C** as a linear combination of **A** and **B**.

(a) $\mathbf{A} = [2, 0, 1]$, $\mathbf{B} = [0, 3, 4]$, $\mathbf{C} = [8, -3, 0]$
(b) $\mathbf{A} = [1, 7, -2]$, $\mathbf{B} = [-1, 5, 1]$, $\mathbf{C} = [7, 1, -10]$
(c) $\mathbf{A} = [1, 2, 0]$, $\mathbf{B} = [1, 1, 0]$, $\mathbf{C} = [1, -4, 0]$
(d) $\mathbf{A} = [1, 1, 1]$, $\mathbf{B} = [1, 2, 3]$, $\mathbf{C} = [5, 0, -5]$

12. For each of the following, prove that **A**, **B**, and **C** are not coplanar and obtain **D** as a linear combination of **A**, **B**, and **C**.

(a) $\mathbf{A} = [1, 0, 0]$, $\mathbf{B} = [1, 1, 0]$,
$\mathbf{C} = [1, 1, 1]$, $\mathbf{D} = [5, 3, -1]$

(b) $\mathbf{A} = [1, 2, -1]$, $\mathbf{B} = [2, 0, 3]$,
$\mathbf{C} = [6, -5, -4]$, $\mathbf{D} = [3, -12, -24]$

(c) $\mathbf{A} = [-1, 3, -1]$, $\mathbf{B} = [4, 2, 1]$,
$\mathbf{C} = [3, 5, 1]$, $\mathbf{D} = [-8, 24, -10]$

(d) $\mathbf{A} = [2, 7, 5]$, $\mathbf{B} = [-1, -8, 3]$,
$\mathbf{C} = [1, 1, -5]$, $\mathbf{D} = [6, 3, 37]$

5-3 COORDINATE VECTORS

We have defined a vector as a triple of numbers. This gives a natural representation of an arbitrary vector as a linear combination of the three special unit vectors $\mathbf{e}_1 = [1, 0, 0]$, $\mathbf{e}_2 = [0, 1, 0]$, and $\mathbf{e}_3 = [0, 0, 1]$. That is,

$$[x, y, z] = x\mathbf{e}_1 + y\mathbf{e}_2 + z\mathbf{e}_3.$$

We remark that these are not the symbols most often used in vector analysis. The more common symbols are **i**, **j**, and **k**. We have avoided using these for two reasons. First, the letters i and j already cause enough confusion, since they are used as symbols with several different meanings in mathematics, physics, and electrical engineering. But a much more important reason is that we are looking forward to a generalization of three-dimensional vectors to a higher number of dimensions. Most of the formulas we have derived will have natural generalizations, but the symbols **i**, **j**, and **k** would have to be replaced by others (normally $\mathbf{e}_1, \mathbf{e}_2, \ldots, \mathbf{e}_n$).

Theorem 5–10 of the previous section shows that any three noncoplanar vectors can be used to express arbitrary vectors in space. Suppose we had three noncoplanar vectors $\mathbf{u}_1$, $\mathbf{u}_2$, and $\mathbf{u}_3$, and

$$\mathbf{A} = a_1\mathbf{u}_1 + a_2\mathbf{u}_2 + a_3\mathbf{u}_3,$$
$$\mathbf{B} = b_1\mathbf{u}_1 + b_2\mathbf{u}_2 + b_3\mathbf{u}_3.$$

Then using the linearity of the dot product, we obtain

$$\mathbf{A} \cdot \mathbf{B} = \sum_{i=1}^{3} \sum_{j=1}^{3} a_i b_j (\mathbf{u}_i \cdot \mathbf{u}_j).$$

This summation contains nine terms in all. It would be much simpler if the vectors $\mathbf{u}_i$ were mutually orthogonal. Then $\mathbf{u}_i \cdot \mathbf{u}_j = 0$ if $i \neq j$, and we would have

$$\mathbf{A} \cdot \mathbf{B} = \sum_{i=1}^{3} a_i b_i |\mathbf{u}_i|^2.$$

Again, this formula would be simplified if each $\mathbf{u}_i$ had magnitude 1. In this case,

$$\mathbf{A} \cdot \mathbf{B} = \sum_{i=1}^{3} a_i b_i,$$

the same formula we had for the dot product in terms of the expansion by the natural unit vectors, $\mathbf{e}_1$, $\mathbf{e}_2$, and $\mathbf{e}_3$.

Definition 5–3. A set of three nonzero vectors, $\mathbf{u}_1$, $\mathbf{u}_2$, and $\mathbf{u}_3$ is called an *orthogonal* set if and only if $\mathbf{u}_i \cdot \mathbf{u}_j = 0$ for all $i \neq j$. It is called an *orthonormal* set if and only if it is an orthogonal set and in addition $|\mathbf{u}_i| = 1$ for all i.

Note that according to this definition, the unit coordinate vectors $\mathbf{e}_1$, $\mathbf{e}_2$, and $\mathbf{e}_3$ are an orthonormal set. The following theorem is a direct consequence of this definition and shows how similar an orthonormal set is in its behavior to the unit coordinate vectors.

Theorem 5–13. Let $\mathbf{u}_1, \mathbf{u}_2, \mathbf{u}_3$ be an orthonormal set of vectors. Then this set of vectors is linearly independent. Given any vector $\mathbf{A}$,

$$\mathbf{A} = (\mathbf{A} \cdot \mathbf{u}_1)\mathbf{u}_1 + (\mathbf{A} \cdot \mathbf{u}_2)\mathbf{u}_2 + (\mathbf{A} \cdot \mathbf{u}_3)\mathbf{u}_3. \tag{5–16}$$

If $\mathbf{A} = a_1\mathbf{u}_1 + a_2\mathbf{u}_2 + a_3\mathbf{u}_3$ and $\mathbf{B} = b_1\mathbf{u}_1 + b_2\mathbf{u}_2 + b_3\mathbf{u}_3$, then

$$\mathbf{A} \cdot \mathbf{B} = a_1b_1 + a_2b_2 + a_3b_3. \tag{5–17}$$

Proof: To see that an orthonormal set is linearly independent we merely need observe that if

$$\lambda_1\mathbf{u}_1 + \lambda_2\mathbf{u}_2 + \lambda_3\mathbf{u}_3 = \mathbf{0},$$

then

$$\begin{aligned} 0 &= \mathbf{0} \cdot \mathbf{u}_1 \\ &= (\lambda_1\mathbf{u}_1 + \lambda_2\mathbf{u}_2 + \lambda_3\mathbf{u}_3) \cdot \mathbf{u}_1 \\ &= \lambda_1(\mathbf{u}_1 \cdot \mathbf{u}_1) + \lambda_2(\mathbf{u}_2 \cdot \mathbf{u}_1) + \lambda_3(\mathbf{u}_3 \cdot \mathbf{u}_1) \\ &= \lambda_1. \end{aligned}$$

In exactly the same way we can compute λ_2 and λ_3 to be equal to zero. Hence the three vectors are linearly independent. But then, as we saw in Theorem 5–10, any vector $\mathbf{A}$ can be expressed as a linear combination of the three orthonormal vectors,

$$\mathbf{A} = a_1\mathbf{u}_1 + a_2\mathbf{u}_2 + a_3\mathbf{u}_3.$$

However, we may then compute

$$\mathbf{A} \cdot \mathbf{u}_1 = (a_1\mathbf{u}_1 + a_2\mathbf{u}_2 + a_3\mathbf{u}_3) \cdot \mathbf{u}_1 = a_1$$

just as above. Similarly we find $\mathbf{A} \cdot \mathbf{u}_2 = a_2$ and $\mathbf{A} \cdot \mathbf{u}_3 = a_3$, which proves the second assertion of the theorem. The final part was done above.

The question which this theorem immediately raises is: can we produce an orthonormal set of vectors from any three linearly independent vectors?

Thinking geometrically it is quite obvious how this must be done. Suppose we have three vectors $\mathbf{A}_1$, $\mathbf{A}_2$, and $\mathbf{A}_3$ which are linearly independent. It is easy to produce a vector with magnitude 1 in the same direction as $\mathbf{A}_1$, namely $\mathbf{u}_1 = \mathbf{A}_1/|\mathbf{A}_1|$. Clearly, it is possible to find a vector orthogonal to $\mathbf{u}_1$ in the plane of $\mathbf{A}_1$ and $\mathbf{A}_2$. Such a vector is $\mathbf{B}_2 = (\mathbf{A}_1 \times \mathbf{A}_2) \times \mathbf{A}_1$. We then can set $\mathbf{u}_2 = \mathbf{B}_2/|\mathbf{B}_2|$. To get a third vector orthogonal to both $\mathbf{u}_1$ and $\mathbf{u}_2$, we only need to take $\mathbf{u}_1 \times \mathbf{u}_2$. This process can be simplified somewhat. Since the vector $\mathbf{u}_3$ is merely required to be orthogonal to the plane of $\mathbf{A}_1$ and $\mathbf{A}_2$, we could just as easily set

$$\mathbf{u}_3 = \frac{\mathbf{A}_1 \times \mathbf{A}_2}{|\mathbf{A}_1 \times \mathbf{A}_2|},$$

and then $\mathbf{u}_2 = \mathbf{u}_3 \times \mathbf{u}_1$. The reader should note how the requirement that $\mathbf{A}_1$, $\mathbf{A}_2$, and $\mathbf{A}_3$ be linearly independent implies that the quantities $|\mathbf{A}_1|$, $|\mathbf{B}_2|$, and $|\mathbf{A}_1 \times \mathbf{A}_2|$ be all nonzero.

Therefore, we see that we have actually proved:

Theorem 5–14. Let $\mathbf{A}_1$ and $\mathbf{A}_2$ be a given pair of noncollinear vectors. Let

$$\begin{aligned} \mathbf{u}_1 &= \frac{\mathbf{A}_1}{|\mathbf{A}_1|}, \\ \mathbf{u}_3 &= \frac{\mathbf{A}_1 \times \mathbf{A}_2}{|\mathbf{A}_1 \times \mathbf{A}_2|}, \qquad (5\text{–}18) \\ \mathbf{u}_2 &= \mathbf{u}_3 \times \mathbf{u}_1. \end{aligned}$$

Then $\mathbf{u}_1$, $\mathbf{u}_2$, and $\mathbf{u}_3$ form an orthonormal set with $\mathbf{u}_1$ parallel to $\mathbf{A}_1$ and $\mathbf{u}_2$ coplanar with $\mathbf{A}_1$ and $\mathbf{A}_2$.

For example, suppose we have the vectors $\mathbf{A}_1 = [6, -3, 2]$ and $\mathbf{A}_2 = [8, 3, 5]$. Then $|\mathbf{A}_1| = [36 + 9 + 4]^{1/2} = 7$, and so

$$\mathbf{u}_1 = [\tfrac{6}{7}, -\tfrac{3}{7}, \tfrac{2}{7}].$$

Also

$$\begin{aligned} \mathbf{A}_1 \times \mathbf{A}_2 &= [-21, -14, 42] \\ &= 7[-3, -2, 6], \end{aligned}$$

and hence $|\mathbf{A}_1 \times \mathbf{A}_2| = 7 \cdot 7 = 49$. Thus

$$\mathbf{u}_3 = [-\tfrac{3}{7}, -\tfrac{2}{7}, \tfrac{6}{7}],$$

and taking the cross product, we have

$$\mathbf{u}_2 = [\tfrac{2}{7}, \tfrac{6}{7}, \tfrac{3}{7}].$$

The reader should verify for himself that these three vectors do indeed form an orthonormal set.

We can now discuss coordinate systems. In our definition of points in space as triples of numbers, we assumed an intrinsic coordinate system. However, we feel that the points of our space have an independent existence, without regard to the particular coordinate system that we happen to use. Similarly vectors, which are thought of as a property of directed line segments, independent of translation, cannot really depend on the coordinate system either, despite the way we defined them.

We discussed the problem of translation earlier and saw that no real change in the properties of space resulted from translation of the coordinate system (which is algebraically equivalent to translation of the entire space). Translation of the coordinate system in space leaves the representation of vectors as triples of numbers unchanged, of course.

We still have the problem of rotation of coordinate systems to consider. In this regard, it is best to make the identification between vectors and points of space and consider both simultaneously. That is, we consider all vectors to be directed line segments with initial points at the origin, and identify the terminal point of the segment with the vector.

In this context, our initial choice of a set of mutually orthogonal coordinate axes corresponds to a choice of an orthonormal set of vectors: the unit vectors in the positive directions along the coordinate axes. The coordinates of a point (or the components of a vector) in terms of this coordinate system are then given by the three coefficients of these unit vectors in the expansion of the vector, for example,

$$\mathbf{A} = a_1\mathbf{u}_1 + a_2\mathbf{u}_2 + a_3\mathbf{u}_3.$$

Formula (5-16) of Theorem 5-13 shows how these coefficients can actually be obtained for a given new coordinate system. For example, the vectors

$$\begin{aligned}\mathbf{u}_1 &= \left[\frac{1}{\sqrt{2}}, \frac{1}{\sqrt{2}}, 0\right],\\ \mathbf{u}_2 &= \left[\frac{1}{\sqrt{3}}, -\frac{1}{\sqrt{3}}, \frac{1}{\sqrt{3}}\right],\\ \mathbf{u}_3 &= \left[\frac{1}{\sqrt{6}}, -\frac{1}{\sqrt{6}}, -\frac{2}{\sqrt{6}}\right]\end{aligned} \tag{5-19}$$

form an orthonormal set. If these are considered to define a coordinate system, say the $x'y'z'$-coordinate system (in that order), then any point X which initially has coordinates (x, y, z) will have coordinates (x', y', z')

in this new coordinate system. To find the relationship between these coordinates, we observe that

$$\mathbf{X} = [x, y, z] = x\mathbf{e}_1 + y\mathbf{e}_2 + z\mathbf{e}_3 = x'\mathbf{u}_1 + y'\mathbf{u}_2 + z'\mathbf{u}_3,$$

and from (5–16) we have

$$x' = (\mathbf{X} \cdot \mathbf{u}_1) = \frac{1}{\sqrt{2}} x + \frac{1}{\sqrt{2}} y,$$

$$y' = (\mathbf{X} \cdot \mathbf{u}_2) = \frac{1}{\sqrt{3}} x - \frac{1}{\sqrt{3}} y + \frac{1}{\sqrt{3}} z,$$

$$z' = (\mathbf{X} \cdot \mathbf{u}_3) = \frac{1}{\sqrt{6}} x - \frac{1}{\sqrt{6}} y - \frac{2}{\sqrt{6}} z.$$

Formula (5–17) is of special interest in connection with the point of view of considering $\mathbf{u}_1$, $\mathbf{u}_2$, and $\mathbf{u}_3$ as defining a new coordinate system. This formula says that the representation of the dot product of two vectors in terms of their components is the same no matter what orthonormal set of vectors is used to define the coordinate system. Despite the fact that our initial definition of the dot product was in terms of a given coordinate system, it is really independent of this choice.

What about the cross product? It too was defined in terms of the intrinsic coordinates. Let us see what happens if we express vectors in terms of another orthonormal set. Suppose that

$$\mathbf{A} = a_1\mathbf{u}_1 + a_2\mathbf{u}_2 + a_3\mathbf{u}_3,$$
$$\mathbf{B} = b_1\mathbf{u}_2 + b_2\mathbf{u}_2 + b_3\mathbf{u}_3.$$

Then if we take the cross product $\mathbf{A} \times \mathbf{B}$, using the linearity and the anticommutative property, we find

$$\mathbf{A} \times \mathbf{B} = (a_2b_3 - a_3b_2)\mathbf{u}_2 \times \mathbf{u}_3 + (a_1b_3 - a_3b_1)\mathbf{u}_1 \times \mathbf{u}_3 + (a_1b_2 - a_2b_1)\mathbf{u}_1 \times \mathbf{u}_2. \qquad (5\text{–}20)$$

Here, we have discarded the terms involving $\mathbf{u}_1 \times \mathbf{u}_1$, $\mathbf{u}_2 \times \mathbf{u}_2$, and $\mathbf{u}_3 \times \mathbf{u}_3$ since they are zero.

Now, we know that $\mathbf{u}_1 \times \mathbf{u}_2$ is orthogonal to both $\mathbf{u}_1$ and $\mathbf{u}_2$, hence $\mathbf{u}_1 \times \mathbf{u}_2 = c\mathbf{u}_3$; but from (5–16) we see that $c = \mathbf{u}_1 \times \mathbf{u}_2 \cdot \mathbf{u}_3$, and so

$$\mathbf{u}_1 \times \mathbf{u}_2 = (\mathbf{u}_1 \times \mathbf{u}_2 \cdot \mathbf{u}_3)\mathbf{u}_3.$$

On the other hand, from identity (5–7)

$$|\mathbf{u}_1 \times \mathbf{u}_2|^2 = |\mathbf{u}_1|^2|\mathbf{u}_2|^2 - (\mathbf{u}_1 \cdot \mathbf{u}_2)^2 = 1,$$

since $\mathbf{u}_1 \cdot \mathbf{u}_2 = 0$, so that $\mathbf{u}_1 \times \mathbf{u}_2 = \pm\mathbf{u}_3$.

If $\mathbf{u}_1 \times \mathbf{u}_2 = \mathbf{u}_3$ (and $\mathbf{u}_1 \cdot \mathbf{u}_2 \times \mathbf{u}_3 = +1$), we say that $\mathbf{u}_1$, $\mathbf{u}_2$, and $\mathbf{u}_3$ constitute a right-handed system of vectors. Let us assume that this is true for the moment. Then with the help of identity (5–1), we have

$$\begin{aligned}\mathbf{u}_2 \times \mathbf{u}_3 &= \mathbf{u}_2 \times (\mathbf{u}_1 \times \mathbf{u}_2)\\ &= (\mathbf{u}_2 \cdot \mathbf{u}_2)\mathbf{u}_1 - (\mathbf{u}_2 \cdot \mathbf{u}_1)\mathbf{u}_2\\ &= \mathbf{u}_1,\end{aligned}$$

and similarly,

$$\begin{aligned}\mathbf{u}_1 \times \mathbf{u}_3 &= \mathbf{u}_1 \times (\mathbf{u}_1 \times \mathbf{u}_2)\\ &= (\mathbf{u}_1 \cdot \mathbf{u}_2)\mathbf{u}_1 - (\mathbf{u}_1 \cdot \mathbf{u}_1)\mathbf{u}_2\\ &= -\mathbf{u}_2.\end{aligned}$$

Substituting these into (5–20), we find that if $\mathbf{u}_1$, $\mathbf{u}_2$, and $\mathbf{u}_3$ constitute a right-handed orthonormal system, then

$$\mathbf{A} \times \mathbf{B} = (a_2b_3 - a_3b_2)\mathbf{u}_1 - (a_1b_3 - a_3b_1)\mathbf{u}_2 + (a_1b_2 - a_2b_1)\mathbf{u}_3. \tag{5–21}$$

Comparing this with formula (4–10), we find that the expansion of the cross product in terms of any right-handed orthogonal coordinate system is the same. Thus the cross product does not depend on the choice of a coordinate system, so long as the chosen system is still right-handed.

The student can easily verify that if the coordinate system is left-handed (that is, if $\mathbf{u}_1 \times \mathbf{u}_2 = -\mathbf{u}_3$), then instead of (5–21) we find a formula for $\mathbf{A} \times \mathbf{B}$ which is the negative of that given in (5–21).

Finally, we remark that if we have any three vectors which are not coplanar, then from Theorem 5–10 we can express any vector $\mathbf{X}$ as a linear combination of these. We can think of the coefficients of these vectors as being the coordinates of the vector $\mathbf{X}$ (or point X) in terms of an oblique coordinate system. The rectangular parallelepiped in Fig. 3–1 would be replaced by a parallelepiped whose edges are parallel to the given vectors (as in Fig. 5–3). While the oblique coordinates are useful in some cases, their use make the formulas for the dot and cross product very complicated.

PROBLEMS

1. Construct an orthonormal set out of the given vectors by the method described in this section.

   (a) $\mathbf{A}_1 = [1, 3, 0]$, $\mathbf{A}_2 = [-1, 1, 0]$
   (b) $\mathbf{A}_1 = [-1, 0, 1]$, $\mathbf{A}_2 = [0, 2, 1]$
   (c) $\mathbf{A}_1 = [2, 1, -3]$, $\mathbf{A}_2 = [1, -1, 2]$
   (d) $\mathbf{A}_1 = [1, 2, 1]$, $\mathbf{A}_2 = [-2, -5, 2]$

2. Express the vector $\mathbf{B} = [2, 2, 2]$ as a linear combination of the orthonormal set $\mathbf{u}_1$, $\mathbf{u}_2$, and $\mathbf{u}_3$ for each part of Problem 1.

3. Prove that the right-hand side of (5–20) reduces to the negative of (5–21) if $\mathbf{u}_1 \times \mathbf{u}_2 = -\mathbf{u}_3$.

4. Is the set of vectors defined by (5–18) a right-handed system? Does this fact depend on $\mathbf{A}_1$ and $\mathbf{A}_2$?

5. Prove that the vectors (5–19) form an orthornormal set. Are they a right-handed system?

6. For each of the orthonormal sets of vectors obtained in Problem 1, find formulas for the coordinates (x', y', z') of a point (x, y, z) when the x'-, y'-, and z'-axes are determined by $\mathbf{u}_1$, $\mathbf{u}_2$, and $\mathbf{u}_3$, respectively.

7. Show that each of the following sets of vectors is an orthonormal set. Give formulas for the coordinates (x', y', z') of a point (x, y, z) when the x'-, y'-, and z'-axes are determined by $\mathbf{u}_1$, $\mathbf{u}_2$, and $\mathbf{u}_3$, respectively. Express $\mathbf{A} = [5, -2, 1]$ as a linear combination of $\mathbf{u}_1$, $\mathbf{u}_2$, and $\mathbf{u}_3$.

(a) $\mathbf{u}_1 = [0, \frac{3}{5}, \frac{4}{5}]$, $\quad \mathbf{u}_2 = [\frac{12}{13}, -\frac{4}{13}, \frac{3}{13}]$, $\quad \mathbf{u}_3 = [\frac{25}{65}, \frac{48}{65}, -\frac{36}{65}]$
(b) $\mathbf{u}_1 = [\frac{4}{9}, \frac{7}{9}, -\frac{4}{9}]$, $\quad \mathbf{u}_2 = [-\frac{8}{9}, \frac{4}{9}, -\frac{1}{9}]$, $\quad \mathbf{u}_3 = [\frac{1}{9}, \frac{4}{9}, \frac{8}{9}]$
(c) $\mathbf{u}_1 = [\frac{2}{3}, -\frac{2}{3}, \frac{1}{3}]$, $\quad \mathbf{u}_2 = [-\frac{11}{15}, -\frac{10}{15}, \frac{2}{15}]$, $\quad \mathbf{u}_3 = [\frac{2}{15}, -\frac{5}{15}, -\frac{14}{15}]$

8. Let $\mathbf{u}_1$, $\mathbf{u}_2$, and $\mathbf{u}_3$ be a right-handed, orthonormal set of vectors. Set

$$\mathbf{N} = \mathbf{e}_1 \times \mathbf{u}_1 + \mathbf{e}_2 \times \mathbf{u}_2 + \mathbf{e}_3 \times \mathbf{u}_3,$$

$$\mathbf{X} = x\mathbf{e}_1 + y\mathbf{e}_2 + z\mathbf{e}_3,$$

and

$$\mathbf{Y} = x\mathbf{u}_1 + y\mathbf{u}_2 + z\mathbf{u}_3.$$

(a) Prove that the angle between $\mathbf{e}_i$ and $\mathbf{N}$ is the same as the angle between $\mathbf{u}_i$ and $\mathbf{N}$ for $i = 1, 2$, and 3.
(b) Show that $|\mathbf{X}| = |\mathbf{Y}|$, and prove that the angle between $\mathbf{X}$ and $\mathbf{N}$ is the same as the angle between $\mathbf{Y}$ and $\mathbf{N}$ for any x, y, and z.
(c) Prove that $\mathbf{X} = \mathbf{Y}$ if $\mathbf{X}$ is collinear with $\mathbf{N}$. [*Hint:* Use (5–16) on both $\mathbf{X}$ and $\mathbf{Y}$.]

Remark: A rotation of space which carries $\mathbf{e}_1$ to $\mathbf{u}_1$, $\mathbf{e}_2$ to $\mathbf{u}_2$, and $\mathbf{e}_3$ to $\mathbf{u}_3$ can be thought of as a function which maps a point X to a point Y, where X and Y are given as above. The vector $\mathbf{N}$ is then the axis of the rotation. Property (b) shows that $\mathbf{N}$ is the axis, and property (c) shows that any rotation must have an axis.

9. Find the axis $\mathbf{N}$ as defined in Problem 8 for each of the sets of vectors in Problem 7. Make a sketch showing these vectors for each of the cases.

10. Let $\mathbf{u}_1$, $\mathbf{u}_2$, and $\mathbf{u}_3$ be any three noncoplanar vectors (they need not form an orthonormal set). Define

$$\mathbf{v}_1 = c(\mathbf{u}_2 \times \mathbf{u}_3), \qquad \mathbf{v}_2 = c(\mathbf{u}_3 \times \mathbf{u}_1), \qquad \mathbf{v}_3 = c(\mathbf{u}_1 \times \mathbf{u}_2),$$

where $c = 1/(\mathbf{u}_1 \cdot \mathbf{u}_2 \times \mathbf{u}_3)$. The $\mathbf{v}_i$ are called a dual basis to the $\mathbf{u}_i$.

(a) Prove that

$$\mathbf{v}_i \cdot \mathbf{u}_j = \begin{cases} 0 & \text{if } i \neq j, \\ 1 & \text{if } i = j. \end{cases}$$

(b) Prove that for any vector **A**,

$$\mathbf{A} = (\mathbf{A} \cdot \mathbf{v}_1)\mathbf{u}_1 + (\mathbf{A} \cdot \mathbf{v}_2)\mathbf{u}_2 + (\mathbf{A} \cdot \mathbf{v}_3)\mathbf{u}_3,$$

and also

$$\mathbf{A} = (\mathbf{A} \cdot \mathbf{u}_1)\mathbf{v}_1 + (\mathbf{A} \cdot \mathbf{u}_2)\mathbf{v}_2 + (\mathbf{A} \cdot \mathbf{u}_3)\mathbf{v}_3.$$

(c) Find the dual basis to **A**, **B**, and **C** in each of the four parts of Problem 12, Section 5–2. Use the results of part (b) of this problem to obtain **D** as a linear combination of **A**, **B**, and **C**.

5–4 PROJECTIONS AND DISTANCE FORMULAS

In Section 3–5 we introduced the projection of vectors in the direction of a line and we have made use of this idea several times in various applications. The formula which was introduced as the definition is not particularly easy to remember by itself. At this point, we would like to exhibit another way of looking at the projection. From this point of view, the formula for the projection can be rederived easily as needed.

Let **A** and $\mathbf{B} \neq \mathbf{0}$ be given vectors. We wish to find the projection of **A** in the direction of the line determined by **B**. The situation is illustrated in Fig. 5–4. Here, the required projection is **P**, and we see that the basic requirements are satisfied when $\mathbf{V} = \mathbf{A} - \mathbf{P}$ is orthogonal to **B**. In order that **P** be collinear with **B**, we must have

$$\mathbf{P} = t\mathbf{B} \tag{5–22}$$

for some scalar t. But then, in order to have **V** orthogonal to **B**, we must have

$$\begin{aligned} \mathbf{V} \cdot \mathbf{B} &= \mathbf{A} \cdot \mathbf{B} - \mathbf{P} \cdot \mathbf{B} \\ &= \mathbf{A} \cdot \mathbf{B} - t\mathbf{B} \cdot \mathbf{B} \\ &= 0. \end{aligned}$$

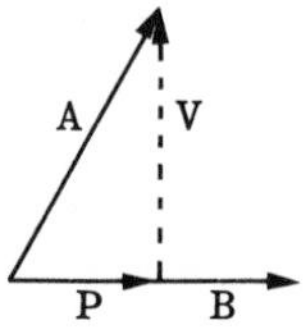

FIGURE 5–4

This will be true only if $t = (\mathbf{A} \cdot \mathbf{B})/(\mathbf{B} \cdot \mathbf{B})$. Using this value in (5–22) yields exactly the formula given in Definition 3–16.

This particular point of view can be extended to give us the definition of the projection of a vector onto a plane.

Definition 5–4. Let **A** be a given vector and M a given plane. Then the *projection* of **A** onto M is a vector **P** which lies in the plane and is such that

$$\mathbf{A} = \mathbf{P} + \mathbf{V}$$

for some vector $\mathbf{V}$ orthogonal to M.

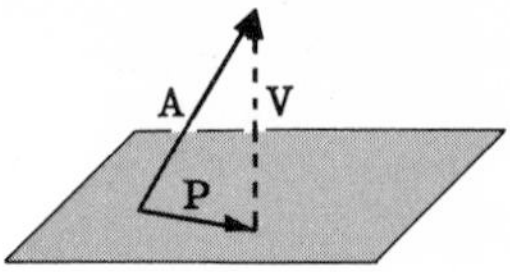

FIGURE 5–5

The contents of this definition are illustrated in Fig. 5–5. From this figure it is easy to see how we can obtain formulas for the projection of a vector onto a plane.

Suppose $\mathbf{N} \neq \mathbf{0}$ is orthogonal to the plane. Then it is clear that we want $\mathbf{V}$ to be collinear with $\mathbf{N}$ to satisfy the requirements of Definition 5–4. Likewise, it seems clear from the figure that $\mathbf{V}$ must actually be the projection of $\mathbf{A}$ in the direction of $\mathbf{N}$. Using this would give

$$\begin{aligned}\mathbf{P} &= \mathbf{A} - \mathbf{V}\\ &= \mathbf{A} - \frac{(\mathbf{A}\cdot\mathbf{N})}{(\mathbf{N}\cdot\mathbf{N})}\mathbf{N}.\end{aligned}$$

This result has been obtained by means of our geometric understanding rather than by formal computation. However, once we have obtained this formula, it is easy to verify it. Direct computation shows that if $\mathbf{P}$ is defined in this way, then $\mathbf{P}\cdot\mathbf{N} = 0$ and hence that $\mathbf{P}$ is parallel to the given plane. Thus, we have proved:

Theorem 5–15. Let M be a plane orthogonal to a vector $\mathbf{N} \neq \mathbf{0}$. Then the projection of a vector $\mathbf{A}$ onto M is given by

$$\mathbf{P} = \mathbf{A} - \frac{(\mathbf{A}\cdot\mathbf{N})}{(\mathbf{N}\cdot\mathbf{N})}\mathbf{N}. \tag{5–23}$$

For example, let us find the projection of $\mathbf{A} = [2, 5, -1]$ onto the plane with equation $3x - y + 2z - 5 = 0$. The normal vector to this plane is $\mathbf{N} = [3, -1, 2]$. Here, $|\mathbf{N}|^2 = 14$ and $\mathbf{A}\cdot\mathbf{N} = -1$. Hence

$$\begin{aligned}\mathbf{P} &= [2, 5, -1] + \tfrac{1}{14}[3, -1, 2]\\ &= [\tfrac{31}{14}, \tfrac{69}{14}, -\tfrac{12}{14}].\end{aligned}$$

In Section 4–3 we derived an expression for the distance from a point to a plane. We now wish to find expressions for the distance between a point and a line and for the distance between two lines.

Suppose that we are given a line L which contains the point A and has the direction $\mathbf{B}$. Thus the line L has parametric equation

$$\mathbf{X} = \mathbf{A} + t\mathbf{B}.$$

We wish to find the distance from a point P to the line L. From geometric considerations it is clear that the required distance is exactly the length of the vector $\overrightarrow{PC}$ from P to a point C on the line which is such that $\overrightarrow{PC}$ is orthogonal to $\mathbf{B}$. This can be verified by noting that if D is any point on the line, then (see Fig. 5-6)

$$\overrightarrow{PD} = \overrightarrow{PC} + \overrightarrow{CD}.$$

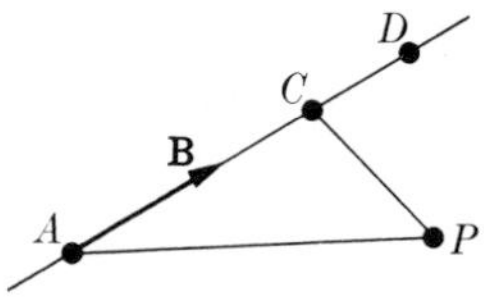

FIGURE 5-6

Since $\overrightarrow{PC}$ is orthogonal to $\mathbf{B}$ and $\overrightarrow{CD}$ is collinear with $\mathbf{B}$, $\overrightarrow{PC}$ and $\overrightarrow{CD}$ must be orthogonal. But then

$$|\overrightarrow{PD}|^2 = |\overrightarrow{PC}|^2 + |\overrightarrow{CD}|^2, \qquad (5\text{-}24)$$

as can be shown by direct calculation or by reference to Theorem 3-8. (The fact that the square of the magnitude of the sum of two orthogonal vectors is the sum of the squares of their magnitudes is exactly the Pythagorean theorem.)

By letting the point D vary along the line L, we see from (5-23) that the minimum distance $|\overrightarrow{PD}|$ is attained when $C = D$, and thus $|\overrightarrow{PC}|$ is the distance from P to L.

To find $\overrightarrow{PC}$ we can proceed in any one of several different ways. Perhaps the easiest way is to note that

$$\overrightarrow{PC} = \overrightarrow{AC} - \overrightarrow{AP}.$$

(We remark that the reader frequently will find it easier to obtain an equation such as this by noting first that $\overrightarrow{AP} + \overrightarrow{PC} = \overrightarrow{AC}$.) The vector $\overrightarrow{AC}$ is the projection of $\overrightarrow{AP}$ onto the direction of $\mathbf{B}$, and hence

$$\overrightarrow{AC} = \frac{(\overrightarrow{AP} \cdot \mathbf{B})}{|\mathbf{B}|^2}\,\mathbf{B},$$

giving

$$\overrightarrow{PC} = \frac{(\overrightarrow{AP} \cdot \mathbf{B})}{|\mathbf{B}|^2}\,\mathbf{B} - \overrightarrow{AP}$$

To find the length of $\overrightarrow{PC}$, we can calculate

$$\begin{aligned}
|\overrightarrow{PC}|^2 &= (\overrightarrow{PC}) \cdot (\overrightarrow{PC}) \\
&= \frac{(\overrightarrow{AP} \cdot \mathbf{B})^2}{|\mathbf{B}|^4}|\mathbf{B}|^2 - 2\,\frac{(\overrightarrow{AP} \cdot \mathbf{B})^2}{|\mathbf{B}|^2} + |\overrightarrow{AP}|^2 \\
&= |\overrightarrow{AP}|^2 - \frac{(\overrightarrow{AP} \cdot \mathbf{B})^2}{|\mathbf{B}|^2} \\
&= \frac{|\overrightarrow{AP} \times \mathbf{B}|^2}{|\mathbf{B}|^2},
\end{aligned}$$

where the last step follows from Eq. (5-7) of Section 5-1.

This same result can also be obtained by observing that if θ is the angle between $\overrightarrow{AP}$ and $\mathbf{B}$, then

$$|\overrightarrow{PC}| = |\overrightarrow{AP}| \sin \theta,$$

while

$$|\overrightarrow{AP} \times \mathbf{B}| = |\overrightarrow{AP}\ | \cdot |\mathbf{B}| \sin \theta.$$

Either way, we have proved

Theorem 5–16. Let L be the line through A with direction $\mathbf{B}$, and let P be a given point. Then the distance from P to L is d, where

$$d = \frac{|\overrightarrow{AP} \times \mathbf{B}|}{|\mathbf{B}|}. \tag{5–25}$$

The point C on L which is closest to P is given by

$$\mathbf{C} = \mathbf{A} + \frac{(\overrightarrow{AP} \cdot \mathbf{B})}{|\mathbf{B}|^2}\mathbf{B}. \tag{5–26}$$

It should be noted that the distance d given by (5–25) will be zero if and only if the point P is on the line.

As an illustration of the use of these formulas, let us find the distance between the line

$$\mathbf{X} = [2, 3, -5] + t[1, -2, 2]$$

and the point $P = (15, 7, 6)$. Here, $\mathbf{B} = [1, -2, 2]$, and $\overrightarrow{AP} = [13, 4, 11]$. Starting with (5–26), we see that the projection of $\overrightarrow{AP}$ in the direction of the line is

$$\overrightarrow{AC} = \frac{\overrightarrow{AP} \cdot \mathbf{B}}{|\mathbf{B}|^2}\mathbf{B} = \frac{27}{9}\mathbf{B} = [3, -6, 6].$$

Hence $\mathbf{C} = \mathbf{A} + \overrightarrow{AC} = [5, -3, 1]$, and

$$\begin{aligned} d &= |\overrightarrow{PC}| = |[10, 10, 5]| \\ &= 5 \cdot |[2, 2, 1]| \\ &= 5 \cdot 3 = 15. \end{aligned}$$

Alternatively, we could compute

$$\overrightarrow{AP} \times \mathbf{B} = [30, -15, -30],$$

and, using (5–25), find

$$d = \frac{|[30, -15, -30]|}{3} = \frac{15 \cdot |[2, -1, -2]|}{3} = 15.$$

Now, we wish to turn to the problem of finding a formula for the distance between two lines. Let L_1 be the line through A_1 with the direction $\mathbf{B}_1$, and let L_2 be the line through A_2 with direction $\mathbf{B}_2$. Suppose that there exist points C_1 and C_2 on L_1 and L_2, respectively, such that $\overrightarrow{C_1C_2}$ is orthogonal to both L_1 and L_2. Then $|C_1C_2|$ is the required distance between L_1 and L_2. This is easily seen by considering the planes orthogonal to $\overrightarrow{C_1C_2}$ through A_1 and A_2, respectively. The lines L_1 and L_2 will be contained in these respective planes (why?), and hence the distance between these planes will be the minimum distance between the lines. (See Fig. 5-7.)

The vector $\overrightarrow{C_1C_2}$ is clearly the projection of the vector $\overrightarrow{A_1A_2}$ in the direction of $\overrightarrow{C_1C_2}$. But since $\overrightarrow{C_1C_2}$ is assumed to be orthogonal to both $\mathbf{B}_1$ and $\mathbf{B}_2$, it must be collinear with $\mathbf{B}_1 \times \mathbf{B}_2$ (assuming that $\mathbf{B}_1$ and $\mathbf{B}_2$ are not collinear). Therefore $\overrightarrow{C_1C_2}$ is the projection of $\overrightarrow{A_1A_2}$ in the direction of $\mathbf{B}_1 \times \mathbf{B}_2$, and hence

$$|\overrightarrow{C_1C_2}| = \frac{|\overrightarrow{A_1A_2} \cdot \mathbf{B}_1 \times \mathbf{B}_2|}{|\mathbf{B}_1 \times \mathbf{B}_2|}. \tag{5-27}$$

This result was obtained under the assumption that points C_1 and C_2 with the required properties exist. The existence of these points can be verified in several different ways, but with the proper point of view it is easy to see.

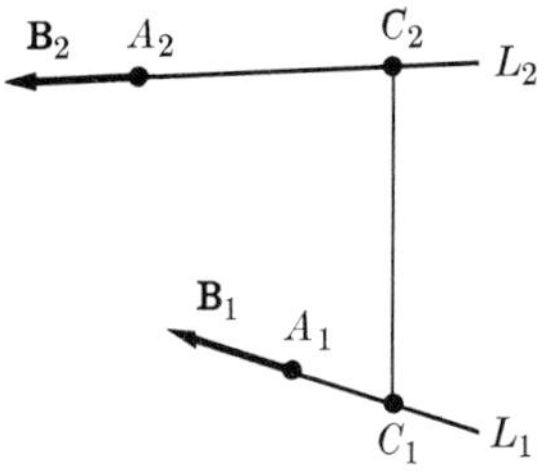

FIGURE 5-7

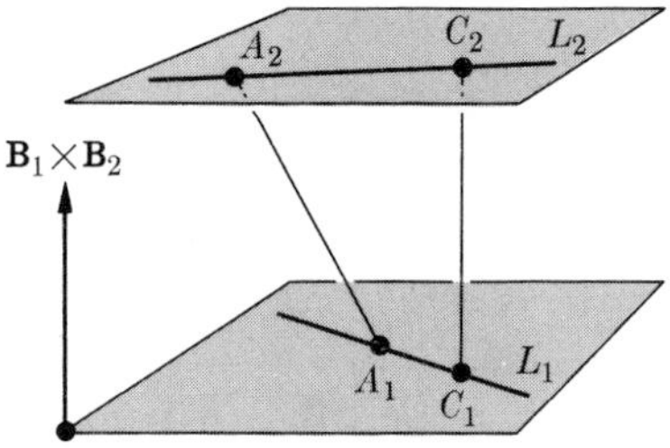

FIGURE 5-8

We suppose that $\mathbf{B}_1$ and $\mathbf{B}_2$ are not collinear. Then $\mathbf{B}_1 \times \mathbf{B}_2 \neq \mathbf{0}$, and we can imagine the planes orthogonal to $\mathbf{B}_1 \times \mathbf{B}_2$ through $\mathbf{A}_1$ and $\mathbf{A}_2$. The line L_1 is in one of these planes and the line L_2 is in the other. If we make the orthogonal projection of the line L_2 into the plane containing L_1, we see that L_1 and the projection of L_2 must intersect. The point of intersection will be the point C_1 (Fig. 5-8).

This rather intuitive argument can be made rigorous quite easily. Introduce an orthonormal set of vectors $\mathbf{u}_1$, $\mathbf{u}_2$, and $\mathbf{u}_3$ such that $\mathbf{u}_1$ is parallel to $\mathbf{B}_1$, $\mathbf{u}_2$ is in the plane determined by $\mathbf{B}_1$ and $\mathbf{B}_2$, and $\mathbf{u}_3$ is collinear with $\mathbf{B}_1 \times \mathbf{B}_2$, by the method of the last section. Then we have

$$\mathbf{B}_1 = b_1\mathbf{u}_1, \qquad \mathbf{B}_2 = c_1\mathbf{u}_1 + c_2\mathbf{u}_2, \tag{5-28}$$

where $b_1 = 1/|\mathbf{B}_1| \neq 0$ and $c_2 \neq 0$, since otherwise $\mathbf{B}_1$ and $\mathbf{B}_2$ would have been collinear. The lines L_1 and L_2 have equations

$$\mathbf{X} = \mathbf{A}_1 + t\mathbf{B}_1, \qquad \mathbf{Y} = \mathbf{A}_2 + s\mathbf{B}_2, \tag{5-29}$$

respectively. If X is an arbitrary point on L_1, having coordinate t, and Y is an arbitrary point on L_2 with coordinate s, then

$$\begin{aligned}\overrightarrow{XY} &= \mathbf{A}_2 - \mathbf{A}_1 + s\mathbf{B}_2 - t\mathbf{B}_1\\ &= (\mathbf{A}_2 - \mathbf{A}_1) + (sc_1 - tb_1)\mathbf{u}_1 + sc_2\mathbf{u}_2.\end{aligned}$$

Let us suppose that $\mathbf{A}_2 - \mathbf{A}_1 = a_1\mathbf{u}_1 + a_2\mathbf{u}_2 + a_3\mathbf{u}_3$. Then

$$\overrightarrow{XY} = (a_1 + sc_1 - tb_1)\mathbf{u}_1 + (a_2 + sc_2)\mathbf{u}_2 + a_3\mathbf{u}_3,$$

and since $\mathbf{B}_1 \times \mathbf{B}_2$ is parallel to $\mathbf{u}_3$, the problem is whether or not we can find values for s and t so that $a_1 + sc_1 - tb_1 = 0$ and $a_2 + sc_2 = 0$. If so, these values when put into (5-29) would give us the required points C_1 and C_2.

However, the second equation,

$$a_2 + sc_2 = 0,$$

can be solved for s, since from (5-28) the number c_2 is not zero. Having solved for s, we can solve for t in the first equation,

$$a_1 + sc_1 - tb_1 = 0,$$

since $b_1 \neq 0$. Therefore the required points C_1 and C_2 exist.

Note that in this proof we are not particularly interested in finding C_1 and C_2. All we are really after is the information that these points exist. With this knowledge, the rest of the calculations are easy.

Theorem 5-17. Let L_1 be the line through A_1 in the direction $\mathbf{B}_1$, and let L_2 be the line through A_2 in the direction $\mathbf{B}_2$. If $\mathbf{B}_1$ and $\mathbf{B}_2$ are not collinear, then the distance between L_1 and L_2 is

$$d = \frac{|\overrightarrow{A_1A_2} \cdot \mathbf{B}_1 \times \mathbf{B}_2|}{|\mathbf{B}_1 \times \mathbf{B}_2|}. \tag{5-30}$$

If $\mathbf{B}_1$ and $\mathbf{B}_2$ are collinear, then the distance between L_1 and L_2 is

$$d = \frac{|\overrightarrow{A_1A_2} \times \mathbf{B}_1|}{|\mathbf{B}_1|}. \tag{5-31}$$

The proof of the second part of this result will be left as one of the problems. It should be noted that the distance d given in this theorem will be zero if and only if the two lines intersect.

As an example, let us find the distance between the lines

$$\mathbf{X} = [1, 0, 5] + t[2, 0, 3]$$

and

$$\mathbf{X} = [4, -1, 2] + t[1, -1, 0].$$

Here, $\mathbf{B}_1 = [2, 0, 3]$ and $\mathbf{B}_2 = [1, -1, 0]$. Hence $\mathbf{B}_1 \times \mathbf{B}_2 = [3, 3, -2]$. Also, $\overrightarrow{A_1A_2} = [3, -1, -3]$. Therefore, the required distance is

$$d = \frac{9 - 3 + 6}{[22]^{1/2}} = \frac{12}{\sqrt{22}}.$$

PROBLEMS

1. For each of the following sets of vectors, find the projection of $\mathbf{A}_3$ onto a plane parallel to both $\mathbf{A}_1$ and $\mathbf{A}_2$.

   (a) $\mathbf{A}_1 = [1, 3, 0]$, $\mathbf{A}_2 = [-1, 1, 0]$, $\mathbf{A}_3 = [1, 2, 1]$
   (b) $\mathbf{A}_1 = [-1, 0, 1]$, $\mathbf{A}_2 = [0, 2, 1]$, $\mathbf{A}_3 = [1, 1, 0]$
   (c) $\mathbf{A}_1 = [2, 1, -3]$, $\mathbf{A}_2 = [1, -1, 2]$, $\mathbf{A}_3 = [3, 0, 4]$
   (d) $\mathbf{A}_1 = [1, 2, 1]$, $\mathbf{A}_2 = [-2, -5, 2]$, $\mathbf{A}_3 = [1, 1, 5]$

2. For each of the sets of vectors in Problem 1, find the projection of $\mathbf{A}_3$ onto a plane orthogonal to $\mathbf{A}_1$.

3. Find s and t such that

$$\overrightarrow{XY} = \mathbf{A}_2 - \mathbf{A}_1 + s\mathbf{B}_2 - t\mathbf{B}_1$$

   is orthogonal to both $\mathbf{B}_1$ and $\mathbf{B}_2$ by direct calculation (without introducing the vectors $\mathbf{u}_1$, $\mathbf{u}_2$, and $\mathbf{u}_3$). Show that the result can be written in the form

$$s = -\frac{[(\mathbf{A}_1 - \mathbf{A}_2) \times \mathbf{B}_1] \cdot [\mathbf{B}_1 \times \mathbf{B}_2]}{|\mathbf{B}_1 \times \mathbf{B}_2|^2},$$

$$t = -\frac{[(\mathbf{A}_1 - \mathbf{A}_2) \times \mathbf{B}_2] \cdot [\mathbf{B}_1 \times \mathbf{B}_2]}{|\mathbf{B}_1 \times \mathbf{B}_2|^2}.$$

4. Set

$$\begin{aligned} A_1 &= (3, 2, 4), & \mathbf{B}_1 &= [1, 0, 1], \\ A_2 &= (1, -3, 1), & \mathbf{B}_2 &= [0, -5, 3], \\ A_3 &= (-2, 1, 2), & \mathbf{B}_3 &= [7, 5, -3], \\ A_4 &= (2, 1, -1), & \mathbf{B}_4 &= [-3, 1, -1], \\ A_5 &= (5, 5, 10), & \mathbf{B}_5 &= [1, 0, 1], \\ P_1 &= (1, 3, 5), & P_2 &= (0, 5, 0), \\ P_3 &= (5, 4, 3), & P_4 &= (-3, 0, 1). \end{aligned}$$

Let L_1 be the line through A_1 in the direction $\mathbf{B}_1$, L_2 the line through A_2 in the direction $\mathbf{B}_2$, etc.

(a) Find the distance from P_i to L_i, for $i = 1, 2, 3$ and 4.
(b) Find the distance from L_1 to each of the other lines.

5. Using Theorem 5–16, prove the second proposition of Theorem 5–17.

6. Let C be a given point and M a given plane. Let L be the line through C orthogonal to M. Then by *the projection of C onto M* we will mean the point D at which the line L cuts the plane. If M is the plane through the point A, orthogonal to $\mathbf{B}$, prove that the projection of C onto M is the point D, where

$$\mathbf{D} = \mathbf{C} - \frac{(\overrightarrow{AC} \cdot \mathbf{B})}{|\mathbf{B}|^2}\mathbf{B}.$$

[*Hint:* Consider Fig. 5–5.]

7. In what way is Problem 6 related to the problem of finding the point on a given plane which is closest to a given point?

5–5 GENERAL METHODS*

The results of Sections 5–2 and 5–3 are of great importance in the general study of vector spaces. These results, however, were obtained with the aid of the properties of the cross product. The cross product is an artifact of the three-dimensional vector space which does not exist (in the same form) in spaces of other dimensions. In this section, it is our purpose to show how certain results obtained in Sections 5–2 and 5–3 can be obtained by methods which do not involve the cross product.

The first topic we wish to discuss is *linear dependence.* Recall that in Definition 5–2, a collection of vectors, $\mathbf{A}_1, \mathbf{A}_2, \ldots, \mathbf{A}_n$, was called *linearly dependent* if and only if there exist scalars λ_i $(i = 1, 2, \ldots, n)$, not all zero, such that

$$\lambda_1\mathbf{A}_1 + \lambda_2\mathbf{A}_2 + \cdots + \lambda_n\mathbf{A}_n = \mathbf{0}. \qquad (5\text{–}32)$$

A set of vectors which is not linearly dependent is called *linearly independent.* Let us now investigate some properties of this concept.

Theorem 5–18. If a collection of vectors contains the zero vector, then the collection is linearly dependent.

---

* The material discussed in this section is not essential to this course, but it does constitute an introduction to some very important topics taken up in later courses. It would be well worth the student's while to study this material. In particular, students interested in applications of mathematics are advised to study the proof of Theorem 5–24 with care.

Proof: If the collection is $\mathbf{A}_1, \mathbf{A}_2, \ldots, \mathbf{A}_{n-1}, \mathbf{0}$, then

$$\lambda_1\mathbf{A}_1 + \lambda_2\mathbf{A}_2 + \cdots + \lambda_{n-1}\mathbf{A}_{n-1} + \lambda_n\mathbf{0} = \mathbf{0}$$

when we set $\lambda_1 = \lambda_2 = \cdots = \lambda_{n-1} = 0$ and $\lambda_n = 1$. Here, not all of the λ_i are zero, since $\lambda_n = 1$.

Theorem 5-19. If a collection of vectors contains two identical vectors, then the collection is linearly dependent.

Proof: Let all of the λ_i in (5-18) be zero except for the coefficients of the two identical vectors. Let one of these have the coefficient $+1$ and the other the coefficient -1. We then have a linear combination of the vectors which is zero, but with some nonzero coefficients.

Theorem 5-20. If a set of vectors is linearly independent, then any nonempty subset of this set is also linearly independent. If a collection of vectors is linearly dependent, then any enlarged collection is also linearly dependent.

Proof: The two parts of this theorem are logically equivalent, so let us prove only the second part. Let $\mathbf{A}_1, \mathbf{A}_2, \ldots, \mathbf{A}_n$ be a linearly dependent collection of vectors. Then there exist λ_i $(i = 1, 2, \ldots, n)$, not all zero, such that

$$\lambda_1\mathbf{A}_1 + \lambda_2\mathbf{A}_2 + \cdots + \lambda_n\mathbf{A}_n = \mathbf{0}.$$

If the enlarged collection is $\mathbf{A}_1, \mathbf{A}_2, \ldots, \mathbf{A}_n, \mathbf{B}_1, \mathbf{B}_2, \ldots, \mathbf{B}_k$, then letting the λ_i be the same as above (and hence not all zero), and all of the μ_i be zero, we have

$$\lambda_1\mathbf{A}_1 + \cdots + \lambda_n\mathbf{A}_n + \mu_1\mathbf{B}_1 + \cdots + \mu_k\mathbf{B}_k = \mathbf{0}.$$

Definition 5-5. A collection of vectors $\mathbf{A}_1, \mathbf{A}_2, \ldots, \mathbf{A}_n$ is called a set of *generators* if and only if every vector can be expressed as a linear combination of these. That is, if $\mathbf{B}$ is any vector, there exist scalars λ_i such that

$$\mathbf{B} = \lambda_1\mathbf{A}_1 + \lambda_2\mathbf{A}_2 + \cdots + \lambda_n\mathbf{A}_n.$$

Directly from this definition we are able to prove

Theorem 5-21. If $\mathbf{A}_1, \mathbf{A}_2, \ldots, \mathbf{A}_n$ is a set of generators, and if $\mathbf{B}$ is any vector, then the collection of vectors $\mathbf{B}, \mathbf{A}_1, \mathbf{A}_2, \ldots, \mathbf{A}_n$ is linearly dependent.

Proof: By the definition, there exist scalars $\lambda_1, \ldots, \lambda_n$ such that

$$\mathbf{B} = \lambda_1\mathbf{A}_1 + \cdots + \lambda_n\mathbf{A}_n.$$

But then

$$\mathbf{B} - \lambda_1\mathbf{A}_1 - \cdots - \lambda_n\mathbf{A}_n = 0,$$

and this collection is linearly dependent (the coefficient of $\mathbf{B}$ is $1 \neq 0$).

Theorem 5–22. Let $\mathbf{A}_1, \mathbf{A}_2, \ldots, \mathbf{A}_n$ be a linearly dependent sequence of nonzero vectors. Then there is some k with $1 \leq k < n$ such that the sequence of vectors $\mathbf{A}_1, \ldots, \mathbf{A}_k$ is linearly independent and $\mathbf{A}_{k+1}$ is a linear combination of these. That is, there exist scalars $\lambda_1, \lambda_2, \ldots, \lambda_k$ such that

$$\mathbf{A}_{k+1} = \lambda_1\mathbf{A}_1 + \lambda_2\mathbf{A}_2 + \cdots + \lambda_k\mathbf{A}_k.$$

Proof: We look at the sequence of vectors, and let k be the *smallest* integer for which the sequence $\mathbf{A}_1, \mathbf{A}_2, \ldots, \mathbf{A}_{k+1}$ is linearly dependent. Since $\mathbf{A}_1$ is nonzero, k must be greater than or equal to one. On the other hand, since the entire sequence is linearly dependent, k is less than n.

Since k is chosen to be the smallest integer such that the sequence $\mathbf{A}_1, \ldots, \mathbf{A}_{k+1}$ is linearly dependent, there exist scalars $\alpha_1, \alpha_2, \ldots, \alpha_{k+1}$, not all zero, such that

$$\alpha_1\mathbf{A}_1 + \alpha_2\mathbf{A}_2 + \cdots + \alpha_{k+1}\mathbf{A}_{k+1} = \mathbf{0}.$$

However, $\alpha_{k+1} \neq 0$, for if $\alpha_{k+1} = 0$, then not all the α_i being zero would imply that the sequence $\mathbf{A}_1, \ldots, \mathbf{A}_k$ is linearly dependent, contradicting the way k was chosen. This equation can then be divided through by α_{k+1} and brought into the form required by the theorem.

Finally we prove

Theorem 5–23. Any four vectors are linearly dependent; and if three vectors are linearly independent, they are a set of generators.

Proof: If we are given four vectors, and if three of them are linearly dependent, then the whole collection is linearly dependent. On the other hand, if three of the vectors are linearly independent and we prove that they are a set of generators, then Theorem 5–21 shows that all four are linearly dependent. So suppose that $\mathbf{A}_1$, $\mathbf{A}_2$, and $\mathbf{A}_3$ are linearly independent. We will prove that they are a set of generators.

The method of proof that we use is called the *method of replacement.* We start with a known set of generators, $\mathbf{e}_1$, $\mathbf{e}_2$, and $\mathbf{e}_3$ (why is this a set of generators?) and add $\mathbf{A}_1$ to this set. By Theorem 5–21 the resulting collection of four vectors $\mathbf{A}_1$, $\mathbf{e}_1$, $\mathbf{e}_2$, and $\mathbf{e}_3$ is linearly dependent. From

Theorem 5–22, we find one of these to be a linear combination of the previous ones.

Suppose, for example, that we can solve for $\mathbf{e}_3$, finding

$$\mathbf{e}_3 = \lambda_1\mathbf{A}_1 + \lambda_2\mathbf{e}_1 + \lambda_3\mathbf{e}_2.$$

But now, we can remove $\mathbf{e}_3$ from the collection $\mathbf{A}_1, \mathbf{e}_1, \mathbf{e}_2, \mathbf{e}_3$ and still have a set of generators. For if $\mathbf{B}$ is an arbitrary vector with

$$\mathbf{B} = \mu_1\mathbf{e}_1 + \mu_2\mathbf{e}_2 + \mu_3\mathbf{e}_3,$$

then

$$\begin{aligned}\mathbf{B} &= \mu_1\mathbf{e}_1 + \mu_2\mathbf{e}_2 + \mu_3(\lambda_1\mathbf{A}_1 + \lambda_2\mathbf{e}_1 + \lambda_3\mathbf{e}_2)\\ &= \mu_3\lambda_1\mathbf{A}_1 + (\mu_1 + \mu_3\lambda_2)\mathbf{e}_1 + (\mu_2 + \mu_3\lambda_3)\mathbf{e}_2\\ &= \mu_1'\mathbf{A}_1 + \mu_2'\mathbf{e}_1 + \mu_3'\mathbf{e}_2.\end{aligned}$$

Next we add $\mathbf{A}_2$ to the collection and look at the sequence $\mathbf{A}_2, \mathbf{A}_1, \mathbf{e}_1, \mathbf{e}_2$ assuming $\mathbf{e}_3$ was the one removed). The same reasoning shows that we can remove another of the vectors. But the one removed will not be $\mathbf{A}_1$ or $\mathbf{A}_2$, since these two are linearly independent. We therefore have a sequence $\mathbf{A}_1, \mathbf{A}_2, \mathbf{e}_i$ (where $\mathbf{e}_i$ is one of the original three) which is still a set of generators.

Finally we add $\mathbf{A}_3$ to the collection, getting $\mathbf{A}_3, \mathbf{A}_2, \mathbf{A}_1, \mathbf{e}_i$. This time, when we remove a vector, it must be $\mathbf{e}_i$, since the collection $\mathbf{A}_3, \mathbf{A}_2, \mathbf{A}_1$ is linearly independent. We are therefore able to conclude that the three vectors are a set of generators, and the theorem is proved.

The reader should study carefully the process used in this proof. We start with a set of generators. When another vector is added, the resulting collection must be linearly dependent. Hence one of the original vectors can be removed and still leave a set of generators. A vector is pushed in at one end, forcing one out at the other. Observe also that in this proof we have made use only of the definitions, the properties of vectors as found in Theorems 3–3 and 3–4, and the fact that there are three special vectors ($\mathbf{e}_1$, $\mathbf{e}_2$, and $\mathbf{e}_3$) which generate the entire space. Theorem 5–23 should be compared with Theorem 5–12. The two are essentially equivalent.

Next, we add to the above assumptions the properties of the dot product as given in Theorem 3–5, and show how we can obtain a close approximation to Theorem 5–14 without having to use the cross product.

Theorem 5–24. Suppose $\mathbf{A}_1$, $\mathbf{A}_2$, and $\mathbf{A}_3$ are linearly independent. Then there exists an orthonormal set $\mathbf{u}_1$, $\mathbf{u}_2$, and $\mathbf{u}_3$ such that $\mathbf{u}_1$ is a scalar multiple of $\mathbf{A}_1$, $\mathbf{u}_2$ is a linear combination of $\mathbf{A}_1$ and $\mathbf{A}_2$, and $\mathbf{u}_3$ is a linear combination of $\mathbf{A}_1$, $\mathbf{A}_2$, and $\mathbf{A}_3$.

Proof: Since $\mathbf{A}_1$, $\mathbf{A}_2$, and $\mathbf{A}_3$ are linearly independent, none can be the zero vector. We start by setting

$$\mathbf{u}_1 = \mathbf{A}_1/|\mathbf{A}_1|$$

just as in Theorem 5–14.

Next we wish to find $\mathbf{u}_2$ coplanar with $\mathbf{A}_1$ and $\mathbf{A}_2$ and orthogonal to $\mathbf{u}_1$. Refer back to Fig. 5–4 for a picture of what we wish to accomplish. In this figure, we let $\mathbf{B} = \mathbf{u}_1$, and $\mathbf{A} = \mathbf{A}_2$. Then the orthogonal vector $\mathbf{V}$, which we call $\mathbf{V}_2$, must be

$$\mathbf{V}_2 = \mathbf{A}_2 - (\mathbf{A}_2 \cdot \mathbf{u}_1)\mathbf{u}_1. \tag{5–33}$$

This same result can also be obtained in a purely algebraic manner. The desired vector $\mathbf{V}_2$ is to be a linear combination of $\mathbf{A}_2$ and $\mathbf{u}_1$. Since it is to be orthogonal to $\mathbf{u}_1$, it cannot be collinear with $\mathbf{u}_1$. We can therefore assume that the desired vector is of the form

$$\mathbf{V}_2 = \mathbf{A}_2 + t\mathbf{u}_1.$$

To find t so that $\mathbf{V}_2$ is orthogonal to $\mathbf{u}_1$, we set $\mathbf{V}_2 \cdot \mathbf{u}_1 = 0$. This gives $\mathbf{A}_2 \cdot \mathbf{u}_1 + t = 0$, and hence $t = -(\mathbf{A}_2 \cdot \mathbf{u}_1)$, resulting in the same vector $\mathbf{V}_2$ as obtained in (5–33).

The vector $\mathbf{V}_2$ is orthogonal to $\mathbf{u}_1$, but it is not of unit length in general. Therefore, we set

$$\mathbf{u}_2 = |\mathbf{V}_2|/\mathbf{V}_2.$$

We can continue this process in a similar manner to find a vector orthogonal to both $\mathbf{u}_1$ and $\mathbf{u}_2$. The desired vector can be determined with the help of the concept of projection (see Fig. 5–5) or directly in the following way. The vector we wish to find is to be a linear combination of $\mathbf{A}_3$, $\mathbf{u}_1$, and $\mathbf{u}_2$. Hence we can assume

$$\mathbf{V}_3 = \mathbf{A}_3 + s\mathbf{u}_1 + t\mathbf{u}_2. \tag{5–34}$$

We can then solve for s and t by using the conditions that $\mathbf{V}_3$ is orthogonal to $\mathbf{u}_1$ and $\mathbf{u}_2$. Setting $\mathbf{V}_3 \cdot \mathbf{u}_1 = 0$ in (5–34) gives

$$\mathbf{A}_3 \cdot \mathbf{u}_1 + s = 0.$$

Similarly, setting $\mathbf{V}_3 \cdot \mathbf{u}_2 = 0$ gives

$$\mathbf{A}_3 \cdot \mathbf{u}_2 + t = 0.$$

Hence we find that

$$\mathbf{V}_3 = \mathbf{A}_3 - (\mathbf{A}_3 \cdot \mathbf{u}_1)\mathbf{u}_1 - (\mathbf{A}_3 \cdot \mathbf{u}_2)\mathbf{u}_2. \tag{5–35}$$

Note that this is merely $\mathbf{A}_3$ minus the projection of $\mathbf{A}_3$ onto the plane determined by $\mathbf{u}_1$ and $\mathbf{u}_2$. The required vector of length 1 is then finally given by

$$\mathbf{u}_3 = \frac{\mathbf{V}_3}{|\mathbf{V}_3|}.$$

The process that we have gone through here is of great theoretical (and in many cases, practical) importance. The method produces an orthonormal set of vectors successively from a given set of vectors by subtracting from each vector its projection on the "plane" determined by the previously determined vectors. Equations (5–33) and (5–35) serve to show how the method proceeds. The process in no way depends on the fact that our vectors are three-dimensional, and can be extended to any vector space with an inner product. It is known as the *Gram-Schmidt orthogonalization process.*

6

The Conic Sections

6–1 THE DEFINITION OF CONIC SECTIONS

In their study of geometry, the early Greek mathematicians gave special consideration to those curves which could be obtained by cutting a right circular cone with a plane. Such curves occupy an important position throughout geometry and analysis, and their properties must be well known to any student planning to do further work in mathematics.

To start our discussion of the conic sections, let us first find the vector form of the equation of a right circular cone. Three things are required in order to define a cone. We must specify a point to be the *vertex* of the cone (A in Fig. 6–1), a vector $\mathbf{N}$ to define the direction of the *axis* of the cone, and an angle θ to be the *half angle* of the cone. A point $X = (x, y, z)$ is on the cone if and only if the vector $\overrightarrow{AX}$ makes the angle θ with $\mathbf{N}$ or $-\mathbf{N}$. This is the same as

$$|(\mathbf{X} - \mathbf{A}) \cdot \mathbf{N}| = \lambda|\mathbf{X} - \mathbf{A}| \cdot |\mathbf{N}|,$$

where $\lambda = \cos\theta$. The absolute value on $(\mathbf{X} - \mathbf{A}) \cdot \mathbf{N}$ is needed to give us both sides of the cone. If the absolute value signs were left off, what points X would satisfy this relation?

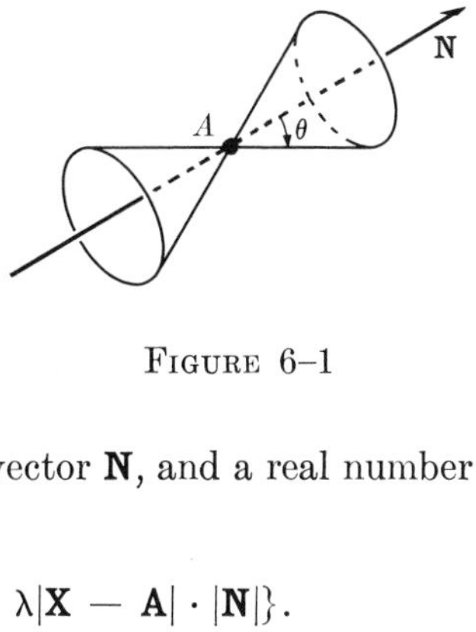

FIGURE 6–1

Definition 6–1. Given a point A, a nonzero vector $\mathbf{N}$, and a real number λ with $0 < \lambda < 1$, a *right circular cone* is

$$\{X = (x, y, z) \mid\ |(\mathbf{X} - \mathbf{A}) \cdot \mathbf{N}| = \lambda|\mathbf{X} - \mathbf{A}| \cdot |\mathbf{N}|\}.$$

The point A is called the *vertex* of the cone; the line $\mathbf{X} = \mathbf{A} + t\mathbf{N}$ is called the *axis* of the cone; and the angle θ with $0 < \theta < \pi/2$ such that $\cos\theta = \lambda$ is called the *half angle* of the cone.

The two sets

$$\{X \mid (\mathbf{X} - \mathbf{A}) \cdot \mathbf{N} = \lambda|\mathbf{X} - \mathbf{A}| \cdot |\mathbf{N}|\},$$
$$\{X \mid (\mathbf{X} - \mathbf{A}) \cdot \mathbf{N} = -\lambda|\mathbf{X} - \mathbf{A}| \cdot |\mathbf{N}|\}$$

are called the *nappes* of the cone.

If X_0 is any point on the cone other than the vertex, then the line $\mathbf{X} = \mathbf{A} + t(\mathbf{X}_0 - \mathbf{A})$ is called a *generator* of the cone.

Although the set defined here is correctly known as a *right circular cone*, we shall just call it a *cone* for the time being. Since only the direction of $\mathbf{N}$ is needed to determine the axis of the cone, we can set $\mathbf{B} = \mathbf{N}/|\mathbf{N}|$ and use this vector of unit length to determine the axis. That is, if $A = (a_1, a_2, a_3)$ and $\mathbf{B} = [b_1, b_2, b_3]$, with $|\mathbf{B}| = 1$, the above relation can be written as

$$|b_1(x - a_1) + b_2(y - a_2) + b_3(z - a_3)| = \lambda[(x - a_1)^2 + (y - a_2)^2 + (z - a_3)^2]^{1/2}.$$

To eliminate the absolute value signs, we can square this equation to obtain

$$[b_1(x - a_1) + b_2(y - a_2) + b_3(z - a_3)]^2 = \lambda^2[(x - a_1)^2 + (y - a_2)^2 + (z - a_3)^2]. \quad (6\text{–}1)$$

This equation is satisfied by the coordinates of each point X on the cone, and if the coordinates of a point satisfy this equation, then that point is on the cone. Therefore, if we specify that $b_1^2 + b_2^2 + b_3^2 = 1$, then (6–1) is the general form of the cartesian equation of a cone.

In order to study the intersection of a cone with a plane we merely have to choose a plane and find the points common to this plane and the cone. The most convenient plane to use is of course the xy-coordinate plane ($z = 0$). If we set $z = 0$ in the equation of the cone, we are left with an equation containing only x and y. This will then be the cartesian equation, in the xy-plane, of the conic section.

Setting $z = 0$ in the equation of the cone given above, expanding and rearranging terms gives an equation of the form

$$Ax^2 + Bxy + Cy^2 + Dx + Ey + F = 0. \quad (6\text{–}2)$$

We can conclude that every conic section in the xy-plane satisfies a general quadratic equation.

To make a more careful study of the conic sections we need to simplify the equations somewhat. This can be done by proper adjustment of the parameters determining the cone. Thus in the position $A = (a_1, a_2, a_3)$ of the vertex of the cone, we can change a_1 and a_2 in any way we may find useful. Such changes merely translate the conic section on the plane. Likewise the direction of the axis $\mathbf{B} = [b_1, b_2, b_3]$ can be altered as desired by changing b_1 and b_2 (keeping $|\mathbf{B}| = 1$). The effect on the conic section will be a rotation in the xy-plane. Since b_3 is the cosine of the angle between $\mathbf{B}$ and the z-axis, fixing it determines the angle between $\mathbf{B}$ and the xy-plane. (See Problem 13, at the end of Section 4–4.)

Let us set $a_2 = 0$ and $b_2 = 0$. This corresponds to assuming that the vertex of the cone is in the xz-plane and that the axis of the cone is in this plane also. Later, we will adjust a_1 as needed to give the greatest simplification. Note that when $b_2 = 0$, b_1 is the cosine of the angle between **B** and the xy-plane.

Substituting these values in the cartesian equation of the cone and setting $z = 0$, we find, after some algebraic manipulation, the equation of the conic to be

$$(\lambda^2 - b_1^2)x^2 - 2[a_1(\lambda^2 - b_1^2) - b_1b_3a_3]x + \lambda^2y^2 = 2b_1b_3a_1a_3 - a_1^2(\lambda^2 - b_1^2) - a_3^2(\lambda^2 - b_3^2). \qquad (6\text{–}3)$$

We will consider various cases of this equation as b_1 is varied while holding fixed λ, the cosine of the half angle of the cone. Changing b_1 corresponds to "tipping" the cone. To fix our picture we will assume that $b_1 \geq 0$, $b_3 \geq 0$, and $a_3 < 0$.

The first case we consider is that when $b_1 = 0$. Then, since $b_1^2 + b_3^2 = 1$ and $b_3 \geq 0$, $b_3 = 1$. For this case, we set $a_1 = 0$. Then Eq. (6–3) becomes

$$\lambda^2x^2 + \lambda^2y^2 = a_3^2(1 - \lambda^2),$$

or

$$x^2 + y^2 = a_3^2\frac{(1 - \lambda^2)}{\lambda^2}. \qquad (6\text{–}4)$$

This is recognized as the equation of a circle (note that $\lambda^2 < 1$), which is as it should be, since with $b_1 = 0$, the cone has its axis orthogonal to the xy-plane (Fig. 6–2).

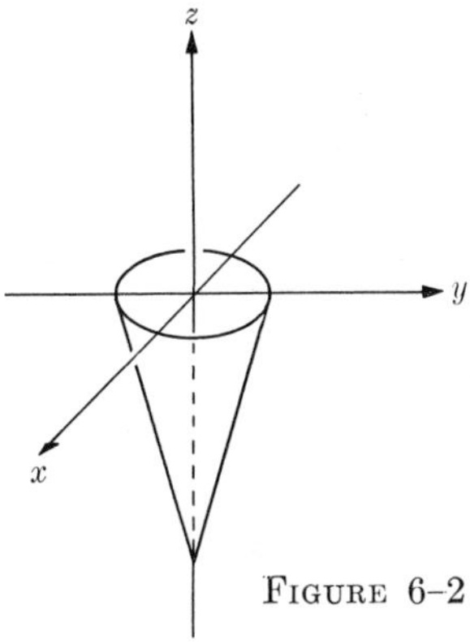

FIGURE 6–2

Let ϕ be the angle between the axis of the cone and the xy-plane. Then $\cos\phi = b_1$. Since the axis of the cone is in the xz-plane, ϕ is also the angle between the axis of the cone and the x-axis. In Fig. 6–3 we show the cross section of the cone in the xz-plane for several possible cases. Letting θ be the half angle of the cone, it is clear that the "bottom" generator of the cone makes an angle of $\phi - \theta$ with the x-axis.

Therefore, if $\theta < \phi$ or equivalently, if $0 < b_1 < \lambda$ (since the cosine decreases as the angle increases), all generators of the cone are pointing "upward" and the xy-plane cuts through a single nappe of the cone. The resulting curve is called an *ellipse* (see Fig. 6–3a).

In this case, we have $0 < \lambda_1^2 - b_1^2 < \lambda^2$. Set $\lambda^2 - b_1^2 = \mu^2$. To simplify Eq. (6–3) as much as possible we set $a_1 = b_1b_3a_3/\mu^2$. That is, we move the vertex of the cone so as to obtain the greatest simplification.

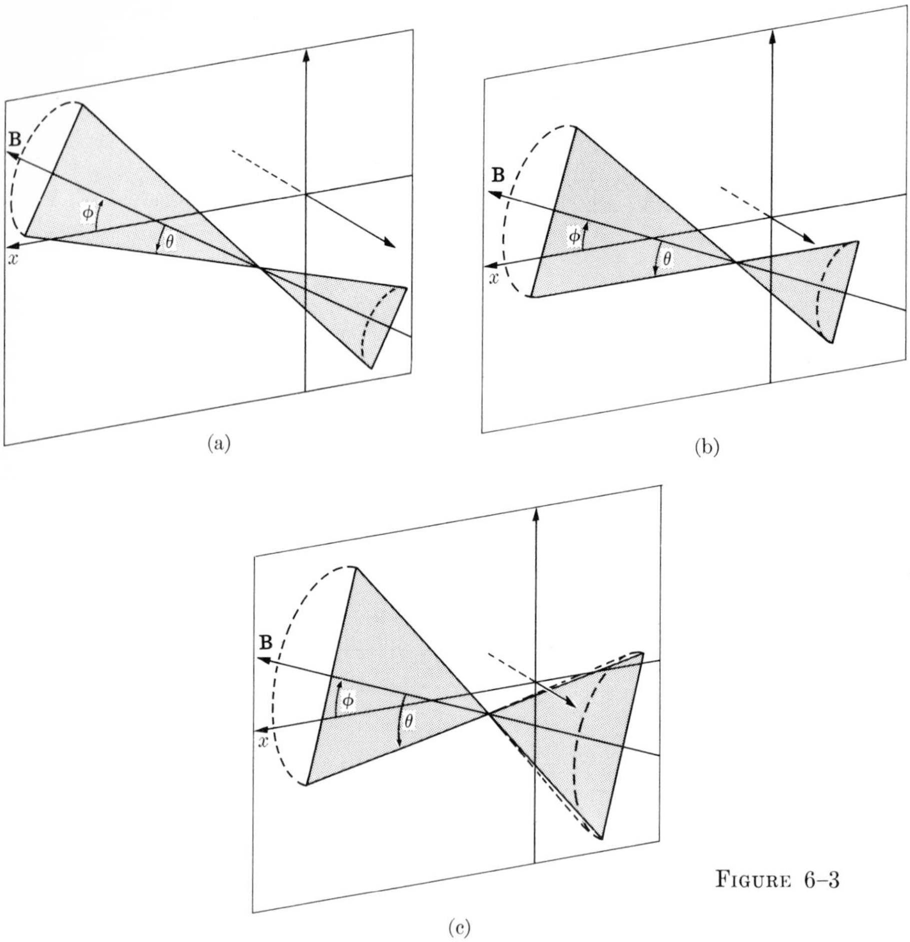

FIGURE 6–3

The result is shown in Fig. 6–4. Equation (6–3) then reduces to

$$\mu^2x^2 + \lambda^2y^2 = k^2. \tag{6–5}$$

Here, the right-hand side of (6–3) reduces to a constant which we have written as a positive constant k^2. To see that this is possible we merely need to observe that the cone must cut the xy-plane somewhere, hence there exist points (x, y) which satisfy (6–3). But the left-hand side of (6–3) reduces to the left-hand side of (6–5), which is positive for any (x, y). Hence the right-hand side must be a positive constant.

The next case to be considered is that for which $b_1 = \lambda$. Here, the half angle of the cone is the same as the angle between its axis and the x-axis. Hence, exactly one of the generators of the cone will be parallel to the

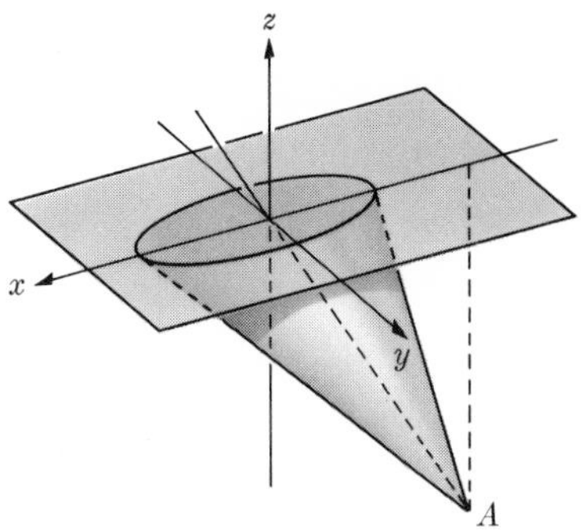

FIGURE 6-4

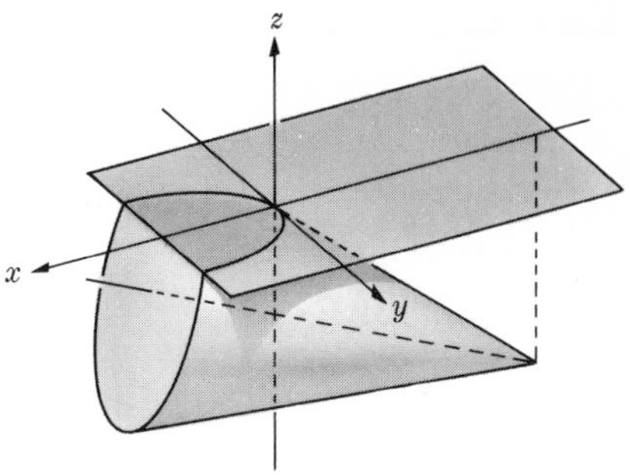

FIGURE 6-5

x-axis (Fig. 6-3b). The intersection will be a single curve which never closes. This conic section is called a *parabola*. Inserting this value into Eq. (6-3), we find that

$$2b_1b_3a_3x + \lambda^2y^2 = 2b_1b_3a_1a_3 - a_3^2(\lambda^2 - b_3^2).$$

In this equation $b_1b_3a_3 \neq 0$ except for certain limiting cases. We may adjust a_1 so that the right-hand side of this equation is zero. Then, dividing through by λ^2, we find that the equation of the parabola has the form

$$y^2 = kx, \tag{6-6}$$

where k is some nonzero constant (Fig. 6-5).

The final case to be considered is that when $0 < \lambda < b_1$. In Fig. 6-3(c) we observe that under this condition the plane $z = 0$ will cut both nappes of the cone. The conic section thus consists of two parts. The resulting curve is called a *hyperbola*.

The coefficient of x^2 in (6-3) is negative, so we set $\lambda^2 - b_1^2 = -\mu^2$. Then we can set $a_1 = -b_1b_3a_3/\mu^2$ to eliminate the coefficient of the x term. The left-hand side of (6-3) then becomes $-\mu^2x^2 + \lambda^2y^2$. From the geometric position of the cone, it is easily seen that there must be two

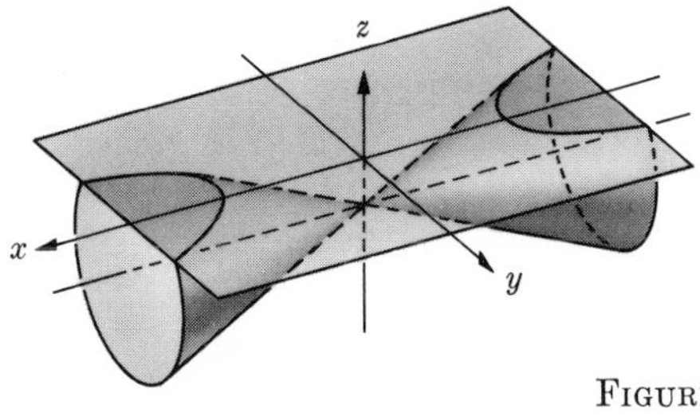

FIGURE 6-6

distinct points on the x-axis which are on the hyperbola. Since at least one of these is not zero, we see that the constant on the right-hand side of (6–3) must be negative. That is, the hyperbola must satisfy an equation of the form

$$-\mu^2 x^2 + \lambda^2 y^2 = -k^2. \tag{6–7}$$

This case is illustrated in Fig. 6–6.

In the above discussion b_1 is the cosine of the angle between the axis of the cone and the x-axis and at the same time the cosine of the angle between the axis of the cone and the xy-plane. Therefore, each of the conic sections considered above satisfies the following formal definition.

Definition 6–2. A *nondegenerate conic section* is the intersection of a right circular cone with a plane which does not pass through the vertex of the cone. Given such a cone and plane, let θ be the half angle of the cone and let ϕ be the angle between the axis of the cone and the plane. Then the resulting conic section is called:

(1) a *circle* if and only if $\phi = \pi/2$,
(2) an *ellipse* if and only if $\pi/2 > \phi > \theta$,
(3) a *parabola* if and only if $\phi = \theta$,
(4) a *hyperbola* if and only if $\theta > \phi$.

The calculations of this section can then be summarized in the following theorem:

Theorem 6–1. The intersection of a right circular cone with the xy-plane is the locus of an equation of the form

$$Ax^2 + Bxy + Cy^2 + Dx + Ey + F = 0.$$

Let λ be the cosine of the half angle of the cone and let b_1 be the cosine of the angle between the axis of the cone and the plane. Set $\mu^2 = |\lambda^2 - b_1^2|$. Then for a suitable location of the cone with respect to the x- and y-axes, an ellipse, a parabola, or a hyperbola will be the locus of the equation

$$\mu^2 x^2 + \lambda^2 y^2 = k^2,$$
$$y^2 = kx,$$

or

$$-\mu^2 x^2 + \lambda^2 y^2 = -k^2,$$

respectively, where k is a nonzero constant whose value depends on the particular conic section in question.

We remark that the size and shape of the conic section is determined completely by three quantities: the half angle of the cone, the angle between the axis of the cone and the plane, and the distance between the vertex of the cone and the plane. The phrase, "suitable location of the cone," found in this theorem should be interpreted as allowing the cone to be moved in any way which does not change any of these three quantities.

PROBLEMS

1. Write the cartesian equations of each of the following cones:
   (a) The cone with vertex at (0, 1, 1), axis parallel to the x-axis, and half angle 60°
   (b) The cone with vertex at (0, 0, 2), axis parallel to $\mathbf{B} = [2, 0, 1]$, and half angle 45°
   (c) The cone with vertex at (0, 0, 1), axis parallel to $\mathbf{B} = [1, 0, 1]$, and half angle 45°

2. Find and simplify as much as possible the cartesian equation of the conic sections obtained as the intersections of the cones of Problem 1 with the xy-plane. Identify each conic section as to type.

3. Prove algebraically that the right-hand side of (6–3) is positive when $0 < \lambda^2 - b_1^2 < \lambda^2$ and when we put $a_1 = b_1 b_3 a_3/(\lambda^2 - b_1^2)$.

4. Let A be the vertex of a right circular cone and let X_0 be any point other than A on the cone. Prove that every point of the line $\mathbf{X} = \mathbf{A} + t(\mathbf{X}_0 - \mathbf{A})$ is on the cone.

5. The intersection of a cone and a plane which passes through the vertex of the cone is a degenerate conic section.
   (a) What is the general form of the equation for the intersection of a right circular cone whose vertex is at (0, 0, 0) with the plane $z = 0$?
   (b) Give an example of a cone in (*a*) in which the conic section consists of the single point (0, 0, 0).
   (c) Give an example of a cone for which the conic section is the single line $x = 0$.
   (d) Give an example of a cone for which the conic section is the pair of lines $x = 0$ and $y = 0$.

6–2 EQUIVALENT DEFINITIONS

There are several other possible ways to define the conic sections. In this section we wish to investigate these alternatives.

It has been known for a long time that if we are given an ellipse, then there are two points in the plane such that the sum of the distances from these points to every point of the ellipse is a constant. This condition can be written in the form:

$$|\mathbf{X} - \mathbf{F}_1| + |\mathbf{X} - \mathbf{F}_2| = 2a,$$

where F_1 and F_2 are the fixed points, a is a constant ($2a$ is used here because it leads to certain simplifications later), and X is any point of the ellipse. In this form, the two fixed points are called the *foci* of the ellipse.

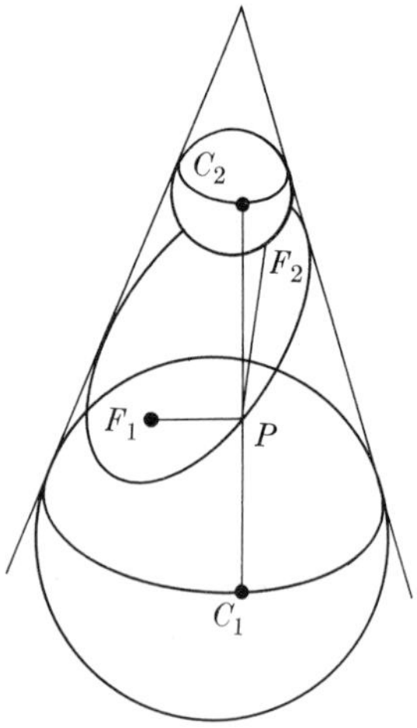

FIGURE 6–7

A simple proof of this property was discovered in the early nineteenth century by the Belgian mathematician Dandelin. The Dandelin proof is illustrated in Fig. 6–7. We imagine a cone and an intersecting plane forming an ellipse. Every point on the central axis of the cone is equidistant from the generators of the cone (see Problem 1 at the end of this section), and hence each point of the central axis is the center of a sphere tangent to the sides of the cone. Exactly two of these spheres would also be tangent to the plane which cuts off the ellipse as shown in Fig. 6–7. The points of tangency, F_1 and F_2, are the foci of the ellipse. Let P be any point of the ellipse. There is a unique generator of the cone through the point P. Let this generator be tangent to the two spheres at C_1 and C_2. Then the distance between C_1 and C_2 is a fixed constant, say $2a$, independent of which point P has been chosen. Now consider the line segments F_1P and F_2P. The two segments F_1P and C_1P are both tangent to the lower sphere from the point P and hence have the same length, $|F_1P| = |C_1P|$. Similarly, $|F_2P| = |C_2P|$, and hence

$$|F_1P| + |F_2P| = |C_1P| + |C_2P| = |C_1C_2| = 2a.$$

We have therefore proved

Theorem 6–2. For any ellipse, there exist a constant a and two points, F_1 and F_2, which are in the plane of the ellipse, such that if X is any point on the ellipse, then

$$|XF_1| + |XF_2| = 2a. \tag{6–8}$$

The points F_1 and F_2 are called the foci of the ellipse.

In an exactly similar manner a focal relation for the hyperbola can be obtained. Two points F_1 and F_2, called the foci of the hyperbola, can be found such that for every point X on the hyperbola, the absolute value of the difference of the distances from X to F_1 and from X to F_2 will be a constant. Verification of this will be left to the reader, with the observation that in the case of the hyperbola the two spheres are in different nappes of the cone.

Theorem 6–3. For any hyperbola, there exist a constant a and two points, F_1 and F_2, which are in the plane of the hyperbola, such that if X is any point on the hyperbola, then

$$\big|\, |XF_1| - |XF_2| \,\big| = 2a. \tag{6–9}$$

The points F_1 and F_2 are called the foci of the hyperbola.

Let us look at another characterization of the conic sections which can be obtained from the introduction of the sphere of the Dandelin proof. This sphere, which is tangent to both the cone and the intersecting plane, is called the Dandelin sphere. The circle consisting of those points at which the Dandelin sphere is tangent to the cone lies in a plane which is orthogonal to the axis of the cone. (See Problem 1 at the end of this section.) In Fig. 6–8 we have indicated this plane together with the cutting plane which determines the conic section. Note that these two planes can be determined for any of the configurations discussed in section 6–1. That is, we are not restricting ourselves to a particular one of the conics (except that the circle does not fall under our discussion here). In Fig. 6–9, where we have redrawn the important features of the geometric configuration which we wish to consider, F is the focus of the conic, that is, the point at which the sphere is tangent to the cutting plane. Just as in the discussion above, we see that if P is an arbitrary point on the conic, then $|FP| = |CP|$ where the line CP is along a generator of the cone and C is the point at which this generator is tangent to the sphere.

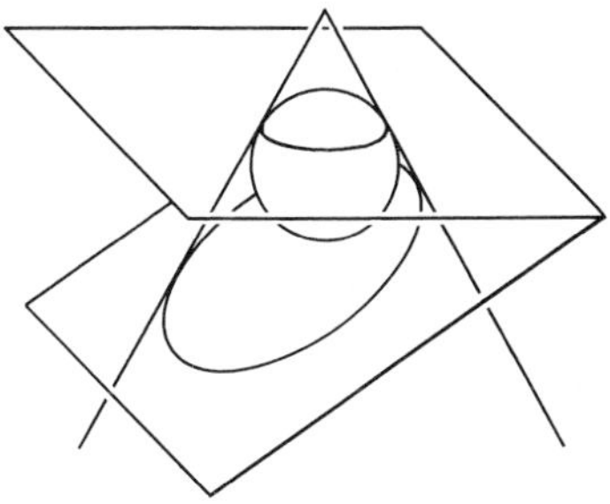

FIGURE 6–8

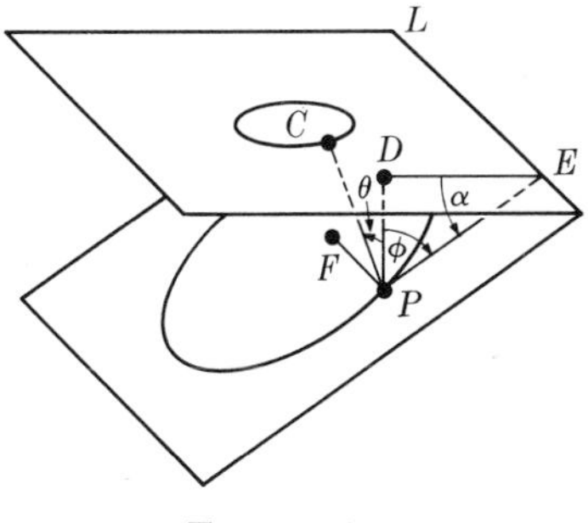

FIGURE 6–9

Let DP be the line segment parallel to the axis of the cone such that D is on the plane through the circle of tangency. Thus DP is orthogonal to this plane. Then if θ is the half angle of the cone, the angle between CP and DP is θ, and hence

$$|DP| = |CP| \cos \theta = |FP| \cos \theta. \tag{6–10}$$

Let L be the line of intersection of these two planes. Then L is orthogonal to the axis of the cone. Let the plane through P orthogonal to L cut this line at E. Then DP is in this plane (since DP is parallel to the axis of the cone and hence is orthogonal to L) and the triangle DEP is a right triangle. Let α be the angle between the two planes and let $\phi = \pi/2 - \alpha$. This angle ϕ is then exactly the angle between the axis of the cone and the plane that was discussed in the last section. Observe that the angle ϕ is the vertex angle of the triangle DPE at P, and therefore

$$|DP| = |PE| \cos \phi. \tag{6–11}$$

Combining this equation with (6–10), we find

$$|FP| = |PE| \frac{\cos \phi}{\cos \theta},$$

or, setting

$$e = \frac{\cos \phi}{\cos \theta}, \tag{6–12}$$

we have

$$|FP| = |PE|e.$$

In this relation, the quantity e is known as the *eccentricity* of the conic and the line of intersection of the planes is called the *directrix* of the conic. When the cutting plane is orthogonal to the axis of the cone and thus yielding a circle, this formula is not strictly applicable since the directrix does not exist. However, in this case we define $e = 0$. If the cutting plane is allowed to tip, e continuously increases while an ellipse is produced. When the plane becomes parallel to a generator of the cone, $\cos \phi = \cos \theta$, $e = 1$, and we have a parabola. For a hyperbola $e > 1$. The maximum value of e for a given cone is $1/\cos \theta$, but this can be made as large as desired by widening the cone and letting θ get close to $\pi/2$ (it can never become $\pi/2$).

In the case of the ellipse or hyperbola, there are two Dandelin spheres and hence two foci. The above argument can be used at either focus. Thus the ellipse and hyperbola have two directrices, one associated with each focus. The parabola, on the other hand, will have a single directrix and focus.

Collecting these results, we have the following theorem.

Theorem 6–4. Let F be a focus of a nondegenerate conic section which is not a circle. Then there exists a line L, called a directrix of the conic, and a constant e, called the eccentricity of the conic, such that for every point X on the conic

$$|XF| = |XE|e, \tag{6–13}$$

where $|XE|$ is the distance from X to the line L. The eccentricity e is less than 1 for an ellipse equal to 1 for a parabola, and greater than 1 for a hyperbola.

PROBLEMS

1. Let the vertex of a cone be at the origin. Let $\mathbf{B}$ be the unit vector defining the axis of the cone, θ be the half angle of the cone and $\lambda = \cos\theta$. Let $\mathbf{R} = r\mathbf{B}$ be a point on the axis of the cone, and suppose that $\mathbf{u}$ is a unit vector along a generator of the cone.
   (a) Let $\mathbf{S}$ be the projection of $\mathbf{R}$ in the direction of $\mathbf{u}$. Prove that
   $$\mathbf{S} = \lambda r\mathbf{u}.$$
   (b) Show that the distance from R to the generator is $|RS| = [1 - \lambda^2]^{1/2}r$, and hence that R is the same distance from all generators.
   (c) Let $\mathbf{T}$ be the projection of $\mathbf{S}$ in the direction of $\mathbf{B}$. Show that
   $$\mathbf{T} = \lambda^2 r\mathbf{B}.$$
   (d) Prove that $\overrightarrow{TS}$ is orthogonal to $\mathbf{B}$ and hence that the points of tangency of the sphere with center R and radius $|RS|$ all lie on a plane orthogonal to $\mathbf{B}$.

2. Using the same cone of Problem 1, let M be the plane through the point Q orthogonal to the unit vector $\mathbf{v}$. Suppose that $\mathbf{Q} = k\mathbf{B}$ where $k \neq 0$. Suppose further that $\mathbf{v}\cdot\mathbf{B} = [1 - \lambda^2]^{1/2}$.
   (a) Prove that the conic section which results is a parabola.
   (b) Show that the distance from the point R of Problem 1 to the plane M is $|k - r|[1 - \lambda^2]^{1/2}$. Prove that the center of the Dandelin sphere for this parabola is at $(k/2)\,\mathbf{B}$.
   (c) At what point is the focus?
   (d) Show that $|\mathbf{B}\times\mathbf{v}| = |\mathbf{B}\times(\mathbf{B}\times\mathbf{v})| = \lambda$.
   (e) Prove that the directrix of the parabola is the line
   $$\mathbf{X} = \mathbf{E}_0 + t(\mathbf{B}\times\mathbf{v}),$$
   where
   $$\mathbf{E}_0 = \frac{k}{2}\left[\lambda^2\mathbf{B} + \frac{(2 - \lambda^2)^{1/2}(1 - \lambda^2)^{1/2}}{\lambda^2}\,\mathbf{B}\times(\mathbf{B}\times\mathbf{v})\right].$$

3. Draw a diagram and give the proof of Theorem 6–3 similar to that given for Theorem 6–2.

4. Let a parabola have a focus F and let L' be a line which cuts the parabola and is parallel to the directrix. Let P be any point of the parabola which is on the same side of L' as the directrix. Let PB be the line segment from P to L' which is orthogonal to L'. Prove that $|FP| + |PB|$ is a constant, independent of P. Make a sketch.

5. Let a solid be made up, as shown in Fig. 6–10, from a cone cut by a plane through its axis and a second plane parallel to a generator so that the line L' of intersection of these two planes is orthogonal to the axis. Let A be the vertex; let B be the point at which a generator meets the parabola; and let BC be a line segment from B to L' orthogonal to L'. Prove that $|AB| + |BC|$ is a constant, independent of the generator chosen.

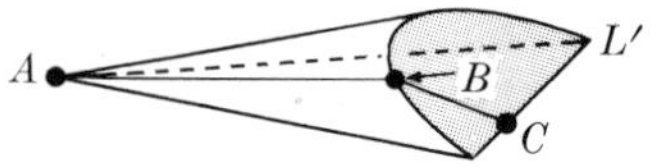

FIGURE 6–10

Remark: This shows that the geodesics (paths of the shortest length) from the tip of the cone to the line L' are all of the same length. If this figure were covered by a sheet of explosive, then by starting the explosion at the point A, a linear explosive front is produced at L'. The reader can easily verify that these paths are indeed geodesics.

6. The usual method used to draw an ellipse is to stick two tacks into a sheet of paper and place a loop of string around these. A curve can then be drawn by placing a pencil point into the loop and moving it about, always holding the loop tight. (See Fig. 6–11.) Prove that the resulting curve satisfies the condition given in Theorem 6–2.

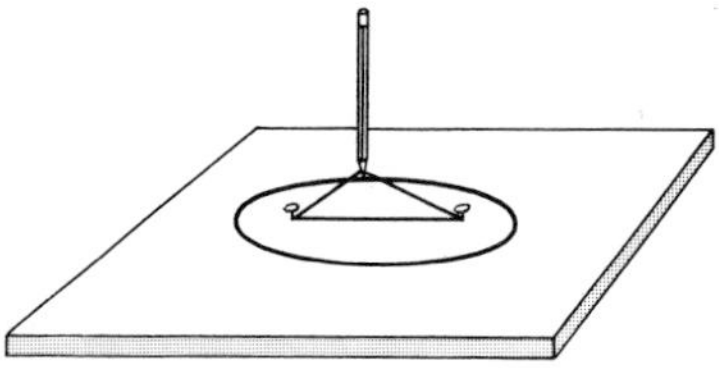

FIGURE 6–11

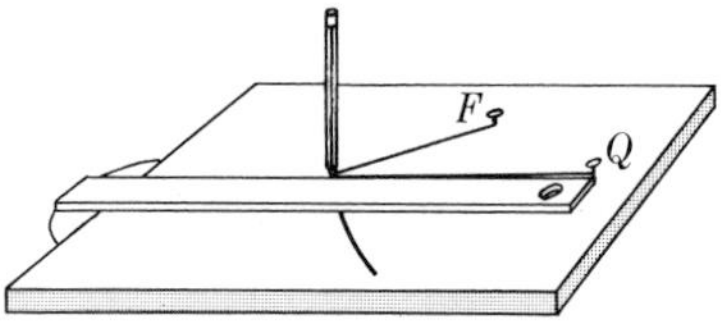

FIGURE 6–12

7. Let a string be fastened at a point F on a drawing board and at the end Q of a T-square (Fig. 6–12). Move the square along the board, holding a pencil point on the edge of the square at a point P so that the string is tight from F to P and from P to Q. As the square is moved, the point P traces out a parabola. Prove that the resulting curve satisfies the condition of Theorem 6–4 with $e = 1$.

6-3 THE ELLIPSE

In the previous sections we have seen several properties of the ellipse. In section 6-1 we saw that a properly located ellipse would satisfy an equation of the form

$$\mu^2x^2 + \lambda^2y^2 = k^2. \tag{6-14}$$

Let us compare this fact with the result of Theorem 6-2, which tells us that each point X of the ellipse satisfies the relation

$$|XF_1| + |XF_2| = 2a. \tag{6-15}$$

Suppose that the foci are on the x-axis, at equal distances on either side of the origin. (Two given points can always be so located by a suitable choice of the coordinate system.) Let F_1 be the point $(-c, 0)$ and F_2 the point $(c, 0)$, where $c > 0$. Then relation (6-15) becomes

$$[(x + c)^2 + y^2]^{1/2} + [(x - c)^2 + y^2]^{1/2} = 2a.$$

Any point (x, y) which satisfies this equation must also satisfy

$$[(x + c)^2 + y^2]^{1/2} = 2a - [(x - c)^2 + y^2]^{1/2},$$

and, squaring, must also satisfy

$$x^2 + 2cx + c^2 + y^2 = 4a^2 - 4a[(x - c)^2 + y^2]^{1/2} + x^2 - 2cx + c^2 + y^2,$$

or

$$4a[(x - c)^2 + y^2]^{1/2} = 4a^2 - 4cx.$$

Squaring again after dividing by 4, we eliminate the last radical, giving

$$a^2[x^2 - 2cx + c^2 + y^2] = a^4 - 2a^2cx + c^2x^2,$$

or

$$(a^2 - c^2)x^2 + a^2y^2 = a^4 - a^2c^2$$
$$= a^2(a^2 - c^2).$$

Dividing through by the right-hand member, we obtain the equation

$$\frac{x^2}{a^2} + \frac{y^2}{a^2 - c^2} = 1. \tag{6-16}$$

Note that since the distance between the foci is $2c$, $2a$ must be greater than $2c$ or the ellipse will not exist. Hence $a^2 - c^2 > 0$. Let us set

$$a^2 - c^2 = b^2, \tag{6-17}$$

then we finally have the equation

$$\frac{x^2}{a^2} + \frac{y^2}{b^2} = 1. \tag{6–18}$$

We have thus shown that any point which satisfies Equation (6–15) satisfies Equation (6–18).

Before continuing with the discussion of (6–18), let us look at the second representation of the ellipse as given in Theorem 6–4. This says that there are a point F, a line L, and a number e, with $0 < e < 1$, such that every point X on the ellipse satisfies the equation

$$|XF| = |XE|e \tag{6–19}$$

where $|XE|$ is the distance from X to the line L.

Let L' be the line through F, orthogonal to L and suppose that X is a point on the line L'. Then, for some scalar t, $\mathbf{X} = \mathbf{F} + t\overrightarrow{FE}$, where E is the point on L closest to F (and also to X). That is, E is the point of intersection of L and L'. Hence

$$|XF| = |t| \cdot |FE|,$$

and

$$\begin{aligned}|XE| &= |\mathbf{E} - \mathbf{X}| \\ &= |\mathbf{E} - \mathbf{F} - tFE| \\ &= |\overrightarrow{FE} - t\overrightarrow{FE}| \\ &= |1 - t| \cdot |FE|.\end{aligned}$$

Therefore,

$$\frac{|XF|}{|XE|} = \frac{|t|}{|1 - t|}.$$

To satisfy requirement (6–19) we must have $t/(1 - t) = \pm e$. Since $0 < e < 1$, there are two possible values of t which will satisfy this, namely $t = e/(1 + e)$ and $t = -e/(1 - e)$. Therefore, there are two points, A and A', on the line L' which satisfy the requirement (6–19).

One of these points, which we denote by A, is between F and L (t is between 0 and 1). The other, A', is so located that F is between A' and L. The reader will find it instructive to observe how the ratio $|XF|/|XE|$ behaves as the point X moves along the line L'.

We are free to locate the focus and directrix as we wish so as to simplify our computations (but, of course, maintaining the same distance between them). Let us place them so that the line L' coincides with the x-axis. That is, so that F is on the x-axis and the directrix L is orthogonal to the x-axis. The two points A and A' found above will also be on the x-axis, and we will suppose that these points are so located that they are at equal distances on either side of the origin. Set

$$A = (a, 0), \qquad A' = (-a, 0), \qquad a > 0,$$
$$F = (c, 0),$$
$$L = \{(x, y) \mid x = d\}.$$

The points A and A' satisfy relation (6–19). That is, $|AF| = |AE|e$, and $|A'F| = |A'E|e$. Since $0 < a < d$, these are equivalent to the equations

$$a - c = (d - a)e,$$
$$a + c = (d + a)e.$$

Adding these equations gives

$$2a = 2de,$$

and subtracting them gives

$$2c = 2ae.$$

Therefore, we may assume that $F = (ae, 0)$ and that the directrix L is the line $x = a/e$, where a is some positive constant.

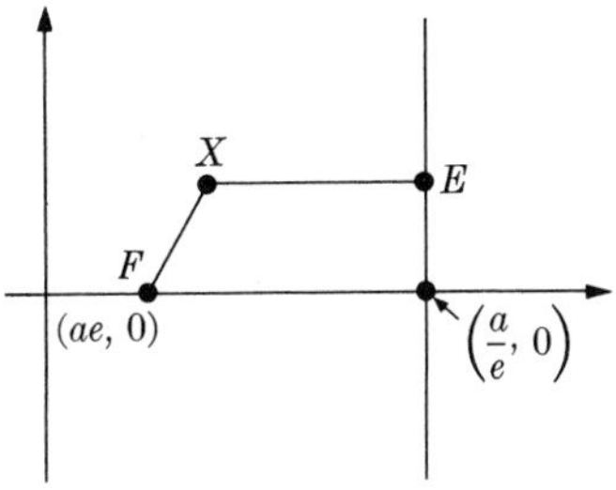

FIGURE 6–13

Let $X = (x, y)$ be an arbitrary point which satisfies the desired relation (6–19) (see Fig. 6–13). Then, we must have

$$[(x - ae)^2 + y^2]^{1/2} = e\left|\frac{a}{e} - x\right|.$$

Squaring this gives

$$x^2 - 2aex + a^2e^2 + y^2 = a^2 - 2aex + e^2x^2,$$

or

$$(1 - e^2)x^2 + y^2 = a^2(1 - e^2).$$

This equation may be divided through by the right-hand member to give

$$\frac{x^2}{a^2} + \frac{y^2}{a^2(1 - e^2)} = 1. \qquad (6\text{–}20)$$

This equation is identical to Eq. (6–18) if we set

$$b^2 = a^2(1 - e^2). \tag{6–21}$$

Let us now investigate the rather delicate question of exactly what implications have been proved. An ellipse is defined as the point set common to a cone and a plane which cuts through a single nappe of the cone. In Theorem 6–1 we showed that if the cone and plane were suitably located, that is, if a coordinate system is suitably chosen, then a point is on the ellipse if and only if it satisfies an equation of the form (6–14). In Section 6–2, we showed that if a point is on the ellipse, it satisfies an equation of the form (6–15) and one of the form (6–19). Here we have shown that if a point satisfies an equation of the form (6–15), then it satisfies one of the form (6–18) and that if a point satisfies (6–19), then it satisfies an equation of the form (6–20). These facts may be summarized in the following diagram.

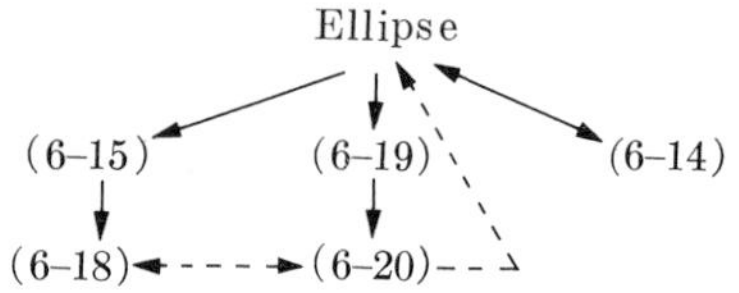

The solid arrows in this diagram indicate the implications we have proved. The dashed double arrow joining (6–18) and (6–20) is meant to indicate that a point which satisfies an equation of either form also satisfies the other. This is clearly true. We merely use (6–21) to go from the one form to the other.

The final implication indicated in this diagram, the arrow from (6–20) to the word "ellipse" is meant to indicate that if a point satisfies an equation of the form (6–20), then it lies on an ellipse with the given eccentricity e. To show this we merely have to set

$$\begin{aligned} A &= \left(-a, 0, -\frac{a(1-e^2)}{e}\right), \\ \mathbf{B} &= \left[\frac{e}{[1+e^2]^{1/2}}, 0, \frac{1}{[1+e^2]^{1/2}}\right], \\ \lambda &= \frac{1}{[1+e^2]^{1/2}} \end{aligned} \tag{6–22}$$

in (6–3) to obtain the equation of a conic section in the xy-plane which is identical to (6–20). The student is asked to verify this as an exercise at the end of this section.

With this result, we see that in the above diagram all the implications hold, and hence that starting at any point in the diagram and following the arrows we can arrive at any other point. In other words, *all of these characterizations of the ellipse are equivalent.* In particular, we have proved the next theorem.

Theorem 6–5. The locus of any equation of the form

$$\frac{x^2}{a^2} + \frac{y^2}{b^2} = 1,$$

where $a > b > 0$, is an ellipse.*

Let us now see what can be determined about the points of an ellipse from the equation given in this theorem. We see that if $|x| > a$, this equation cannot be satisfied, so that all points of the ellipse must have x-coordinates between $-a$ and $+a$. Similarly the y-coordinates of all points of the ellipse must be between $-b$ and $+b$.

When $x = -a$, only $y = 0$ can satisfy the equation. When $-a < x < a$, there will be exactly two values of y satisfying the equation, and hence exactly two points of the ellipse with this value for their x-coordinate. In particular, when $x = 0$, $y = +b$ and $-b$ are the two values for y. When $x = a$, there is again only the single value $y = 0$ which can satisfy the equation.

The ellipse also has a number of symmetry properties. To discuss these properties we first need a definition.

Definition 6–3. Two points P_1 and P_2 are *symmetric* with respect to a line L if and only if the line L is orthogonal to, and bisects the line segment P_1P_2. A set of points S is *symmetric* with respect to a line L if and only if for each point P in S, there is also a point P' in S such that P and P' are symmetric with respect to the line L.

This definition corresponds to our usual notion of symmetry. It can easily be converted to an analytic condition in special cases. For example,

Theorem 6–6. If S is the set of all points (x, y) in the plane which satisfy a functional relationship $f(x\ y) = 0$, and if for every x and y, $f(x, -y) = f(x, y)$, then S is symmetric with respect to the x-axis. Similarly, if for every x and y, $f(-x, y) = f(x, y)$, then S is symmetric with respect to the y-axis.

---

* Compare this with Theorem 6–4.

It should be noted that this is not an "if and only if" theorem. The condition given here gives us what is called a *sufficient condition.* If it is satisfied then the set is symmetric. It is not, however, a *necessary condition.* The locus of $f(x, y) = 0$ can be symmetric with respect to one of the axes without the corresponding condition in this theorem being satisfied. The proof of this theorem is left as an exercise.

Now, the equation of the ellipse satisfies the requirements of the above theorem [letting $f(x, y) = x^2/a^2 + y^2/b^2 - 1$]; hence we can conclude that the ellipse is symmetric with respect to both the x- and y-axes. This is a most remarkable result. It is "obvious" to most people that if a plane intersects a cone at an angle, the figure which results must be egg-shaped, fatter at the end which is at the wider part of the cone. Indeed, when Albrecht Dürer, one of the great inventors of descriptive geometry, discovered an accurate method for the construction of an ellipse in the early sixteenth century, he allowed his "knowledge" to affect the construction so as to obtain an egg-shaped figure. An illustration from one of Dürer's books showing this error can be found on page 614 of Volume 1 of *The World of Mathematics*, edited by James R. Newman.

Let us now collect the information we have found about the ellipse. In Fig. 6–14 we show a diagram of the ellipse together with the other relationships which have been developed. The dashed rectangle is centered at the origin and is made up of the lines $x = \pm a$ and $y = \pm b$. The ellipse itself lies within this rectangle, touching the four sides of the rectangle at the points where the axes cross the sides. The origin is called the *center* of the ellipse (later we will discuss the case of an ellipse whose center is located at a point other than the origin).

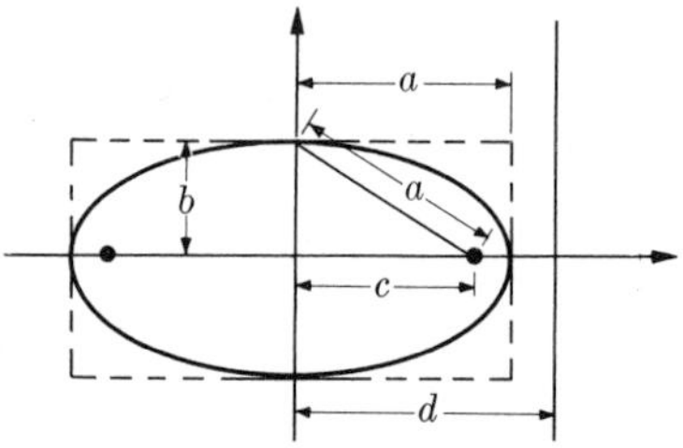

FIGURE 6–14

Note that $a > b$ (since $b^2 = a^2 - c^2$), hence the rectangle is longer in the x-direction than it is in the y-direction. The x-axis (which is the line through the two foci) is called the *principal axis* of the ellipse. The y-axis, which is the line through the center orthogonal to the principal axis, we call the *conjugate axis* of the ellipse. In traditional usage, these axes are called the *major* and *minor* axes respectively. These terms will not be used here, but the reader should be aware of them. Strictly speaking, both of these axes should be called principal axes to conform with modern usage in physics and applied mathematics, but our present terminology will suffice.

The two points at which the principal axis cuts the ellipse [the points $(-a, 0)$ and $(a, 0)$ in Fig. 6–14] are called the *principal vertices* (or just the *vertices*) of the ellipse. The points where the conjugate axis cuts the ellipse (points $(0, -b)$ and $(0, b)$ in this case) are called the *conjugate vertices* of the ellipse. When we refer to a *vertex*, without specifying the type, we mean a principal vertex.

The quantities a and b are respectively called the *principal* and *conjugate dimensions* of the ellipse. In traditional usage, these are called the semimajor axis and semiminor axis.

Let us collect these terms into a formal definition.

Definition 6–4. Let F_1 and F_2 be the foci of an ellipse E. Then we define the following quantities in the ellipse.

(1) The *center*, C, is the midpoint of the line segment F_1F_2.
(2) The *principal axis* is the line L through F_1 and F_2.
(3) The *conjugate axis* is the line L' through C orthogonal to L.
(4) The *principal vertices* are the points A_1 and A_2 of intersection of E and the principal axis L.
(5) The *conjugate vertices* are the points B_1 and B_2 of intersection of E with the conjugate axis L'.
(6) The *principal dimension* is

$$a = |CA_1| = |CA_2|.$$

(7) The *conjugate dimension* is

$$b = |CB_1| = |CB_2|.$$

(8) The *focal dimension* is

$$c = |CF_1| = |CF_2|.$$

The relationships between the quantities listed in this definition and the other properties of the ellipse are given by the following theorem.

Theorem 6–7. Let a, b, and c be the principal, conjugate, and focal dimensions of an ellipse with eccentricity e. Let d be the distance from the center of the ellipse to either directrix. Then the five quantities a, b, c, d, and e are related by the three equations

$$a^2 = b^2 + c^2, \qquad c = ae, \qquad d = a/e. \tag{6–23}$$

With one exception, if any two of these three quantities are specified, the remaining three are uniquely determined by these relationships. These three equations can easily be remembered by keeping Fig. 6–14 in mind. In this figure, the center, the focus, and the point $(0, b)$ form the vertices of a right triangle whose sides are of length b and c. The hypotenuse of this triangle is, by symmetry, exactly half of the sum of the distances from the foci to the point $(0, b)$, and hence must be a. Thus the Pythagorean relation for this triangle gives the first of the three equations.

To remember the other two relations, it is only necessary to remember that c and d are ae and a/e, and that $e < 1$. This fact together with a recollection of the figure will tell you which is which.

The above discussion could be repeated step for step interchanging the roles of x and y. The result would be an ellipse with equation

$$\frac{x^2}{b^2} + \frac{y^2}{a^2} = 1,$$

where as before $a > b$. The resulting ellipse would have its principal axis coinciding with the y-axis, and would appear as in Fig. 6–15.

The same relations between the quantities a, b, c, d, and e hold for this case as well.

Students often seem to have difficulty in recalling which dimension is a and which is b when faced with an actual equation. The following procedure is therefore recommended. When an equation of the form

$$\frac{x^2}{p^2} + \frac{y^2}{q^2} = 1$$

is given, set $x = 0$ and note that $y = \pm q$. The two points $(0, q)$ and $(0, -q)$ may then be marked on a coordinate plane. Similarly, setting $y = 0$ we find the points $(p, 0)$ and $(-p, 0)$ on the ellipse. Mark these points on the plane, and draw the rectangle determined by these four points (as in the figures). The ellipse may then be sketched within the rectangle and the various other quantities determined with a being the larger of p and q.

For example, if we are given the equation

$$\frac{x^2}{4} + \frac{y^2}{9} = 1,$$

we immediately recognize it as the equation of an ellipse of the type shown in Fig. 6–15. In this ellipse, the principal dimension is $a = 3$ and the conjugate dimension is $b = 2$. The focal dimension is then $c = \sqrt{a^2 - b^2} = \sqrt{5}$. The eccentricity is $e = c/a = \sqrt{5}/3$, and hence $d = a/e =$

$9/\sqrt{5}$. We therefore have for this ellipse the following properties.

center: (0, 0)
eccentricity: $e = \sqrt{5}/3$
principal axis: $x = 0$
conjugate axis: $y = 0$
foci: $(0, \sqrt{5})$, $(0, -\sqrt{5})$
principal vertices: (0, 3), (0, −3)
conjugate vertices: (2, 0), (−2, 0)
directrices: $y = 9\sqrt{5}/5$, $y = -9\sqrt{5}/5$

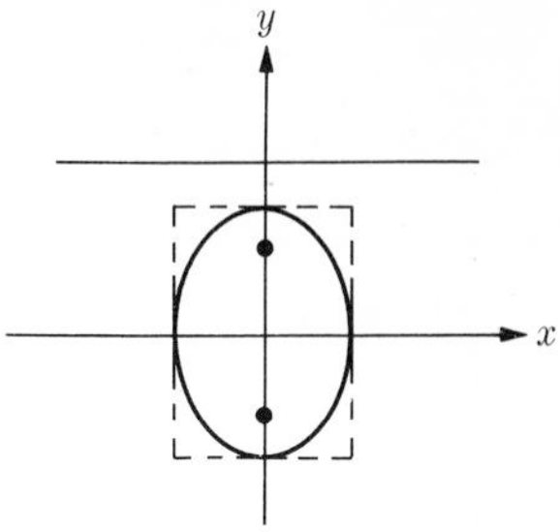

FIGURE 6–15

Going in the other direction, we may wish to find the equation of an ellipse satisfying certain given conditions. For example, what is the equation of the ellipse with foci at (−3, 0), (3, 0), and having a vertex at (5, 0)? Note that this must be a principal vertex, since it lies on the line through the foci.

Here, $a = 5$, $c = 3$, and hence $b^2 = a^2 - c^2 = 25 - 9 = 16$. Therefore, $b = 4$ and the equation is

$$\frac{x^2}{25} + \frac{y^2}{16} = 1.$$

(How do we know that 25 divides the x^2 rather than the y^2?)

PROBLEMS

1. Using the given relations between a, b, c, d, and e for the ellipse, find formulas for the following:
   (a) b, c, and d in terms of a and e only
   (b) c, d, and e in terms of a and b only
   (c) b, d, and e in terms of a and c only
   (d) b, c, and e in terms of a and d only
   (e) a, d, and e in terms of b and c only
   (f) a, b, and c in terms of b and e only
   (g) a, b, and d in terms of c and e only
   (h) a, b, and e in terms of c and d only
   (i) a, b, and c in terms of d and e only

2. (a) From the relations given in Theorem 6–7, find an equation which involves b, d, and e only.
   (b) Using the result of part (a), show that in any ellipse $b \leq d/2$.
   (c) Prove that when $b < d/2$, there are two different ellipses with the same values for b and d.
   (d) If $b = d/2$, what is the eccentricity of the ellipse? What are a and c?

3. Show that exactly the same equation for an ellipse results if the focus-directrix form is assumed with the focus at $(-ae, 0)$ and the line $x = -a/e$ as the directrix.

4. For each of the following equations, make a sketch of the ellipse. Give the coordinates of the foci, and the principal and conjugate vertices. Give the equations of both directrices. Show these on the sketch. Give the eccentricity.

(a) $\dfrac{x^2}{16} + \dfrac{y^2}{25} = 1$ (b) $\dfrac{x^2}{169} + \dfrac{y^2}{25} = 1$

(c) $\dfrac{x^2}{81} + \dfrac{y^2}{16} = 1$ (d) $\dfrac{x^2}{100} + \dfrac{y^2}{144} = 1$

(e) $\dfrac{x^2}{5} + \dfrac{y^2}{4} = 1$ (f) $3x^2 + 4y^2 = 1$

(g) $6x^2 + 15y^2 = 60$ (h) $\dfrac{x^2}{5} + 20y^2 = 5.$

5. Give the equation of the ellipse with center at the origin, x-axis as the principal axis, and satisfying the conditions given:
   (a) One (principal) vertex is at (3, 0) and one focus is at (1, 0)
   (b) One vertex is at (3, 0) and a directrix is $x = 4$
   (c) One vertex is at (3, 0) and the eccentricity is $\frac{1}{5}$
   (d) One focus is at (4, 0) and the eccentricity is $\frac{3}{5}$
   (e) One focus is at (4, 0) and a directrix is $x = 10$
   (f) One focus is at (4, 0) and the conjugate dimension is 3
   (g) A directrix is $x = 5$ and the eccentricity is $\frac{4}{5}$

6. Sketch and give the quantities asked for in Problem 4 for each of the ellipses found in Problem 5.

7. Prove that the cone defined by the quantities A, $\mathbf{B}$, and λ given by (6–22) intersects the plane $z = 0$ in the ellipse whose equation, as given by (6–3), reduces to (6–20).

8. Prove Theorem 6–6.

6–4 THE HYPERBOLA

We will now derive the standard form for the equation of the hyperbola from the focal property given in Theorem 6–3:

$$\big|\,|XF_1| - |XF_2|\,\big| = 2a. \tag{6–24}$$

In this representation, we will let $F_1 = (c, 0)$, $F_2 = (-c, 0)$, and $X = (x, y)$. Then this equation can be written as

$$\left|[(x - c)^2 + y^2]^{1/2} - [(x + c)^2 + y^2]^{1/2}\right| = 2a. \tag{6–25}$$

Any pair (x, y) which satisfies this equation will satisfy one of the pair of equations

$$[(x - c)^2 + y^2]^{1/2} - [(x + c)^2 + y^2]^{1/2} = \pm 2a,$$

or equivalently,

$$[(x - c)^2 + y^2]^{1/2} = [(x + c)^2 + y^2]^{1/2} \pm 2a.$$

Squaring gives

$$x^2 - 2cx + c^2 + y^2 = x^2 + 2cx + c^2 + 4a^2 \pm 4a[(x + c)^2 + y^2]^{1/2},$$

or equivalently,

$$\mp 4a[(x + c)^2 + y^2]^{1/2} = 4cx + 4a^2.$$

Dividing by 4 and squaring again gives

$$a^2x^2 + 2a^2cx + a^2c^2 + a^2y^2 = c^2x^2 + 2a^2cx + a^4.$$

This can be simplified to give

$$(c^2 - a^2)x^2 - a^2y^2 = a^2c^2 - a^4.$$

Dividing through by the right-hand member finally gives

$$\frac{x^2}{a^2} - \frac{y^2}{c^2 - a^2} = 1. \tag{6–26}$$

If we set

$$c^2 - a^2 = b^2, \tag{6–27}$$

this can then be written as

$$\frac{x^2}{a^2} - \frac{y^2}{b^2} = 1. \tag{6–28}$$

Every point (x, y) which satisfies (6–24) must therefore satisfy (6–28).

However, we should check whether or not the definition of b^2 in (6–27) is permissible. The distance between the two foci is $2c$. If X is an arbitrary point on the hyperbola, let l be the smaller of the two distances $|XF_1|$ and $|XF_2|$, and m the larger. Then from the triangle inequality (Fig. 6–16), we have $m < l + 2c$. Therefore,

$$2a = m - l < 2c,$$

or $a < c$, which shows that the left-hand side of (6–27) is a positive quantity.

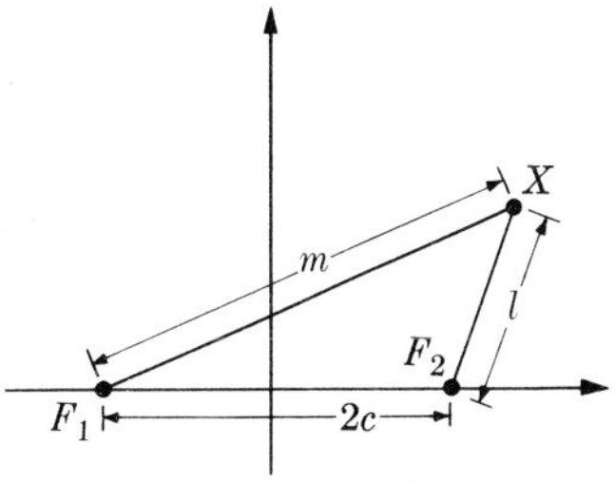

FIGURE 6–16

Next we will derive the equation of the hyperbola from the focus-directrix property of Theorem 6–10. We assume that we are given a point F, a line L, and a real number $e > 1$.

Just as in the last section, let L' be the line through F, orthogonal to L, and let E be the intersection of L and L'. Then, as before, we find that if X is any point of L', then $\mathbf{X} = \mathbf{F} + t\overrightarrow{FE}$, and

$$\frac{|XF|}{|XE|} = \frac{|t|}{|1 - t|}.$$

To satisfy the property of Theorem 6–10, we must have

$$|XF| = |XE|e. \tag{6–29}$$

Again, (6–29) will hold when $t = e/(1 + e)$ or $t = e/(e - 1)$. These two values of t will give us two points, A_1 and A_2, on L' which satisfy (6–29). These points are on opposite sides of the directrix and one is between the directrix and the focus.

We may now assume that the focus and directrix have been so located on the plane that L' coincides with the x-axis, and A_1 and A_2 are at equal distances on either side of the origin. Let $A_1 = (a, 0)$, $A_2 = (-a, 0)$, $F = (c, 0)$, where $a > 0$ and $c > 0$, and suppose the directrix has the equation $x = d$. From the locations of A_1 and A_2 in relation to the focus and the directrix, we have

$$-a < d < a < c.$$

Since the points A_1 and A_2 must satisfy (6–29), we find the two equations

$$c - a = (a - d)e,$$
$$c + a = (a + d)e.$$

Adding and subtracting these equations give

$$2c = 2ae$$

and

$$2a = 2de.$$

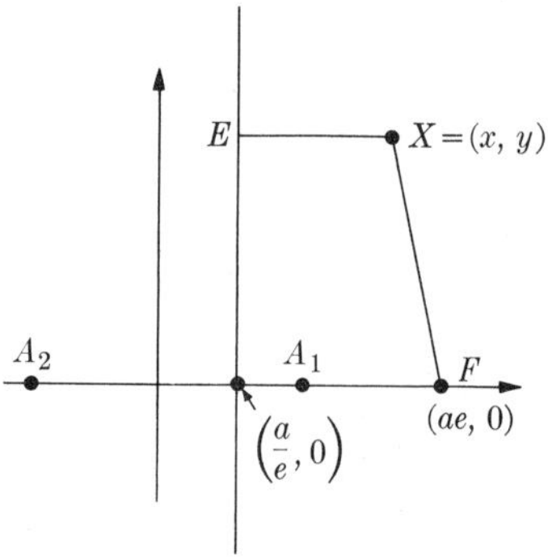

FIGURE 6–17

Therefore $c = ae$ and $d = a/e$, just as in the case of an ellipse (except now $e > 1$).

Let $X = (x, y)$ be an arbitrary point on the ellipse. Then (6–29) must be satisfied. In this case (see Fig. 6–17), (6–29) is equivalent to

$$[(x - ae)^2 + y^2]^{1/2} = e\left|x - \frac{a}{e}\right|$$
$$= |ex - a|.$$

Squaring this relation gives the equivalent equation

$$(x - ae)^2 + y^2 = (ex - a)^2,$$

or

$$x^2 - 2aex + a^2e^2 + y^2 = e^2x^2 - 2aex + a^2.$$

This is again equivalent to

$$(e^2 - 1)x^2 - y^2 = a^2(e^2 - 1),$$

or

$$\frac{x^2}{a^2} - \frac{y^2}{a^2(e^2 - 1)} = 1, \tag{6–30}$$

which is in the same form as (6–28) if we set

$$b^2 = a^2(e^2 - 1), \tag{6–31}$$

(noting that $e > 1$ and hence $e^2 - 1 > 0$).

We thus have found the equation

$$\frac{x^2}{a^2} - \frac{y^2}{b^2} = 1$$

for the hyperbola with focus at $(c, 0)$ and directrix $x = d$, where $c = ae$ and $d = a/e$. Connecting these quantities are the three relations

$$\begin{aligned} a^2 + b^2 &= c^2, \\ c &= ae, \\ d &= a/e. \end{aligned} \tag{6–32}$$

The problem of showing that the forms (6–26) and (6–30) are equivalent to the definition will be left as an exercise.

We therefore have

Theorem 6–8. Any hyperbola in the xy-plane can be so located that it is the locus of an equation of the form

$$\frac{x^2}{a^2} - \frac{y^2}{b^2} = 1,$$

and the locus of any such equation is a hyperbola. For a hyperbola with this equation, relations (6–32) connect the quantities a, b, c, d, and e, where e is the eccentricity and c and d are the distances from the origin to the focus and directrix respectively.

From Eq. (6–28) we see, just as in the case of the ellipse, that the hyperbola is symmetric with respect to both the x-axis and to the y-axis. The origin, the point at which these two axes of symmetry intersect, is called the *center* of the hyperbola.

In Fig. 6–18 we sketch the hyperbola determined by an equation of the form (6–28). The four quantities a, b, c, and d are indicated in this sketch. The dashed lines outline a rectangle centered at the origin with sides of length $2a$ and $2b$ just as in the case of an ellipse. The hyperbola, however, lies outside of this rectangle.

The line passing through two foci, in this case the x-axis, we call the *principal axis* of the hyperbola. The two points at which the hyperbola crosses this line [the points $(a, 0)$, $(-a, 0)$ in the figure] are called the *vertices* of the hyperbola. The line through the center, orthogonal to the principal axis (in this case the y-axis, is called the *conjugate axis* of the hyperbola. Note that there are no conjugate vertices for the hyperbola.

The quantities a and b are called the *principal* and *conjugate dimensions* of the hyperbola respectively.

The two lines shown in Fig. 6–18 forming the diagonals of the dashed rectangle have a special relation to the hyperbola. In this figure each branch of the hyperbola is shown to lie completely within one of the angles formed by these lines and the points of the hyperbola are shown to be close to the points of these lines as $|x|$ and $|y|$ become large. The proof of Theorem 6–9 will show that this is actually true. These lines are called the *asymptotes* of the hyperbola.

Definition 6–5. Let F_1 and F_2 be the foci of a hyperbola H. Then we define the following terms.

(1) The *center* C is the midpoint of the line segment F_1F_2.

(2) The *principal axis* is the line L through F_1 and F_2.

(3) The *conjugate axis* is the line L' through C, orthogonal to L.

(4) The *vertices* are the points A_1 and A_2 of intersection of H and L.

(5) The *principal dimension* is

$$a = |CA_1| = |CA_2|.$$

(6) The *focal dimension* is

$$c = |CF_1| = |CF_2|.$$

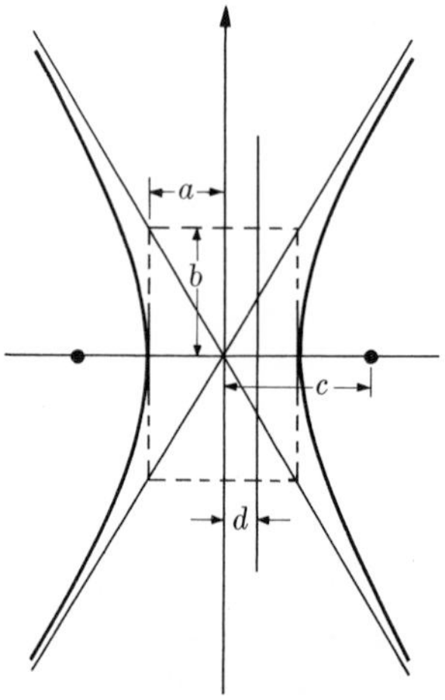

FIGURE 6–18

(7) The *conjugate dimension* is b, where

$$b^2 = c^2 - a^2.$$

(8) The *asymptotes* are the two lines through the center which are the diagonals of the rectangle whose sides are parallel to L and L', whose center is C, and whose dimensions are $2a$ and $2b$, the sides of length $2b$ passing through the vertices.

Theorem 6–9. Each branch of the hyperbola lies completely within one of the angles formed by the asymptotes. Points of the hyperbola which are far from the center are arbitrarily close to the asymptotes.

Proof: The asymptotes of the hyperbola (6–28) have equations

$$\begin{aligned} \frac{x}{a} + \frac{y}{b} &= 0, \\ \frac{x}{a} - \frac{y}{b} &= 0, \end{aligned} \tag{6–33}$$

(why?). To prove our assertions, it suffices to show them to be true for the one line $x/a - y/b = 0$ and for the points of the hyperbola both of whose coordinates x and y are greater than zero. By symmetry, the results will then hold true for all points of the hyperbola.

What must be shown is that if (x_1, y_1) is any point of the hyperbola with both x_1 and $y_1 > 0$, and if (x_1, y_2) is a point on the line $x/a - y/b = 0$, then $y_2 > y_1$, and also that as x_1 becomes large, the distance between the point (x_1, y_1) and the line becomes small.

Both of these remarks can be proved from the fact that if (x_1, y_1) is on the hyperbola, then

$$1 = \frac{x_1^2}{a^2} - \frac{y_1^2}{b^2} = \left(\frac{x_1}{a} - \frac{y_1}{b}\right)\left(\frac{x_1}{a} + \frac{y_1}{b}\right). \tag{6–34}$$

If (x_1, y_2) is on the line $x/a - y/b = 0$, then

$$\frac{x_1}{a} - \frac{y_2}{b} = 0.$$

Hence if $y_1 \geq y_2$, then we would have

$$\frac{x_1}{a} - \frac{y_1}{b} \leq \frac{x_1}{a} - \frac{y_2}{b} = 0,$$

and the product on the right-hand side of (6–34) would be nonpositive (we are supposing $x_1 > 0$ and $y_1 > 0$, remember). This is a contradiction. Therefore, $y_1 < y_2$ as we wished to show.

To see the second assertion, we recall that the distance from a point (x_1, y_1) to the line $x/a - y/b = 0$ is given by

$$\delta = \frac{ab}{[a^2 + b^2]^{1/2}} \left(\frac{x_1}{a} - \frac{y_1}{b}\right)$$

(why?). But from (6–34) we have

$$\delta = \frac{ab}{[a^2 + b^2]^{1/2}} \left(\frac{x_1}{a} - \frac{y_1}{b}\right) = \frac{ab}{[a^2 + b^2]^{1/2}} \frac{1}{\left(\frac{x_1}{a} + \frac{y_1}{b}\right)}$$

$$< \frac{ab}{[a^2 + b^2]^{1/2}} \frac{1}{\frac{x_1}{a}} = \frac{a^2 b}{x_1[a^2 + b^2]^{1/2}}.$$

Here we have used the assumption that $y_1 > 0$. It is clear that as we allow x_1 to increase, the quantity δ becomes very small. In fact, we can make it as small as we desire by choosing x_1 large enough.

If the above development is repeated, interchanging the roles of x and y, we would obtain an equation of the form

$$\frac{x^2}{b^2} - \frac{y^2}{a^2} = -1. \tag{6–35}$$

The hyperbola determined by this equation is of the type shown in Fig. 6–19. The eccentricity and distances from the center to the focus and directrix are determined by the same formulas, (6–32), for this hyperbola. The principal axis in this case is the y-axis and the conjugate axis is the x-axis.

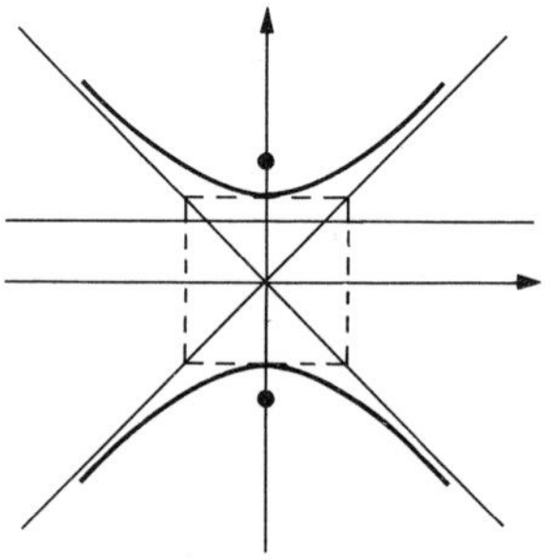

FIGURE 6–19

Students sometimes find it difficult to remember which type of hyperbola goes with which of the two types of equations. Rather than attempting to memorize this information, it is probably easier to proceed as follows when occasion arises. Suppose an equation is given, say $x^2/3^2 - y^2/4^2 = 1$. We know that the hyperbola crosses its principal axis at the two vertices, and has no points in common with its conjugate axis. Setting $x = 0$ in the given equation, we see that there are no values of y which can satisfy the equation, and hence $x = 0$ must be the conjugate axis for this hyperbola. The vertices can be found by setting $y = 0$ and solving for x. The vertices and the foci are on the principal axis, which is the x-axis ($y = 0$) in this case. The hyperbola is thus of the type shown in Fig. 6-18.

For this hyperbola then, $a = 3$ and $b = 4$. Therefore, $c = [a^2 + b^2]^{1/2} = 5$, $e = c/a = 5/3$, and $d = a/e = \frac{9}{5}$. We can thus list for this hyperbola the following properties.

center: $(0, 0)$
eccentricity: $e = 5/3$
principal axis: $y = 0$
conjugate axis: $x = 0$
vertices: $(3, 0)$, $(-3, 0)$
foci: $(5, 0)$, $(-5, 0)$
directrices: $x = 9/5$, $x = -9/5$

asymptotes: $\frac{x}{3} - \frac{y}{4} = 0$, $\frac{x}{3} + \frac{y}{4} = 0$

As another illustrative example, let us find the equation of the hyperbola whose center is at the origin, which has one focus at $(0, 10)$, and which has the line $2x - y = 0$ as one of its asymptotes. Here the hyperbola must be one whose equation is of the form (6-35). An asymptote to the hyperbola of this form is $x/b - y/a = 0$. This has the slope a/b, while the given asymptote has slope 2. Hence we must have

$$a^2 + b^2 = 100,$$
$$a/b = 2.$$

From these equations we find $a = 2b$ and hence

$$5b^2 = 100,$$
$$b^2 = 20,$$
$$a^2 = 80.$$

Thus the desired equation is

$$\frac{x^2}{20} - \frac{y^2}{80} = -1.$$

Note well that unlike the case of the ellipse, a need not be larger than b. Any pair of positive values are possible for the principal and conjugate dimensions of a hyperbola.

PROBLEMS

1. Show the same equation for the hyperbola results if the focus is assumed to be $(-ae, 0)$ and the directrix $x = -a/e$.

2. For the hyperbola defined by the given equation, give the principal and conjugate dimensions, the coordinates of the vertices and the foci, the equations of the directrices and asymptotes, and the eccentricity. Make a sketch for each, showing all relevant items.

(a) $\frac{x^2}{64} - \frac{y^2}{36} = 1$ (b) $\frac{x^2}{144} - \frac{y^2}{25} = -1$

(c) $\frac{x^2}{4} - \frac{y^2}{9} = -1$ (d) $\frac{y^2}{16} - \frac{x^2}{16} = 1$

(e) $\frac{x^2}{9} = 1 + \frac{y^2}{16}$ (f) $x^2 - 4y^2 = -1$

(g) $x^2 - 9y^2 = 36$

3. Find the equation of the hyperbola with center at the origin satisfying the given conditions.
   (a) One vertex at $(5, 0)$ and eccentricity 2
   (b) One vertex at $(0, 8)$ and one focus at $(0, 18)$
   (c) One focus at $(4, 0)$ and eccentricity $5/2$
   (d) One focus at $(6, 0)$ and one directrix being $x = 2$
   (e) One vertex at $(0, 8)$ and one asymptote being $2x - y = 0$
   (f) One directrix being $x = 4$ and one asymptote being $x + 4y = 0$

4. Suppose H is the hyperbola determined by the equation

$$\frac{x^2}{a^2} - \frac{y^2}{b^2} = 1.$$

What is the equation of the hyperbola H' whose principal axis and principal dimension are the conjugate axis and conjugate dimension of H and whose conjugate axis and conjugate dimension are the principal axis and principal dimension of H? What is the relationship between the asymptotes of H and H'? These two are called *conjugate hyperbolas.*

5. During the second world war sound ranging units were used to locate enemy artillery. These units operated as follows. Three sound detectors were placed on a straight line which was nearly orthogonal to the direction of the gun to be located. When the sound of the gun was picked up, the time difference between the arrival of the sound at the right-hand and center detectors and the time difference between the arrival of the sound at the left-hand and center detectors were determined. From a table, each time difference was used to determine an angle. On a map lines were drawn with the determined angles through the points half way between the corresponding detectors (see Fig. 6–20). The enemy gun was then located as being at the point at which these lines intersected.

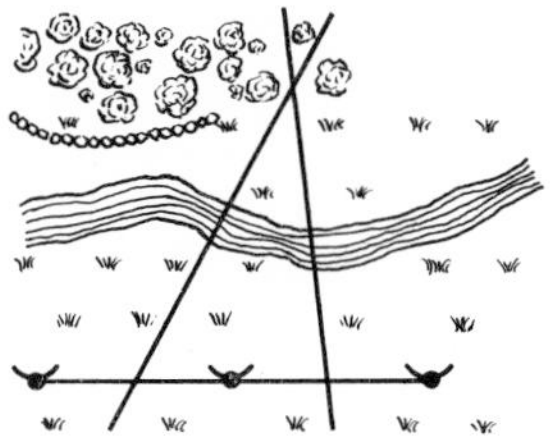

FIGURE 6–20

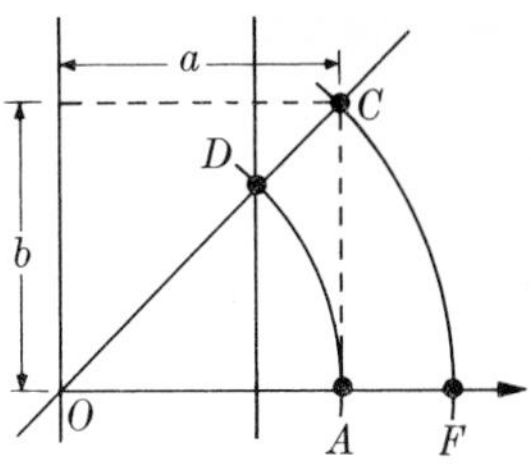

FIGURE 6–21

In practice, the sound ranging units observed that when the enemy gun was relatively close, the position located in this manner was usually slightly beyond the actual position.

Explain why the gun is located on the intersection of two hyperbolas. For a given pair of detectors and a given time difference at these detectors, how could you determine the actual hyperbola? The lines read from the tables were the asymptotes of these hyperbolas. Why were these lines used? Explain the observed discrepancy.*

6. Prove that a point satisfies an equation of the form (6–26) if and only if it satisfies one of the form (6–30). Given a and $e > 1$, show that the equation of the intersection of the xy-plane with the cone having vertex $A = (0, 0, -a\sqrt{e^2 - 1})$, axis in the direction $\mathbf{B} = [1, 0, 0]$, and $\lambda = 1/e$ is (6–30). Draw a diagram similar to that in the last section to show that the focal properties are equivalent to the definition of the hyperbola.

7. Prove that the following geometric construction locates the focus and the directrix of a hyperbola. Let O be the origin, C a corner of the rectangle whose sides are $2a$ and $2b$ and which is centered at the origin as shown in Fig. 6–21, and A the point at which one side of the rectangle crosses the x-axis. (A is thus a vertex of the hyperbola.) With center at O draw a circle with radius $|OC|$. This circle cuts the x-axis at F, a focus of the hyperbola. Also with center at O, draw a circle with radius $|OA|$. This circle cuts the asymptote (the line through O and C) at a point D which is on the directrix.

8. Find a geometric construction similar to that in Problem 7 to locate the directrix of an ellipse.

9. To what extent do any two of the five quantities a, b, c, d, and e for a given hyperbola determine the other three? Prepare a table for all possible determinations.

10. Let θ be the angle between the principal axis and one of the asymptotes of a hyperbola whose eccentricity is e. Prove that $e = \sec\theta$.

---

* A friend of the author was in such a unit during the second world war, and, despite the fact that he became a mathematician, it was not until many years later that he realized that his activities had anything to do with the focal properties of the hyperbola.

6–5 THE PARABOLA

While we had two different conditions which could be used to determine an ellipse or a hyperbola, Theorem 6–4 gives us only one condition which can be used to derive the general equation of a parabola. This condition says that all points on the parabola are at the same distance from a given point, the focus, and a given line, the directrix.

To derive the equation of a parabola, let us start by assuming that the focus F is at the point $(p, 0)$, and that the directrix is the line $x = -p$. Then if P is a point of the parabola with coordinates (x, y), we must have,

$$|PE| = |PF|, \tag{6–36}$$

where $|PE|$ is the distance from P to the line, and hence

$$|x + p| = [(x - p)^2 + y^2]^{1/2}.$$

This equation can be squared to give the equivalent equation

$$x^2 + 2px + p^2 = x^2 - 2px + p^2 + y^2,$$

which simplifies to

$$y^2 = 4px. \tag{6–37}$$

This is then the equation of the desired parabola. The set of points which satisfy this equation has the general appearance shown in Fig. 6–22. This figure is based on the case $p > 0$. The x-axis, which is the line passing through the focus orthogonal to the directrix is the *axis* of the parabola. The parabola has no second axis so that we do not have to speak of this as the principal axis, although that is actually what it is.

The point at which the axis cuts the parabola, the origin in this case, is called the *vertex* of the parabola. The eccentricity is, of course, 1 as is necessary to fit in with the focus-directrix form of the definition of the ellipse and hyperbola.

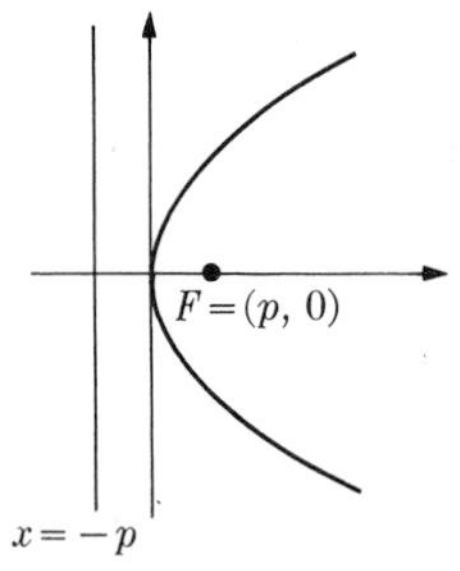

FIGURE 6–22

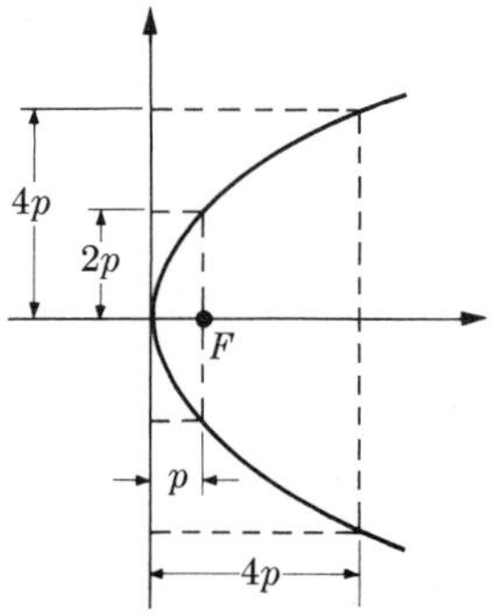

FIGURE 6–23

Definition 6–6. Let F be the focus and L' the directrix of a parabola P. Then

(1) the *axis* of the parabola is the line L through F orthogonal to L';
(2) the *vertex* of the parabola is the point of intersection of L with P.

A fairly good sketch of the parabola can be made, as shown in Fig. 6–23, by sketching in two rectangles. The smaller rectangle is made up of the lines $x = 0$, $x = p$, $y = 2p$, and $y = -2p$. The larger rectangle, which is actually two squares, is made up of the lines $x = 0$, $x = 4p$, $y = 4p$, and $y = -4p$. The parabola then can be sketched in as shown. Essentially, we use here the fact that if p is the distance from the vertex to the focus, the parabola is of "height" $2p$ at the focus and of "height" $4p$ at the distance $4p$ from the vertex.

We observe from Eq. (6–37) that the parabola is symmetric with respect to the x-axis, that is with respect to its axis. This is the only axis of symmetry for the parabola.

When $p < 0$ in Eq. (6–37), the parabola will "open out" to the left as in Fig. 6–24 (b). The axis is still the x-axis, however.

If we interchange the roles of x and y, we get an equation of the form

$$x^2 = 4py. \tag{6–38}$$

The appearance of the parabola in this case is as shown in Fig. 6–24(c) and (d).

For any given equation it is easy to determine which type of figure is involved. If x, for example, is the squared variable, as in (6–38), and if the point (x, y) is on the parabola, then so is $(-x, y)$. This means that the y-axis must be the axis of symmetry. Since x^2 is always positive, $4py$ must be positive also. Hence every point (x, y) on the parabola must be such that y is of the same sign as p. In this way, any given equation of this type can be analyzed. Conversely, the type of equation required for a given parabola is easily determined.

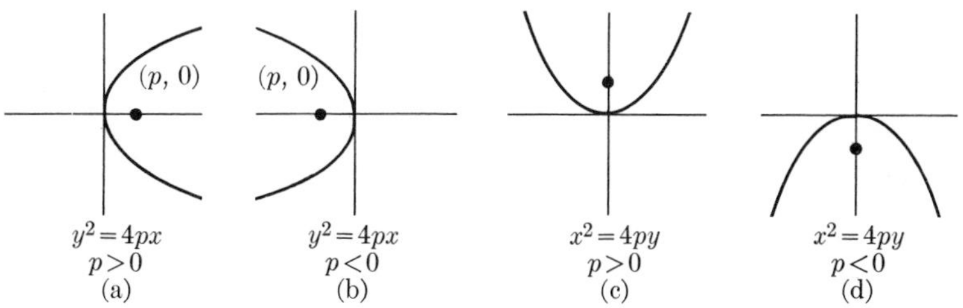

FIGURE 6–24

For example,

$$x^2 + 8y = 0$$

is the equation of a parabola. Rewriting this as

$$x^2 = 4(-2)y,$$

we recognize it as a parabola of the type shown in Fig. 6-24(d). Its focus is at (0, −2) and its directrix is the line $y = 2$.

Similarly, the equation of the parabola with vertex at (0, 0) and focus (−3, 0) must be

$$\begin{aligned} y^2 &= 4(-3)x \\ &= 12x. \end{aligned}$$

PROBLEMS

1. For each of the following parabolas, give the coordinates of the focus and the equations of the axis and the directrix. Sketch the parabola.

   (a) $x^2 = 16y$ (b) $y^2 = -6x$
   (c) $x^2 + 2y = 0$ (d) $x - 12y^2 = 0$
   (e) $4x^2 + 5y = 0$ (f) $2x + 15y^2 = 0$
   (g) $4x^2 = y$ (h) $3x^2 - 8y = 0$

2. Find the equation of each of the parabolas with vertex at (0, 0) and satisfying the following conditions.

   (a) focus at (2, 0) (b) focus at (−3, 0)
   (c) focus at $(\frac{1}{2}, 0)$ (d) focus at (0, −2)
   (e) focus at $(0, -\frac{1}{3})$ (f) focus at (0, 5)
   (g) directrix $x = -\frac{1}{2}$ (h) directrix $x = 7$
   (i) directrix $y = \frac{3}{5}$ (j) directrix $y = -\frac{2}{5}$

3. Show that the cone with

$$\lambda = 1/\sqrt{2}, \qquad \mathbf{B} = [1/\sqrt{2}, 0, 1/\sqrt{2}], \qquad \text{and} \qquad A = (0, 0, -2p)$$

   intersects the plane $z = 0$ in the parabola with equation

$$y^2 = 4px.$$

4. (a) Using directly the definition of the parabola as given by (6-36), find the equation of the parabola with focus at (4, 3) and directrix $4x + 3y + 25 = 0$.
   (b) Find the equation of the parabola with vertex at (0, 0) and focus at (1, −1).
   (c) Find the equation of the parabola with directrix $x + y = 0$ and vertex at (0, 2).

6–6 GENERAL QUADRATIC EQUATIONS WITHOUT CROSS PRODUCT TERMS

If we make a translation of all of the points of the plane through a distance h in the x-direction and a distance k in the y-direction, then the origin is translated to the point (h, k) and a point which has coordinates (x', y') is translated to the point with coordinates $(x' + h, y' + k)$. Suppose that (x, y) is an arbitrary point of the translated plane, and that (x', y') is the point which is translated into (x, y). Then $x = x' + h$ and $y = y' + k$, or

$$\begin{aligned} x' &= x - h, \\ y' &= y - k. \end{aligned} \tag{6–39}$$

Now suppose we have a point set which we wish to translate. As a specific example, suppose we are considering the points of an ellipse (see Fig. 6–25). That is, we have a set of points (x', y') which satisfy the equation

$$\frac{x'^2}{a^2} + \frac{y'^2}{b^2} = 1.$$

After the translation the coordinates (x, y) of the points of the translated ellipse must satisfy the equation

$$\frac{(x - h)^2}{a^2} + \frac{(y - k)^2}{b^2} = 1. \tag{6–40}$$

In other words, (6–40) is the equation of the ellipse after translation.

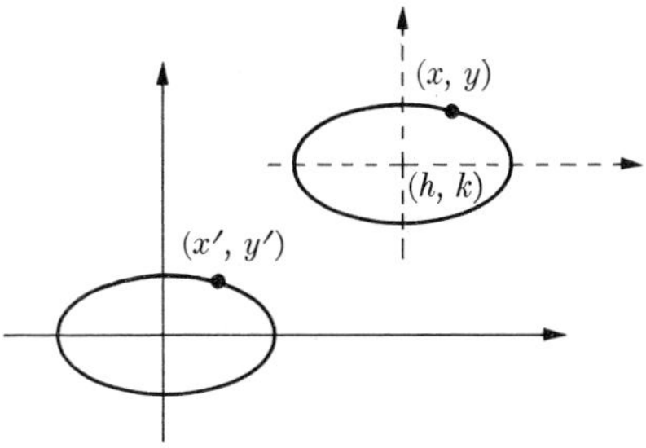

FIGURE 6–25

It is sometimes useful to think of a translation in terms of the change of position of the coordinate axes. Thus we may first think of a translation as being a function which maps the points of the $x'y'$-plane to the points of the xy-plane, which we think of as an entirely separate plane. The resulting loci in their respective planes are identical except for their

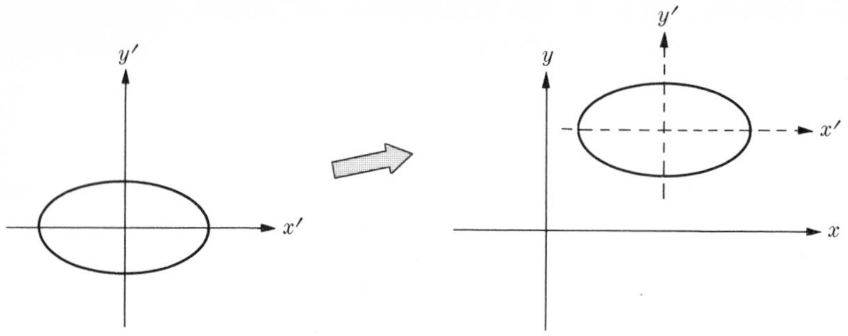

FIGURE 6-26

location with respect to the coordinate axes. In Fig. 6-26 we have illustrated this point of view. Note, however, that we can reconstruct the left-hand side of this figure if we view the dashed lines on the right-hand side as the x'- and y'-axes. This fact may be clarified, perhaps, by looking at some specific examples.

The first type of problem we investigate is the problem of finding the equation of a locus in a nonstandard position. For example, what is the equation of the parabola with focus (1, 6) and vertex (−3, 6)? Plotting these points, as in Fig. 6-27, we see that the axis of the parabola must be the line $y = 6$, which is shown as a broken line. Adding the line $x = -1$, and thinking of these two lines as the x'- and y'-axes, we see that the desired parabola would have an equation of the form

$$y'^2 = 4 \cdot 4\, x'$$

in the $x'y'$-plane. However, the x-, y- and x'-, y'-axes are related by the equations

$$x' = x + 3,$$
$$y' = y - 6.$$

Recall that these equations are most easily determined by observing that the point $x' = 0$, $y' = 0$ must be the same as $x = -3$, $y = 6$. Inserting these values into the equation of the parabola, we find the desired equation to be

$$(y - 6)^2 = 16(x + 3).$$

Another type of problem which often occurs is that of identifying the locus of a given equation. Again it is often easiest to simplify the equation by a change of the variables such as given by Eqs. (6-39), and view the new equation as the equation of the same locus in terms of a new coordinate system. Thus, for example, if we are given an equation such as (6-40), we can introduce new coordinates x' and y', satisfying (6-39) so as to simplify the equation. From (6-39) we see that the new axes, $x' = 0$

and $y' = 0$, are the lines $x = h$ and $y = k$. The quantities, points, and lines associated with the conic in the new coordinate system can then be identified and located in terms of the original coordinate system.

The ellipse whose equation is (6–40) has a focal distance $c = [a^2 - b^2]^{1/2}$, and eccentricity c/a, directrix distance $d = a/e$, but its center is at the point (h, k). Its principal axis is the x'-axis, or, in other words, $y = k$. Its conjugate axis is the line $x = h$. Note that the center is the point at which the left-hand side of (6–40) vanishes, and the axes are the lines parallel to the coordinate axes through this center. The quantity c is the distance between the center and the foci, and hence the foci of the ellipse determined by (6–40) are the points $(h + c, k)$ and $(h - c, k)$. Similarly, we see that the vertices are the points $(h + a, k)$ and $(h - a, k)$. The directrices will be the lines $x = h + d$ and $x = h - d$.

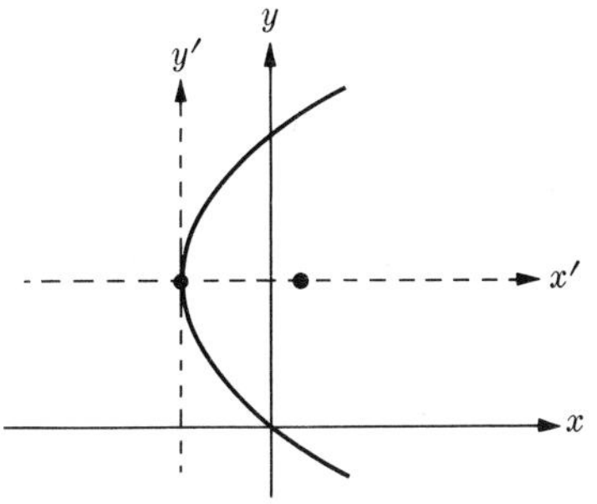

FIGURE 6–27

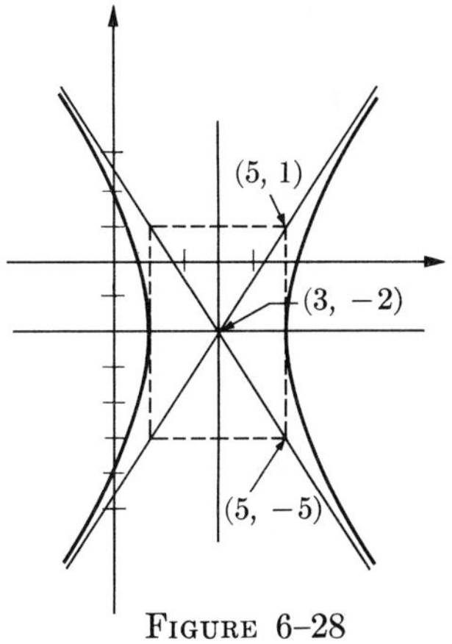

FIGURE 6–28

Exactly similar reasoning will apply to the translation of any of the conic sections discussed in the previous sections. An equation such as

$$\frac{(x-3)^2}{4} - \frac{(y+2)^2}{9} = 1$$

is easily identified as the equation of a hyperbola with center at $(3, -2)$. Its asymptotes are the lines

$$\frac{x-3}{2} \pm \frac{y+2}{3} = 0,$$

as may be discovered directly from the equation, thinking of the new coordinate system as defined by Eqs. (6–39), or equivalently, found with the help of a sketch as in Fig. 6–28. It is seen that one asymptote is the line passing through $(3, -2)$ and $(5, 1)$ while the other asymptote is the line through (3, −2) and (5, −5). The other quantities connected with this hyperbola can be determined in a manner similar to that discussed above. The methods are best learned by doing a few examples, such as the problems at the end of this section.

Now, we wish to consider the general quadratic equation

$$Ax^2 + Bxy + Cy^2 + Dx + Ey + F = 0, \tag{6–41}$$

and to discuss the possible point sets which can satisfy such an equation. In this section, we will restrict ourselves to a discussion of equations of the type (6–41) in which $B = 0$, that is, to general quadratic equations without cross product terms.

Suppose that in such an equation,

$$Ax^2 + Cy^2 + Dx + Ey + F = 0, \tag{6–42}$$

both A and C are zero (strictly speaking, we do not then have a quadratic equation). The equation is then seen to be the equation of a straight line. A straight line is actually a degenerate case of a conic section (see Problem 2 at the end of this section), but we are more interested in the cases in which (6–42) is a true quadratic equation, where A and C are not both zero.

First, let us consider the case in which $A \neq 0$, and $C = E = 0$. Equation (6–42) is then of the form

$$Ax^2 + Dx + F = 0,$$

a simple quadratic equation in x. If this quadratic equation has no roots, then there are no points satisfying the equation. If it has a single root r, then the line $x = r$ is the set of all points satisfying the given equation. If there are two distinct roots, then two parallel lines constitute the set of points satisfying Eq. (6–42). This last locus is an especially degenerate case since it cannot be obtained by the intersection of a cone and plane in any way, but requires the cone to degenerate into a cylinder.

The discussion of the case when (6–42) reduces to a quadratic equation in y alone is similar.

Now suppose $A \neq 0$, $C = 0$, and $E \neq 0$. Then, by completing the square, the Dx term can be combined with the Ax^2, and the Ey term can be combined with the resulting constant term to give an equation of the form

$$A(x - h)^2 + E(y - k) = 0.$$

This is easily recognized as the equation of a translated parabola.

A similar discussion shows that when $A = 0$, $C \neq 0$, and $D \neq 0$, Eq. (6–42) again determines a parabola.

We are left then with only the cases in which $A \neq 0$ and $C \neq 0$. By completing the square, Eq. (6–42) then can always be reduced to an equation of the form

$$A(x - h)^2 + C(y - k)^2 = m, \tag{6–43}$$

where m is some constant. Again, we may consider various cases.

First, if $A = C$ in (6–43), then this is the equation of a circle when $m \neq 0$ and is of the same sign as A and C. If $m = 0$, only the single point (h, k) satisfies the equation, and if $m \neq 0$ but is of opposite sign to A and C, then there are no points which satisfy (6–43).

Secondly, if $A \neq C$, but both are of the same sign, then (6–43) determines a translated ellipse, a single point, or has no locus at all depending on whether m is of the same sign as A and C, zero, or of opposite sign.

Finally, if A and C are of opposite signs, then (6–43) determines a translated hyperbola when $m \neq 0$. If $m = 0$, however, the set of points satisfying (6–43) is a pair of intersecting straight lines, which are the asymptotes of the hyperbolas determined when $m \neq 0$.

Theorem 6–10. The locus of Eq. (6–42) is one of the following:

(1) the empty set
(2) a single point
(3) a single line, parallel to one of the coordinate axes
(4) two parallel lines, parallel to one of the coordinate axes
(5) two intersecting lines whose slopes are the negatives of one another
(6) a circle
(7) a nondegenerate conic section whose principal axis is parallel to one of the coordinate axes.

This theorem has been proved, except for a few details, in the discussion given above. These remaining details are left as exercises.

The methods used in the above discussion can be applied in practice to actually determine the set of points satisfied by any equation of the form (6–42). The trick is merely to complete the square on each variable whose squared term appears.

For example, what is the locus of

$$x^2 + 4y^2 + 2x - 24y + 33 = 0?$$

To answer this question, we proceed as follows:

$$\begin{aligned} x^2 + 2x + \quad 4(y^2 - 6y) \quad &= -33, \\ x^2 + 2x + 1 + 4(y^2 - 6y + 9) &= -33 + 1 + 36, \\ (x+1)^2 + 4(y-3)^2 &= 4, \\ \frac{(x+1)^2}{4} + \frac{(y-3)^2}{1} &= 1. \end{aligned}$$

This we recognize as an ellipse with center at $(-1, 3)$ and principal axis parallel to the x-axis. Here, $a = 2$, $b = 1$, $c = \sqrt{3}$, $e = \sqrt{3}/2$, and $d = 4/\sqrt{3} = 4\sqrt{3}/3$. Thus for this ellipse, we have the following:

center: $(-1, 3)$
eccentricity: $e = \sqrt{3}/2$
principal axis: $y = 3$
conjugate axis: $x = -1$
foci: $(-1 + \sqrt{3}, 3)$, $(-1 - \sqrt{3}, 3)$
principal vertices: $(1, 3)$, $(-3, 3)$
conjugate vertices: $(-1, 4)$, $(-1, 2)$
directrices: $x = -1 + 4\sqrt{3}/3$, $x = -1 - 4\sqrt{3}/3$

We remark that it is usually helpful to make a sketch as an aid in determining these quantities.

PROBLEMS

1. Sketch each of the following conic sections. Identify each; give the coordinates of the center, foci, and vertices, and the equations of the axes, directrices, and asymptotes (if any). What is the eccentricity of each?

(a) $\dfrac{(x-1)^2}{9} - \dfrac{(y-3)^2}{16} = -1$
(b) $(x-3)^2 = 16(y+2)$
(c) $\dfrac{(x+1)^2}{9} + \dfrac{(y-7)^2}{25} = 1$
(d) $x^2 - 2x + 8y + 41 = 0$
(e) $16x^2 + 25y^2 - 96x + 50y - 231 = 0$
(f) $x^2 - 4y^2 - 14x + 45 = 0$
(g) $y^2 - 6x - 4y + 7 = 0$
(h) $x^2 - 4y^2 + 6x - 4y + 4 = 0$
(i) $9x^2 + 9y^2 - 54x + 6y + 66 = 0$
(j) $4x^2 - 25y^2 + 40x + 50y + 75 = 0$

2. Describe how the intersection of a cone and a plane can be: (a) a single straight line, (b) two intersecting lines, (c) a single point.

3. Find the equation of the conic section determined in each of the following cases:

   (a) The ellipse with foci at $(3, -2)$ and $(3, 6)$, and with principal dimension 5
   (b) The hyperbola of eccentricity 2 with a focus at $(4, 1)$ and directrix (associated with this focus) $x = 1$
   (c) The parabola with focus at $(7, 6)$ and directrix $y = 4$
   (d) The ellipse with center at $(3, 5)$, a focus at $(3, 8)$ and a vertex at $(3, 9)$
   (e) The hyperbola with asymptotes

$$4x + y - 11 = 0,$$
$$4x - y - 13 = 0,$$

   and a vertex at $(3, 1)$

4. Find the equation of the conic section having eccentricity e, a focus at $(1, 0)$ and an associated vertex at $(0, 0)$. What happens to this equation and its locus as e approaches 0? as e approaches 1 from below? from above?

5. What are the possible loci of (6–42) if

   (a) $AC > 0$?
   (b) $AC = 0$?
   (c) $AC < 0$?

6. Show that the lines of parts (3) and (4) of Theorem 6–10 must be parallel to one of the coordinate axes.

7. Prove that when case (5) occurs in Theorem 6–10, the two lines have slopes which are negatives of one another.

8. Give a specific example illustrating each of the first five cases of Theorem 6–10.

7

Quadratic Curves and Surfaces

7–1 ROTATION OF AXES

In the last section we considered the effect of translations upon loci in the plane. We now wish to consider the effect of another euclidean motion, rotation.

We will consider only the case of rotations about the origin. Rotations about any other center can be studied by translating the center of rotation to the origin, performing the rotation, and translating the center back to the original position.

As before, we can think of this euclidean motion as a function which maps the points of the xy-plane onto the points of a (separate) $x'y'$-plane. However, the relative positions of points are unchanged, and this mapping can be illustrated by drawing two sets of coordinate axes in the same plane. A given point will have different coordinates with respect to the different axes, as in Fig. 7–1.

Theorem 5–13 (on page 160) tells us how to determine the coordinates of the point in the new coordinate system. Let $\mathbf{e}_1'$ and $\mathbf{e}_2'$ be the unit vectors in the directions of the new x'- and y'-axes. Then from Theorem 5–13, we have for any point X

$$\begin{aligned}\mathbf{X} &= (\mathbf{X}\cdot\mathbf{e}_1')\mathbf{e}_1' + (\mathbf{X}\cdot\mathbf{e}_2')\mathbf{e}_2'\\ &= x'\mathbf{e}_1' + y'\mathbf{e}_2'.\end{aligned}$$

Hence the point has coordinates (x', y') with respect to the new coordinate system, where

$$\begin{aligned}x' &= \mathbf{X}\cdot\mathbf{e}_1',\\ y' &= \mathbf{X}\cdot\mathbf{e}_2'.\end{aligned} \tag{7–1}$$

To find the new coordinates all we have to do is compute these dot products. But we must first know $\mathbf{e}_1'$ and $\mathbf{e}_2'$. Let us suppose that the new coordinate system is located so that the x'-axis makes a signed angle of θ with the original x-axis, as in Fig. 7–1. Then the signed angle from the y-axis to the x'-axis is $\theta - \pi/2$ (why?), and the signed angles from the

x- and y-axes to the y'-axis are $\theta + \pi/2$ and θ respectively. Therefore,

$$\begin{aligned} \mathbf{e}_1' \cdot \mathbf{e}_1 &= \cos\theta, \\ \mathbf{e}_1' \cdot \mathbf{e}_2 &= \cos(\theta - \pi/2) = \sin\theta, \\ \mathbf{e}_2' \cdot \mathbf{e}_1 &= \cos(\theta + \pi/2) = -\sin\theta, \\ \mathbf{e}_2' \cdot \mathbf{e}_2 &= \cos\theta. \end{aligned}$$

Using these relations and Theorem 5–13 again [$\mathbf{e}_1' = (\mathbf{e}_1' \cdot \mathbf{e}_1)\mathbf{e}_1 + (\mathbf{e}_1' \cdot \mathbf{e}_2)\mathbf{e}_2$, etc.], we have

$$\begin{aligned} \mathbf{e}_1' &= \cos\theta\, \mathbf{e}_1 + \sin\theta\, \mathbf{e}_2, \\ \mathbf{e}_2' &= -\sin\theta\, \mathbf{e}_1 + \cos\theta\, \mathbf{e}_2. \end{aligned} \tag{7–2}$$

For a given point $X = (x, y)$ in the original coordinate system, we can use relations (7–2) to obtain the change of coordinates in (7–1). Doing so, we find

$$\begin{aligned} \mathbf{X} \cdot \mathbf{e}_1' &= (x\mathbf{e}_1 + y\mathbf{e}_2) \cdot (\cos\theta\, \mathbf{e}_1 + \sin\theta\, \mathbf{e}_2) \\ &= x\cos\theta + y\sin\theta, \end{aligned}$$

and

$$\begin{aligned} \mathbf{X} \cdot \mathbf{e}_2' &= (x\mathbf{e}_1 + y\mathbf{e}_2) \cdot (-\sin\theta\, \mathbf{e}_1 + \cos\theta\, \mathbf{e}_2) \\ &= -x\sin\theta + y\cos\theta. \end{aligned}$$

We have thus proved the theorem below.

Theorem 7–1. If a point (x, y) has coordinates (x', y') in a new coordinate system which has been rotated through the signed angle θ, then

$$\begin{aligned} x' &= x\cos\theta + y\sin\theta, \\ y' &= -x\sin\theta + y\cos\theta. \end{aligned} \tag{7–3}$$

Let us illustrate the use of these formulas by finding the equation of the hyperbola whose principal axis is the line $y = x$, whose asymptotes are

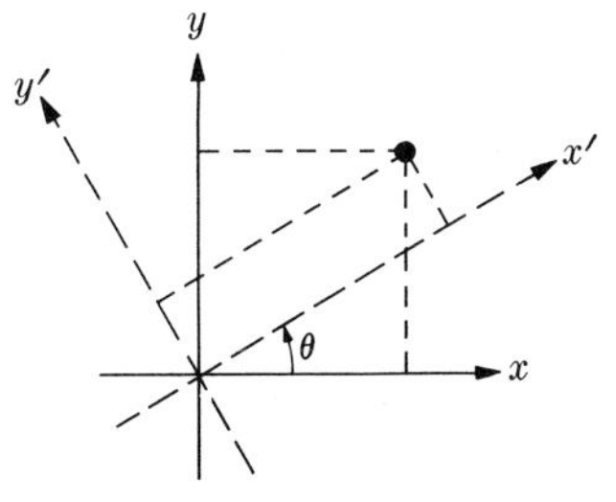

FIGURE 7–1

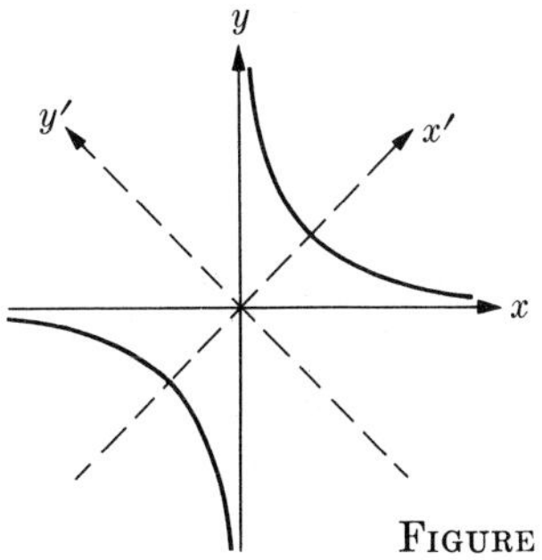

FIGURE 7–2

the lines $x = 0$ and $y = 0$, and which has a vertex at the point (1, 1) (Fig. 7-2). Introduce a new coordinate system whose x'-axis is the principal axis of this hyperbola. Then, from relations (7-3) we have

$$x' = \frac{1}{\sqrt{2}}(x + y),$$
$$y' = \frac{1}{\sqrt{2}}(-x + y). \tag{7-4}$$

The line $x = 0$ is the line $x' - y' = 0$ in these new coordinates (why?), and the other asymptote is the line $x' + y' = 0$. These can be obtained by solving the relations (7-4) for x and y in terms of x' and y'. The vertex is at the point $(\sqrt{2}, 0)$ in terms of these coordinates.

The equation of the required hyperbola in the (x',y')-coordinate system is therefore

$$\frac{x'^2}{2} - \frac{y'^2}{2} = 1.$$

From (7-4) this is

$$\tfrac{1}{4}(x + y)^2 - \tfrac{1}{4}(-x + y)^2 = 1,$$

or after some simplification,

$$xy = 1. \tag{7-5}$$

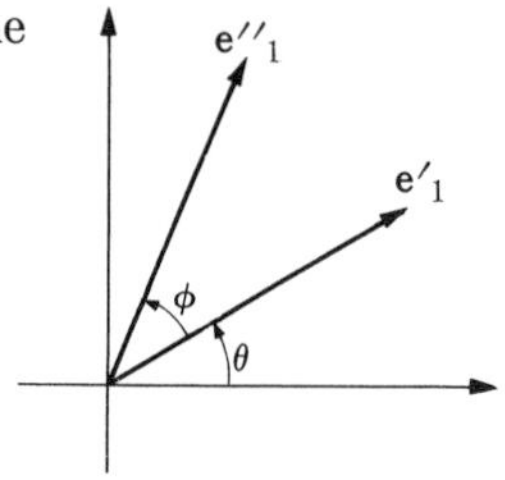

FIGURE 7-3

In the next section we will be looking at the opposite problem: how to find a rotation which will simplify a given equation. For this, we will find it useful to have some relations which are consequences of the trigonometric sum formulas. These were derived in Section 2-7, but we can repeat the derivation here. Indeed, these formulas can be derived by using the methods of this section. Let us suppose that the vector $\mathbf{e}_1'$ results from a rotation of $\mathbf{e}_1$ through an angle θ, and that $\mathbf{e}_1''$ results from a rotation of $\mathbf{e}_1$ through an angle $\theta + \phi$, or equivalently, from the rotation of $\mathbf{e}_1'$ through an angle of ϕ (see Fig. 7-3). Then

$$\begin{aligned}\mathbf{e}_1'' &= \cos(\theta + \phi)\mathbf{e}_1 + \sin(\theta + \phi)\mathbf{e}_2\\ &= \cos\phi\,\mathbf{e}_1' + \sin\phi\,\mathbf{e}_2'.\end{aligned}$$

However, $\mathbf{e}_1'$ and $\mathbf{e}_2'$ are given by Eqs. (7-2), and substituting these values into the second equation above, we have

$$\begin{aligned}\cos(\theta + \phi)\mathbf{e}_1 + \sin(\theta + \phi)\mathbf{e}_2 &= \cos\phi(\cos\theta\,\mathbf{e}_1 + \sin\theta\,\mathbf{e}_2)\\ &\quad + \sin\phi(-\sin\theta\,\mathbf{e}_1 + \cos\theta\,\mathbf{e}_2)\\ &= (\cos\theta\cos\phi - \sin\theta\sin\phi)\mathbf{e}_1\\ &\quad + (\sin\theta\cos\phi + \cos\theta\sin\phi)\mathbf{e}_2.\end{aligned}$$

Since the two sides of this equation are identical, we have proved

$$\begin{aligned} \cos(\theta + \phi) &= \cos\theta\cos\phi - \sin\theta\sin\phi, \\ \sin(\theta + \phi) &= \sin\theta\cos\phi + \cos\theta\sin\phi. \end{aligned} \tag{7–6}$$

PROBLEMS

1. Find formulas similar to (7–2) for $\mathbf{e}_1$ and $\mathbf{e}_2$ in terms of $\mathbf{e}_1'$ and $\mathbf{e}_2'$.
2. Use the results of Problem 1 to obtain formulas for x and y in terms of x' and y'.
3. Find x and y in terms of x' and y' by solving Eqs. (7–3). How does this result compare with the answer to Problem 2?
4. Find the equation of the hyperbola whose principal and conjugate dimensions are a and b, whose center is at the origin, having the y-axis as an asymptote, and such that a vertex is in the first quadrant. Can you solve the resulting equation for y as a function of x?
5. Find the equation of the ellipse whose foci are at (3, 4) and (—3, —4) and whose principal dimension is 13. Use the methods of this section.
6. Find the equation of the ellipse of Problem 5 directly from the focal property, as was done in Section 6–3. Compare with the result of Problem 5. Which method is easier?
7. Starting from Equations (7–6) prove the following:

$$\begin{aligned} \sin 2\theta &= 2\sin\theta\cos\theta \\ \cos 2\theta &= \cos^2\theta - \sin^2\theta \\ \cos 2\theta &= 2\cos^2\theta - 1 \\ \cos 2\theta &= 1 - 2\sin^2\theta \\ \cos^2\theta &= \tfrac{1}{2}[1 + \cos 2\theta] \\ \sin^2\theta &= \tfrac{1}{2}[1 - \cos 2\theta] \\ \tan^2\theta &= \frac{1 - \cos 2\theta}{1 + \cos 2\theta} \\ \tan\theta &= \frac{1 - \cos 2\theta}{\sin 2\theta} \\ \tan\theta &= \frac{\sin 2\theta}{1 + \cos 2\theta} \end{aligned}$$

8. Prove:

$$\begin{aligned} \tan(\theta + \phi) &= \frac{\tan\theta + \tan\phi}{1 - \tan\theta\tan\phi} \\ \tan(\theta - \phi) &= \frac{\tan\theta - \tan\phi}{1 + \tan\theta\tan\phi} \end{aligned}$$

7-2 GENERAL QUADRATIC EQUATIONS

In the first section of the last chapter we found that the intersection of a cone with the xy-plane is the set of points which satisfy a quadratic equation, that is, it is the locus of an equation of the form

$$Ax^2 + Bxy + Cy^2 + Dx + Ey + F = 0. \tag{7-7}$$

In this section we wish to investigate the converse property, i.e. to determine what point sets will satisfy an arbitrary equation of the form (7-7).

If $B = 0$ in Eq. (7-7), then we know that the equation represents a conic section, a degenerate conic section, or the empty set, as was discussed in Section 6-6. We will see that the same result holds for Eq. (7-7) by showing that in a suitably rotated coordinate system the cross product term xy will not occur, and hence in this coordinate system the results of Section 6-6 will apply.

Let us suppose that the (x',y')-coordinate system is rotated through an angle θ with respect to the x-, y-axes. Then from (7-3) we have

$$\begin{aligned} x' &= x\cos\theta + y\sin\theta, \\ y' &= -x\sin\theta + y\cos\theta. \end{aligned}$$

If these relations are solved for x and y in terms of x' and y' (see Problems 2 and 3 in the last section) we find

$$\begin{aligned} x &= x'\cos\theta - y'\sin\theta, \\ y &= x'\sin\theta + y'\cos\theta, \end{aligned} \tag{7-8}$$

and hence, we can compute

$$\begin{aligned} x^2 &= x'^2\cos^2\theta - 2x'y'\cos\theta\sin\theta + y'^2\sin^2\theta, \\ y^2 &= x'^2\sin^2\theta + 2x'y'\cos\theta\sin\theta + y'^2\cos^2\theta, \\ xy &= x'^2\cos\theta\sin\theta + x'y'(\cos^2\theta - \sin^2\theta) - y'^2\cos\theta\sin\theta. \end{aligned}$$

Therefore, in terms of the rotated coordinate system, the point set satisfying Eq. (7-7) will satisfy the equation

$$A'x'^2 + B'x'y' + C'y'^2 + D'x' + E'y' + F' = 0,$$

where

$$\begin{aligned} A' &= A\cos^2\theta + B\cos\theta\sin\theta + C\sin^2\theta, \\ B' &= 2(C - A)\cos\theta\sin\theta + B(\cos^2\theta - \sin^2\theta), \\ C' &= A\sin^2\theta - B\cos\theta\sin\theta + C\cos^2\theta, \\ D' &= D\cos\theta + E\sin\theta, \\ E' &= -D\sin\theta + E\cos\theta, \\ F' &= F. \end{aligned} \tag{7-9}$$

Using the relations of Problem 7 of the last section, we see that

$$B' = (C - A) \sin 2\theta + B \cos 2\theta.$$

By proper choice of θ, this expression can be made zero. Indeed, if we set

$$\sin 2\theta = \frac{B}{\Lambda}, \qquad \cos 2\theta = \frac{C - A}{\Lambda}, \tag{7-10}$$

where

$$\Lambda = [B^2 + (C - A)^2]^{1/2}, \tag{7-11}$$

then $B' = 0$.

The values on the right-hand side of Eqs. (7-10) are the sine and cosine of some angle 2θ since the sum of their squares is one. The only possible way in which this could fail is if $\Lambda = 0$. However, in order for Λ to be zero, we would have to have $B = 0$ and $C - A = 0$. Since we were trying to eliminate B from (7-7) by this process, this would mean that Eq. (7-7) was already in the desired form to begin with. It is interesting to note that in this case, Eq. (7-7) represents a circle (if its locus is nondegenerate).

Using the identities of Problem 7 of the last section, we find from (7-10) that

$$\begin{aligned} \cos^2\theta &= \frac{1}{2}\left(1 - \frac{C - A}{\Lambda}\right) = \frac{1}{2\Lambda}[\Lambda - (C - A)], \\ \sin^2\theta &= \frac{1}{2}\left(1 + \frac{C - A}{\Lambda}\right) = \frac{1}{2\Lambda}[\Lambda + (C - A)], \\ \cos\theta \sin\theta &= \mathrm{B}/2\Lambda. \end{aligned} \tag{7-12}$$

Putting these values into (7-9), we find that when the angle θ is determined by (7-10) we have

$$\begin{aligned} A' &= \tfrac{1}{2}[(C + A) + \Lambda], \\ B' &= 0, \\ C' &= \tfrac{1}{2}[(C + A) - \Lambda]. \end{aligned} \tag{7-13}$$

The values for D' and E' are similarly determined by using the values determined by (7-12). There is here, however, a matter of choice. Equations (7-12) determine $\cos^2\theta$ and $\sin^2\theta$. There are in general four possible angles θ between 0 and 2π which will satisfy these requirements, but only two of these will also satisfy $\cos\theta \sin\theta = B/2\Lambda$. Generally, it probably is most convenient to choose the angle in the first or fourth quadrant, which corresponds to taking the positive root for $\cos\theta$, and the appropriate root for $\sin\theta$ so that $\sin\theta\cos\theta = B/2\Lambda$.

In practical problems, it probably is unwise to try to memorize these formulas. If Eqs. (7–13) cannot be referred to, it is better to start with Eqs. (7–8) and work the relations out in full. An example will show how this may be done. Let us attempt to find the point set which satisfies the equation

$$9x^2 - 6xy + 17y^2 - 288 = 0.$$

We set $x = x' \cos\theta - y' \sin\theta$ and $y = x' \sin\theta + y' \cos\theta$, getting

$$9[x'^2 \cos^2\theta - 2x'y' \cos\theta \sin\theta + y'^2 \sin^2\theta] - 6[x'^2 \cos\theta \sin\theta + x'y' (\cos^2\theta - \sin^2\theta) + y'^2 \cos\theta \sin\theta] + 17[x'^2 \sin^2\theta + 2x'y' \cos\theta \sin\theta + y'^2 \cos^2\theta] - 288 = 0,$$

or

$$[9 \cos^2\theta - 6 \cos\theta \sin\theta + 17 \sin^2\theta]x'^2 + [16 \cos\theta \sin\theta - 6(\cos^2\theta - \sin^2\theta)]x'y' + [9 \sin^2\theta - 6 \cos\theta \sin\theta + 17 \cos^2\theta]y'^2 - 288 = 0.$$

The expression which we wish to eliminate is

$$\begin{aligned} 16 \cos\theta \sin\theta - 6(\cos^2\theta - \sin^2\theta) &= 8 \sin 2\theta - 6 \cos 2\theta \\ &= 2[4 \sin 2\theta - 3 \cos 2\theta]. \end{aligned}$$

This will be zero if we set

$$\sin 2\theta = \tfrac{3}{5},$$
$$\cos 2\theta = \tfrac{4}{5}.$$

In this case,

$$\begin{aligned} \cos\theta \sin\theta &= \tfrac{1}{2} \sin 2\theta = \tfrac{3}{10}, \\ \cos^2\theta &= \tfrac{1}{2}(1 + \cos 2\theta) = \tfrac{9}{10}, \\ \sin^2\theta &= \tfrac{1}{2}(1 - \cos 2\theta) = \tfrac{1}{10}. \end{aligned}$$

Substituting in these values, we have the equation

$$8x'^2 + 18y'^2 - 288 = 0,$$

or

$$\frac{x'^2}{36} + \frac{y'^2}{16} = 1.$$

This we immediately recognize as an ellipse with the x'-axis as its principal axis and with principal and conjugate dimensions 6 and 4 respectively.

Since $\sin\theta \cos\theta$ is positive, we can choose the positive roots for $\sin\theta$ and $\cos\theta$, giving $\cos\theta = 3/\sqrt{10}$ and $\sin\theta = 1/\sqrt{10}$. The x'-axis can thus be sketched in by drawing the line through the origin and (3, 1). It is then easy to make a sketch of the ellipse as in Fig. 7–4. How have the coordinates given in Fig. 7–4 been determined? What are the coordinates of the foci?

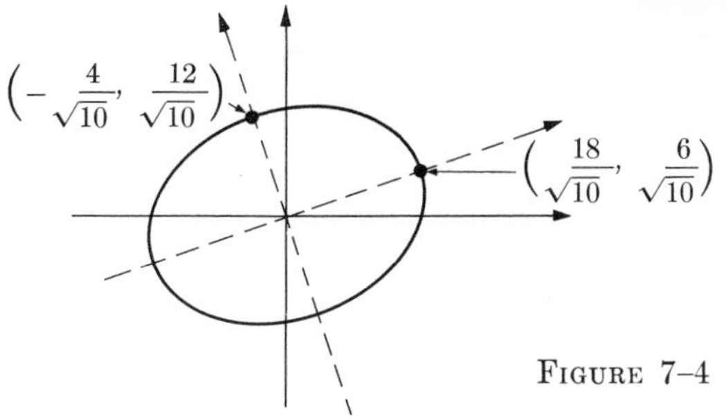

FIGURE 7-4

In order to see whether a given equation of the form (7-7) represents an ellipse, hyperbola, or parabola, it is not necessary to do all of this computation. We will show that the expression $B^2 - 4AC$ remains unchanged under rotation of coordinates, hence this expression will be the same as $-4A'C'$ when the coordinates are so chosen that $B' = 0$. But the equation

$$A'x'^2 + C'y'^2 + D'x + E'y + F' = 0$$

will represent an ellipse if $A'C' > 0$, a parabola if $A'C' = 0$, and a hyperbola if $A'C' < 0$ (without considering degenerate cases, or the possibility of no locus). First, however, we must prove the invariance of this expression.

Theorem 7-2. If the equation

$$Ax^2 + Bxy + Cy^2 + Dx + Ey + F = 0$$

becomes

$$A'x'^2 + B'x'y' + C'y'^2 + D' + E'y' + F' = 0$$

under a rotation of the coordinate system, then

$$C' + A' = C + A,$$

$$B'^2 + (C' - A')^2 = B^2 + (C - A)^2,$$

and

$$B'^2 - 4A'C' = B^2 - 4AC.$$

Proof: First we observe from the relations (7-9) that

$$\begin{aligned} C' + A' &= A(\cos^2\theta + \sin^2\theta) + C(\cos^2\theta + \sin^2\theta) \\ &= C + A, \end{aligned}$$

so that $C + A$ is invariant under the rotation.

Next we compute

$$C' - A' = (C - A)(\cos^2\theta - \sin^2\theta) - 2B\cos\theta\sin\theta$$
$$= (C - A)\cos 2\theta - B\sin 2\theta.$$

Likewise,

$$B' = (C - A)\sin 2\theta + B\cos 2\theta.$$

Therefore,

$$\begin{aligned} B'^2 + (C' - A')^2 &= (C - A)^2\sin^2 2\theta + 2B(C - A)\sin 2\theta\cos 2\theta \\ &\quad + B^2\cos^2 2\theta + (C - A)^2\cos^2 2\theta \\ &\quad - 2B(C - A)\sin 2\theta\cos 2\theta + B^2\sin^2 2\theta \\ &= B^2 + (C - A)^2. \end{aligned}$$

Hence the expression $B^2 + (C - A)^2$, which is Λ^2, is also invariant under the rotation.

Finally, we merely need to observe that

$$\begin{aligned} B'^2 - 4A'C' &= B'^2 + (C' - A')^2 - (C' + A')^2 \\ &= B^2 + (C - A)^2 - (C + A)^2 \\ &= B^2 - 4AC. \end{aligned}$$

We immediately obtain the following theorem as a corollary.

Theorem 7–3. The set of points satisfying the equation

$$Ax^2 + Bxy + Cy^2 + Dx + Ey + F = 0$$

is an ellipse, a point, or an empty set if $B^2 - 4AC < 0$. It is a parabola, two parallel lines, or a line if $B^2 - 4AC = 0$. It is a hyperbola or a pair of intersecting lines if $B^2 - 4AC > 0$.

For example, the equation that we considered above,

$$9x^2 - 6xy + 17y^2 - 288 = 0,$$

was found to be the equation of an ellipse. For this equation,

$$B^2 - 4AC = 36 - 4 \cdot 9 \cdot 17 < 0,$$

and hence this information could have been obtained from an application of Theorem 7–3.

It is relatively easy to remember that $B^2 - 4AC$ remains unchanged when the coordinate system is rotated. If the student can also remember that $C + A$ is invariant under the rotation, then he knows all he needs in order to obtain the coefficients of the transformed equation. We wish to rotate the coordinate system so that $B' = 0$. If this is done, we will then have the relations

$$-4A'C' = B^2 - 4AC,$$
$$C' + A' = C + A.$$

Knowing A, B, and C, we can solve these equations for A' and C'.

Again using the above example,

$$9x^2 - 6xy + 17y^2 - 288 = 0,$$

we have

$$-4A'C' = -576,$$
$$C' + A' = 26.$$

From the first equation we have $A' = 144/C'$. Substituting this into the second equation gives $C' + 144/C' = 26$, or

$$C'^2 - 26C' + 144 = 0.$$

This gives $C' = 18$ or 8, and hence $A' = 8$ or 18, respectively. If we use the first pair, we find the transformed equation

$$8x'^2 + 18y'^2 - 288 = 0.$$

This process gives us the transformed equation, but it does not tell us the angle through which the coordinate system has been rotated. The latter can be obtained in another way, however. The last equation tells us that we have an ellipse whose principal dimension is 6 and whose conjugate dimension is 4. The center is at the origin, which is unchanged by the rotation. Hence, if we could find the coordinates of a principal vertex in the (x,y)-coordinate system, then we could locate the ellipse as in Fig. 7-4.

The coordinates of a principal vertex can, however, be found easily by finding a point on the locus whose distance from the origin is 6 (the same process will work equally well in the case of a hyperbola). That is, we wish to solve the pair of equations,

$$9x^2 - 6xy + 17y^2 - 288 = 0,$$
$$x^2 + y^2 = 36,$$

simultaneously. Multiplying the second equation by 9 and subtracting gives

$$-6xy + 8y^2 = -36,$$

and hence,

$$x = \frac{4y^2 - 18}{3y} = \frac{4y}{3} + \frac{6}{y}.$$

Combining this with $x^2 + y^2 = 36$ gives

$$\frac{16}{9}y^2 + 16 + \frac{36}{y^2} + y^2 = 36,$$

or

$$25\,y^4 - 180\,y^2 + 324 = 0.$$

A positive root of this equation is $y^2 = \frac{36}{10}$. From this we have $x^2 = 36 - y^2 = \frac{324}{10}$. If we insert these values into the original equation of the locus, we find

$$-6xy + \frac{648}{10} = 0.$$

This is satisfied when we take the roots for x and y to have the same sign. Thus, we can choose the positive roots, and find the point $(18/\sqrt{10}, 6/\sqrt{10})$ to be one of the principal vertices.

PROBLEMS

1. Prove that the relations of (7–13) follow from (7–9) and (7–12).

2. Show that there are in general four possible angles θ between 0 and 2π such that

$$(C - A)\sin 2\theta + B\cos 2\theta = 0.$$

How are these four angles related to each other?

3. For each of the following equations, find and sketch the locus, first by using relations (7–13) directly, and then by working out the relations in full, starting from Eqs. (7–8).

(a) $9x^2 + 24xy + 16y^2 + 100x - 40y + 100 = 0$
(b) $5x^2 + 8xy + 5y^2 - 9 = 0$
(c) $x^2 + 2\sqrt{3}\,xy - y^2 + 1 = 0$
(d) $3x^2 - 6xy + y^2 - 4 = 0$

4. If the expression $F(x, y) = Ax^2 + Bxy + Cy^2$ is evaluated at points of the unit circle, that is, at points where $x = \cos\phi$ and $y = \sin\phi$, we have

$$V(\phi) = F(\cos\phi, \sin\phi) = A\cos^2\phi + B\cos\phi\sin\phi + C\sin^2\phi.$$

Show that

$$V(\phi) = \tfrac{1}{2}[(C + A) + B\sin 2\phi - (C - A)\cos 2\phi].$$

Show also that

$$V(\phi) = \tfrac{1}{2}[(C + A) + \Lambda\cos(2\theta - 2\phi)],$$

where Λ is defined as in (7–11) and θ is the angle determined as in (7–10). For what value of ϕ is this expression a maximum? a minimum?

5. Equations (7–13) give A' and C' for the coordinate system in which $B' = 0$. What is $A'C'$ in terms of A, B, and C according to these equations? Does this offer another proof of Theorem 7–3?

7–3 THE QUADRIC SURFACES

The general quadratic equation in the three variables x, y, and z is

$$Ax^2 + By^2 + Cz^2 + Hxy + Jyz + Kxz + Dx + Ey + Fz + G = 0. \tag{7–14}$$

In this section we wish to discuss the point sets in the three-dimensional space which can satisfy such an equation. These are called the *quadric surfaces.*

Just as in the case of quadratic equations in two variables, there always exists a rotation of the coordinate system such that the cross product terms in (7–14) can be eliminated. The proof of this would take too much time to give here and is more difficult than might appear at first glance. For, suppose we consider the z-axis as fixed and rotate the x- and y-axes. As was shown in the last section, this can be done so as to eliminate the xy term. It might seem that we could continue by holding the new y-axis fixed and rotating the (new) x-axis and z-axis to eliminate the xz term. However, if we try to do this we find that the yz term generates a new xy term (why?)

Actually, several proofs are available. One in particular results from an extension of the observations made in Problem 4 of the last section, but it too requires techniques we do not want to develop at this point. Instead, we will just assume that this has been accomplished and study only equations of the form

$$Ax^2 + By^2 + Cz^2 + Dx + Ey + Fz + G = 0. \tag{7–15}$$

The character of the locus of this equation changes drastically as the various coefficients in it take on positive, negative, or zero values. Since there are seven coefficients with three possibilities for each coefficient, there are a total of $3^7 = 2187$ possible cases to consider. We can, however, cut the number of these cases down to a reasonable size by making a few observations.

First, if any one of the three coefficients A, B, or C is not zero, then we can make the corresponding coefficient D, E, or F respectively zero.

This can be done by means of a translation (completing the square in that variable).

For example, we could write

$$\begin{aligned} x^2 + 2y^2 - z^2 + 4x - 4y + 6z - 10 \\ &= (x+2)^2 + 2(y-1)^2 - (z-3)^2 - 3 \\ &= x'^2 + 2y'^2 - z'^2 - 3. \end{aligned}$$

Secondly, if any of the coefficients D, E, or F is nonzero while the corresponding quadratic coefficient is zero, then we can make $G = 0$, again by means of a translation. An example of this would be

$$\begin{aligned} x^2 + 2y^2 - 6z + 8 &= x^2 + 2y^2 - 6(z - \tfrac{4}{3}) \\ &= x^2 + 2y^2 - 6z'. \end{aligned}$$

Thirdly, if one of the three coefficients A, B, or C is nonzero, we can assume it to be A, interchanging the roles of the coordinates if necessary (this is a particular case of rotation of coordinates, but one which is quite simple). Furthermore, we can assume A to be positive in this case, since we can multiply (7–15) through by -1 if necessary.

Fourthly, if two of the coefficients A, B, or C are nonzero, then again by interchanging coordinates if necessary, we can assume them to be A and B.

Finally, if A, B, and C are all nonzero, then at least two are of the same sign. We may assume these two to be A and B, and furthermore that both are positive (why?).

On page 233 we give a table which lists all of the pertinent cases remaining after the above reductions have been made. In this table, a zero means that the coefficient is zero; a $+$ or $-$ indicates that the coefficient is nonzero and positive or negative respectively; an x indicates that the coefficient is nonzero (the sign being immaterial in that case); and a zero in parentheses indicates that the coefficient can be assumed to be zero because of one of the above comments. A blank space means that the coefficient in that case does not matter. There are 18 cases listed in this table. The only cases which have been left out are those in which A, B, C, D, E, and F are all zero (why has this been left out?). Of these eighteen cases, nine are fairly trivial in one way or another, and the remaining nine are of considerable interest. These are indicated by an asterisk in the table.

We turn now to an analysis of these nine interesting cases. Each time, we attempt to build up a picture of the locus satisfying the equation by considering the curves which result when a plane parallel to one of the coordinate planes is allowed to cut the surface.

Case		A	B	C	D	E	F	G	Locus
I	1	0	0	0	x				Plane
II	1	+	0	0	(0)	0	0	+	Empty set
	2	+	0	0	(0)	0	0	0	Plane
	3	+	0	0	(0)	0	0	—	Two parallel planes
	4*	+	0	0	(0)	x		(0)	Parabolic cylinder
III	1	+	+	0	(0)	(0)	0	+	Empty set
	2	+	+	0	(0)	(0)	0	0	Line
	3*	+	+	0	(0)	(0)	0	—	Elliptic cylinder
	4*	+	+	0	(0)	(0)	x	(0)	Elliptic paraboloid
IV	1	+	—	0	(0)	(0)	0	0	Two intersecting planes
	2*	+	—	0	(0)	(0)	0	x	Hyperbolic cylinder
	3*	+	—	0	(0)	(0)	x	(0)	Hyperbolic paraboloid
V	1	+	+	+	(0)	(0)	(0)	+	Empty set
	2	+	+	+	(0)	(0)	(0)	0	Single point
	3*	+	+	+	(0)	(0)	(0)	—	Ellipsoid
VI	1*	+	+	—	(0)	(0)	(0)	+	Hyperboloid of two sheets
	2*	+	+	—	(0)	(0)	(0)	0	Elliptic cone
	3*	+	+	—	(0)	(0)	(0)	—	Hyperboloid of one sheet

Case II (4). **The Parabolic Cylinder**

In this case the equation can be written as

$$x^2 + Ey + Fz = 0$$

after dividing through by A. We assume E to be nonzero. Any plane orthogonal to the x-axis cuts the surface in a straight line, the line with equation

$$Ey + Fz + a^2 = 0$$

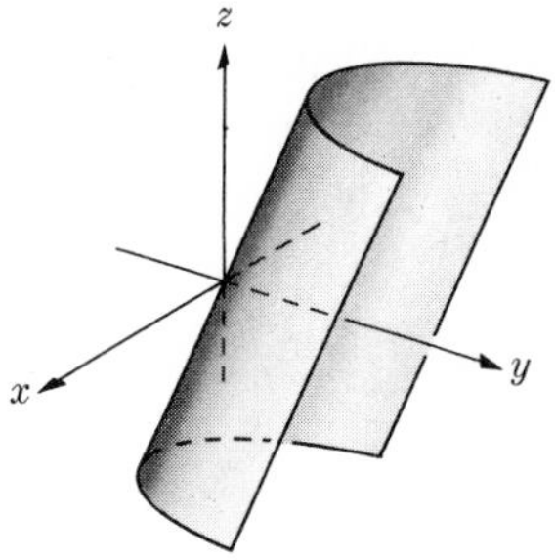

Figure 7–5

where $x = a$ is the cutting plane. All such lines are parallel and the resulting surface is called a *cylinder* (Fig. 7–5), since it can be generated by a set of parallel lines. Any plane orthogonal to the z-axis cuts the cylinder in a parabola and all such parabolas are translates of one another in the y-, z-directions. The vertices lie on a straight line in the yz-plane, and the axes of the parabolas are all parallel to the y-axis.

Note that we can make a rotation in the yz-plane so that $Ey + Fz = E'y'$. Then the surface becomes particularly simple.

Case III (3). **The Elliptic Cylinder**

By dividing through by G, we can assume the equation to be in the form

$$\frac{x^2}{a^2} + \frac{y^2}{b^2} = 1,$$

where we have written the coefficients of x^2 and y^2 in this form to indicate that they are positive. This is the equation of an ellipse in the xy-plane; and since z does not appear in the equation, if any point is on the locus, then the entire line through that point parallel to the z-axis will also be on the locus. The surface is therefore again a cylinder, but this time an *elliptic cylinder* (Fig. 7–6).

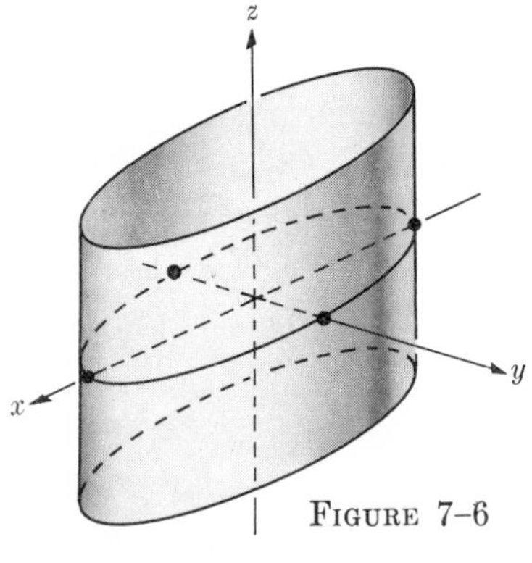

Figure 7–6

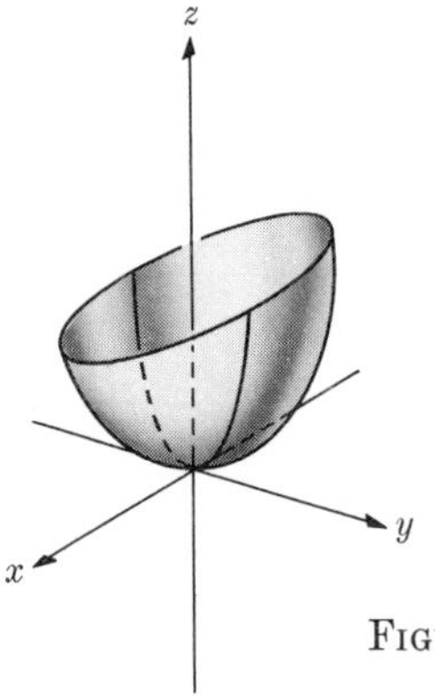

Figure 7–7

Case III (4). **The Elliptic Paraboloid**

The equation can be divided through by $|F|$ and written in the form

$$\frac{x^2}{a^2} + \frac{y^2}{b^2} = \pm z.$$

The two cases here are similar, and we will discuss only the one with the positive sign on z. The negative sign would merely invert the locus. Assuming the positive sign on z, there are no points with negative z which satisfy the locus. Setting $z = c^2$, we see that the intersection of the surface with a plane orthogonal to the z-axis is an ellipse. All such ellipses are similar (have the same eccentricity). A plane orthogonal to the x- (or y-) axis cuts the surface in a parabola. In particular, the planes $x = 0$ and $y = 0$ cut the surfaces in parabolas which pass through the vertices of the above ellipses. The surface is illustrated in Fig. 7–7.

CASE IV (2). **The Hyperbolic Cylinder**

Dividing the equation through by $|G|$ we obtain an equation of the form

$$\frac{x^2}{a^2} - \frac{y^2}{b^2} = \pm 1.$$

This is the equation of a hyperbola in the xy-plane. The principal axis is the x-axis or the y-axis depending on the sign of the right-hand side. Again, the surface is a cylinder with generators parallel to the z-axis (Fig. 7–8).

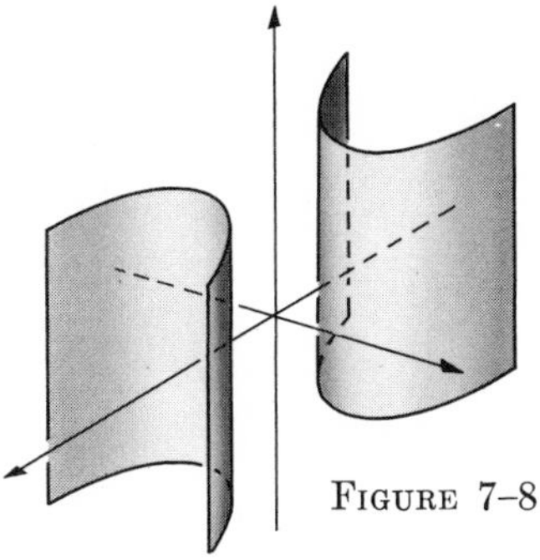

FIGURE 7–8

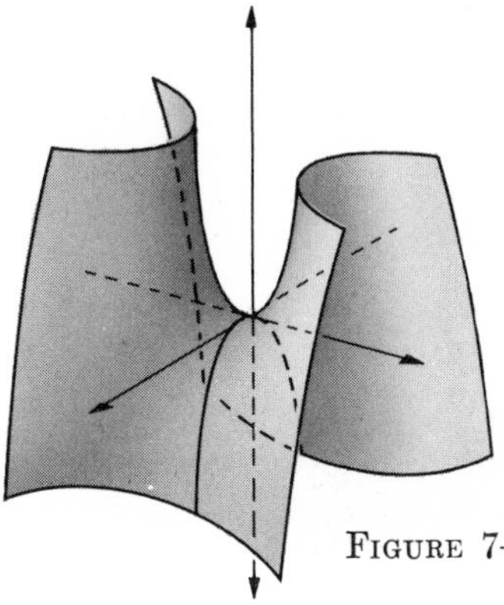

FIGURE 7–9

CASE IV (3). **The Hyperbolic Paraboloid**

By dividing through by $|F|$ we can obtain the equation

$$\frac{x^2}{a^2} - \frac{y^2}{b^2} = \pm z.$$

We will consider only the case with $-z$ on the right-hand side. The other case is similar. The cross sections of this surface in planes orthogonal to the x-axis are parabolas, opening upward. The cross sections in planes orthogonal to the y-axis are parabolas which open downward. Finally, the cross sections in planes orthogonal to the z-axis are hyperbolas (except when $z = 0$). When $z > 0$, these have their principal axis in the yz-plane. When $z < 0$, the principal axis is in the xz-plane. For $z > 0$, the vertices of these hyperbolas lie on the parabola $y^2 = b^2 z$. For $z < 0$, the vertices are on the parabola $x^2 = -a^2 z$. When $z = 0$ we find

$$\left(\frac{x}{a} - \frac{y}{b}\right)\left(\frac{x}{a} + \frac{y}{b}\right) = 0.$$

The locus of this equation is a pair of intersecting lines. A surprising property of this surface is the fact that through every point of the surface there exist two distinct straight lines which lie on the surface. This is shown in Problem 8 at the end of this section.

This surface, as illustrated in Fig. 7–9, is probably the most interesting of the quadric surfaces.

CASE V (3). **The Ellipsoid**

This equation can be divided through by $-G$ to give an equation of the form

$$\frac{x^2}{a^2} + \frac{y^2}{b^2} + \frac{z^2}{c^2} = 1.$$

Every cross section of this surface in a plane orthogonal to one of the axes is an ellipse (or a point, or nothing). The ellipses orthogonal to a given axis are all similar. The surface is sketched in Fig. 7–10.

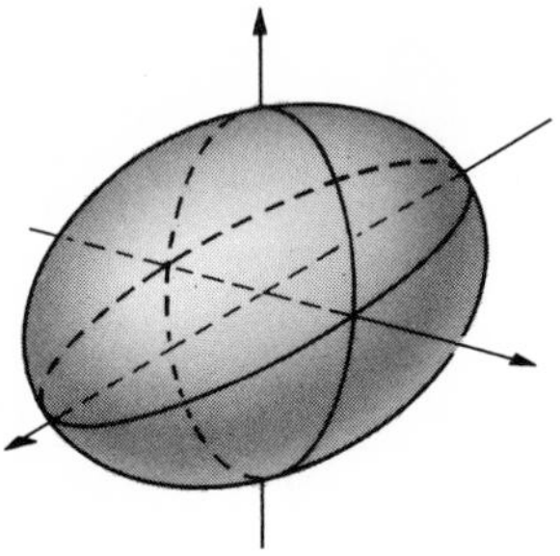

FIGURE 7–10

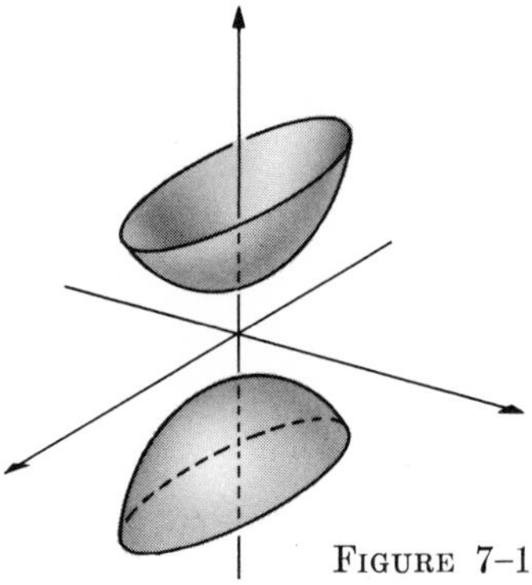

FIGURE 7–11

CASE VI (1). **The Hyperboloid of Two Sheets**

The equation in this case can be brought to the form

$$\frac{x^2}{a^2} + \frac{y^2}{b^2} - \frac{z^2}{c^2} = -1.$$

Every cross section in a plane orthogonal to the z-axis is an ellipse (or a point, or nothing) and all of these ellipses are similar. The cross sections in planes orthogonal to the x-axis or y-axis are hyperbolas, with principal axis parallel to the z-axis in the xz- or yz-plane. There are no points on the locus for $-c < z < c$ and the surface is in two parts (as shown in Fig. 7–11).

CASE VI (2). **The Elliptic Cone**

When the coefficient G is zero, the equation can be written as

$$\frac{x^2}{a^2} + \frac{y^2}{b^2} - \frac{z^2}{c^2} = 0.$$

The cross sections in planes orthogonal to the z-axis are ellipses (except when $z = 0$). The cross sections in planes orthogonal to the x- and y-axes are, in general, hyperbolas. However, when $x = 0$ or $y = 0$ these cross sections are a pair of intersecting lines. In fact, it is easy to verify that if any point is on the locus, then the entire straight line through this point and the origin is on the locus. This is the characteristic property of a cone. This surface is shown in Fig. 7–12.

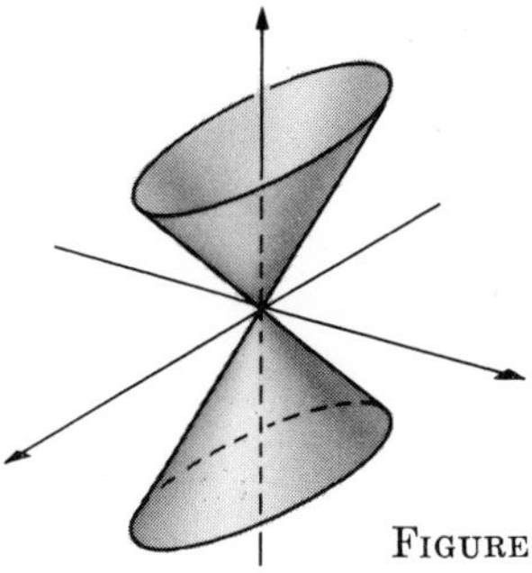

FIGURE 7–12

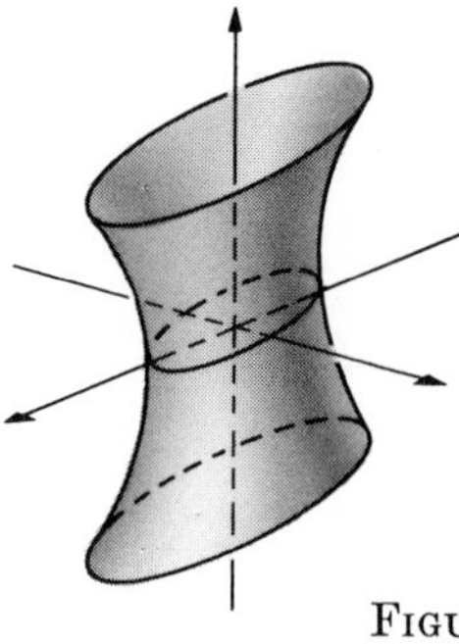

FIGURE 7–13

CASE VI (3). **The Hyperboloid of One Sheet**

The equation in this case can be brought to the form

$$\frac{x^2}{a^2} + \frac{y^2}{b^2} - \frac{z^2}{c^2} = 1.$$

The analysis is similar to that of the hyperboloid of two sheets. The difference here is that every plane orthogonal to the z-axis intersects the locus in an ellipse. The locus therefore does not fall into two parts. The planes $x = 0$ and $y = 0$ intersect the locus in hyperbolas whose principal axes are orthogonal to the z-axis. The resulting surface is as shown in Fig. 7–13. Notice that hyperbolas in the xz- and yz-planes pass through the vertices of the ellipses found as intersections of the surface with planes orthogonal to the z-axis.

This surface also has the property of being made up of straight lines. This is proved in Problem 7 at the end of this section.

There is a special case which can occur in each of six of the above cases. Whenever two of the coefficients A, B, and C are equal (and of the same sign) we will have a *surface of revolution*. When $A = B$ we would have surfaces of revolution about the z-axis. This means that if (x_0, y_0, z_0) is on the surface, then all points of the circle in the plane $z = z_0$ with center at $(0, 0, z_0)$ are also on the locus. This follows from the fact that a point (x_1, y_1, z_0) is on this circle if and only if

$$x_1^2 + y_1^2 = x_0^2 + y_0^2.$$

Thus if the quadratic equation is of the form

$$Ax^2 + Ay^2 + \cdots = 0,$$

this condition is satisfied.

Surfaces of revolution can be visualized easily. If, for example, it is a surface of revolution about the z-axis, we can find the curve of intersection of the surface with the xz-plane (setting $y = 0$) and imagine this curve being rotated about the z-axis to generate the surface.

Surfaces of revolution are of such importance that most of them are given special names.

In case III (3), if $A = B$ the elliptic cylinder becomes a *right circular cylinder*. Similarly, in case VI (2) the elliptic cone becomes a *right circular cone*.

If $A = B$ in the elliptic paraboloid of case III (4), we obtain a surface of revolution which is called just a *paraboloid*. In cases VI (1) and (3) we have hyperboloids of revolution, of two and one sheets respectively.

Finally, if two of the coefficients are equal in the equation of the ellipsoid, we obtain a surface known as a *spheroid*. Assuming that $A = B$, a spheroid has an equation of the type

$$\frac{x^2}{a^2} + \frac{y^2}{a^2} + \frac{z^2}{c^2} = 1.$$

If $c > a$, then the spheroid looks something like a football and is called a *prolate spheroid*. If $c < a$, then surface is called an *oblate spheroid*. The oblate spheroid looks like a curling stone (or like a volleyball that is being sat upon). What happens when $c = a$?

The reader is expected to learn the names (together with the forms) of the various quadric surfaces, but he should not attempt to memorize which forms of the equation go with which of the surfaces. Rather, when faced with the problem of identifying a quadric surface, say,

$$4x^2 - y^2 + z^2 - 8y + 4z + 11 = 0, \tag{7–16}$$

he should proceed by working up a picture of the surface by considering the cross sections in the planes parallel to the coordinate planes. For example, Eq. (7–16) would be rewritten

$$4x^2 - (y + 4)^2 + (z + 2)^2 = 9,$$

or

$$\frac{x^2}{9/4} - \frac{(y + 4)^2}{9} + \frac{(z + 2)^2}{9} = 1. \tag{7–17}$$

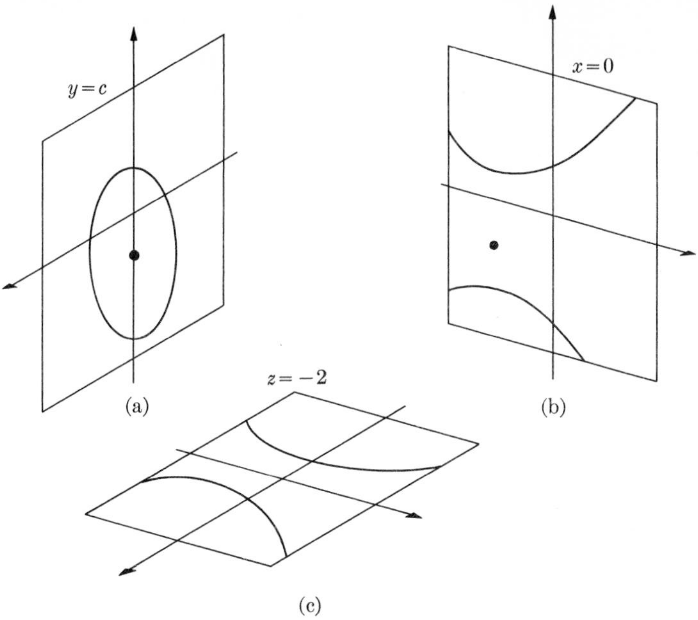

FIGURE 7–14

In choosing the cross sections to consider first, we prefer to find planes in which the cross sections are ellipses (or circles). If such planes exist, it is usually easiest to build up the picture by starting with them. In (7–17) we see that any plane $y = c$ will intersect the surface in an ellipse. The resulting ellipse has its center at $x = 0$, $z = -2$. Its principal axis will be the line $x = 0$ and its conjugate axis the line $z = -2$ (all of these being in the plane $y = c$). (See Fig. 7–14a.)

All of these ellipses are similar, and they can easily be determined by the location of their vertices. The principal vertices are the points of intersection of the surface with the plane $x = 0$, that is, the points on

$$-\frac{(y+4)^2}{9} + \frac{(z+2)^2}{9} = 1.$$

This is a hyperbola in the yz-plane with center at $y = -4$, $z = -2$ (see Fig. 7–14b).

The conjugate vertices of the ellipses are the points of intersection of the surface with the plane $z = -2$. These are the points in this plane which satisfy the equation

$$\frac{x^2}{9/4} - \frac{(y+4)^2}{9} = 1,$$

and hence lie on a hyperbola with center $x = 0$, and $y = -4$ (Fig. 7–14c).

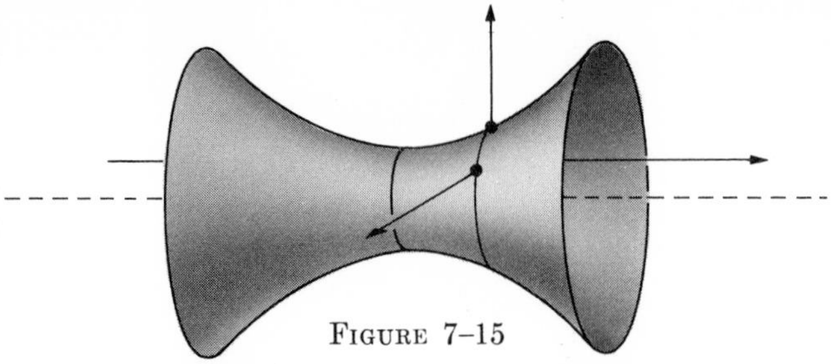

FIGURE 7–15

Collecting the information, we see that the surface is a hyperboloid of one sheet whose axis is the line $x = 0, z = -2$. The surface is as shown in Fig. 7–15.

PROBLEMS

1. Show that nine cases of the above table which were not discussed in the text have loci as listed in the table.

2. What relationship exists between the two intersecting planes of case IV (1) and the hyperbolic cylinder of IV (2) when A, B, and C are the same in the two equations? What relations hold between the planes of IV (1) and hyperbolic paraboloid IV (3)?

3. What relationship exists between the elliptic cone of case VI (2) and the surfaces of cases VI (1) and (3) when A, B, and C are the same in the two equations?

4. Identify the surfaces defined by each of the following equations. Discuss the intersections of planes parallel to the coordinate planes. Sketch the surface.

   (a) $x^2 + 4z^2 = 0$
   (b) $y^2 + 9z^2 - 36x = 0$
   (c) $4x^2 + 9y^2 + 36z^2 - 36 = 0$
   (d) $4x^2 - y^2 + 4z^2 + 12 = 0$
   (e) $x^2 - 16z^2 + 48y = 0$
   (f) $y^2 - 4z^2 + 16 = 0$
   (g) $6y^2 - 4x + z = 0$
   (h) $6x^2 + 4y^2 + 4z^2 - 12 = 0$

5. Follow the same directions as in problem 4.

   (a) $4x^2 - y^2 + 12z^2 - 36 = 0$
   (b) $y^2 + 4z^2 - 16 = 0$
   (c) $y^2 - 9z^2 = 0$
   (d) $9x^2 + 9z^2 - 4y = 0$
   (e) $x^2 - 8y^2 - 8z^2 = 0$
   (f) $8x^2 + y^2 - 8z^2 - 32 = 0$
   (g) $9x^2 + 4y^2 + 9z^2 - 36 = 0$
   (h) $z^2 - x + 2y = 0$

6. Identify the surface defined by each of the following equations. Discuss the intersections of planes parallel to the coordinate planes. Sketch the surface.

   (a) $x^2 - y^2 + 4z^2 + 6x - 8z + 14 = 0$
   (b) $4x^2 + 9z^2 - 12y + 6 = 0$
   (c) $6x^2 + 2y^2 + z^2 - 24x + 8y - 4z = 0$
   (d) $9y^2 - 4z^2 + 10x = 0$
   (e) $4x^2 - y^2 + 4z^2 + 16 = 0$
   (f) $x^2 + 4y^2 - 3z^2 - 2x - 12z - 11 = 0$
   (g) $x^2 - 4z^2 + 6x = 0$

7. Let $X_0 = (x_0, y_0, 0)$ be any point on the intersection of the hyperboloid of one sheet

$$\frac{x^2}{a^2} + \frac{y^2}{b^2} - \frac{z^2}{c^2} = 1$$

with the plane $z = 0$. Show that every point of the lines

$$\mathbf{X} = \mathbf{X}_0 + t\mathbf{B}$$

is on the hyperboloid for

$$\mathbf{B} = [a^2y_0, -b^2x_0, abc],$$

or

$$\mathbf{B} = [-a^2y_0, b^2x_0, abc].$$

8. Let $X_0 = (x_0, 0, z_0)$ be any point on the intersection of the hyperbolic paraboloid

$$\frac{x^2}{a^2} - \frac{y^2}{b^2} + z = 0$$

with the plane $y = 0$. Show that every point of the lines $\mathbf{X} = \mathbf{X}_0 + t\mathbf{B}$ is on the hyperbolic paraboloid for

$$\mathbf{B} = [a^2, ab, -2x_0],$$

or

$$\mathbf{B} = [a^2, -ab, -2x_0].$$

9. A quadric surface is called *central* if and only if there is a point P, called the *center*, such that whenever the point X is on the conic then so is the point X', where

$$\mathbf{X}' = \mathbf{P} - \overrightarrow{PX}$$

(i.e., $\overrightarrow{PX'} = -\overrightarrow{PX}$).
Which of the quadric surfaces defined in this section are central? What are their centers?

7-4 POLAR COORDINATES

We have made an identification between points of the cartesian plane and vectors. Thus, if X is the point (x, y), we identify it with the vector

$$\mathbf{X} = \overrightarrow{OX} = x\mathbf{e}_1 + y\mathbf{e}_2$$

(O being the origin). The vector can then be thought of as determining the point. However, we can specify a vector by giving its length and direction instead of its cartesian coordinates.

If $\mathbf{X}$ is an arbitrary nonzero vector in the cartesian plane, then $|\mathbf{X}|$ is its magnitude and $\mathbf{e}_r = \mathbf{X}/|\mathbf{X}|$ is a unit vector in the same direction. Here, we use the subscript r to indicate that the unit vector is in the radial direction. A subscript θ would be more to the point, since this vector depends on θ, but standard usage calls for $\mathbf{e}_r$ with the dependence on θ being understood.

Since $\mathbf{e}_r \cdot \mathbf{e}_1 = \cos\theta$ and $\mathbf{e}_r \cdot \mathbf{e}_2 = \sin\theta$ (why?), we have $\mathbf{e}_r = \cos\theta\, \mathbf{e}_1 + \sin\theta\, \mathbf{e}_2$. We thus have the motivation for the definition of polar coordinates.

Definition 7–1. The *polar coordinates* of a point X in the cartesian plane are a pair of real numbers (r, θ) such that

$$\mathbf{X} = r\mathbf{e}_r, \tag{7–18}$$

where

$$\mathbf{e}_r = \cos\theta\mathbf{e}_1 + \sin\theta\mathbf{e}_2. \tag{7–19}$$

Several comments must be made about this definition. First of all, it is clear that any given pair of real numbers (r, θ) determine a unique point from these two conditions. Normally we think of the number r as being $|\mathbf{X}|$, the distance of the point in question from the origin, but this is not necessary in this definition. The number r could just as well be $-|\mathbf{X}|$. This, however, is the only other possibility (why?).

On the other hand, a given point has many different sets of polar coordinates, an infinite number in fact. If a point is fixed and we set $r = |\mathbf{X}|$, then there is exactly one θ_0 with $0 \leq \theta_0 < 2\pi$ satisfying the requirements of the definition. Any angle $\theta = \theta_0 + 2\pi k$, $k = 0, \pm 1, \pm 2, \ldots$ will also satisfy the definition. Choosing the other possibility $r = -|\mathbf{X}|$ requires the angle $\theta_1 = \theta_0 + \pi$. Here again we can add any multiple of 2π and still satisfy the conditions.

Polar coordinates are useful in many applications. In particular, they may be used to specify a curve in the plane, just as with cartesian coordinates. In general, this is done by giving an equation of the form

$$r = f(\theta) \tag{7–20}$$

to specify the locus. We sometimes find θ as a function of r, or find an equation in both r and θ, but equations of the form (7–20) are the type which occur most often.

There are two types of questions which arise. First, given an equation of the form (7–20), what is its locus? Second, given a curve in the plane, what is the polar coordinate form of its equation? Both of these questions will be considered with the help of a few examples. We note first that the conversion from polar coordinates to cartesian coordinates or vice versa is aided by the relations

$$\begin{aligned} x &= r\cos\theta, \\ y &= r\sin\theta, \\ r^2 &= x^2 + y^2, \end{aligned} \tag{7–21}$$

which are easily proved from the definition. Some caution is required in the use of these relations, however. When they are used to transform from one kind of coordinate to the other, we must always check that no extraneous points have been introduced into the locus, and that no points have been lost.

Let us now look at a few loci defined by their equations in polar coordinates. The general method of analysis is to determine a number of points on the locus, and to discuss the behavior of r as θ varies to see how to connect these points. A sketch may then be made.

Example I. THE CIRCLE

$$r = a.$$

Here, r is a constant function of θ. The locus is the set of all points at the distance $|a|$ from the origin. (Why the absolute value?) It is therefore a circle with radius $|a|$, centered at the origin.

Example II. THE CIRCLE

$$r = 2a \cos \theta. \tag{7–22}$$

When $\theta = 0$, the point $(2a, 0)$ is determined. As θ increases from 0 to $\pi/2$, r decreases (if $a > 0$) from $2a$ to zero. When θ goes from $\pi/2$ to π, r is negative and we get points in the fourth quadrant. When $\theta = \pi$, $r = -2a$ and we discover that we again have the point $(2a, 0)$. As θ increases from π to 2π, the points previously obtained are obtained again, since $\cos(\theta + \pi) = -\cos\theta$. (See Fig. 7–16.)

Any point satisfying this equation must also satisfy

$$r^2 = 2a\, r \cos \theta,$$

and hence from (7–21) must also satisfy

$$x^2 + y^2 = 2ax.$$

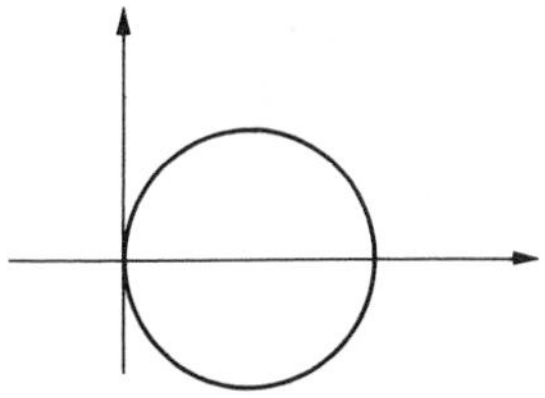

FIGURE 7–16

This, however, is the equation of a circle with center at $(a, 0)$ and radius $|a|$. This discussion shows that the locus of $r(r - 2a\cos\theta) = 0$ is exactly this circle. This equation was obtained from (7–22) by multiplying by r. No points of the locus of (7–21) will have been lost by this process. However, an extraneous point may have been introduced into the new locus. When $r = 0$, the new equation is satisfied. Hence this point is on the locus we have obtained, but may not be on the locus of (7–22). We see, however, that when $\theta = \pi/2$, the point $r = 0$ results in (7–21). Therefore, the locus of (7–21) is exactly the circle described here.

Example III. THE 4-LEAFED ROSE

$$r = a \cos 2\theta \qquad (a > 0). \tag{7–23}$$

A discussion such as given above shows that the locus of this equation is as shown in Fig. 7–17. The dashed lines, at $\theta = \pm\pi/2, \pm 3\pi/2$, are the rays at which $r = 0$. Drawing these in helps to sketch the locus. Note the order in which the leaves are traced out as θ goes from 0 to 2π: first, the upper side of the right-hand leaf, then the left side of the bottom leaf, and so on.

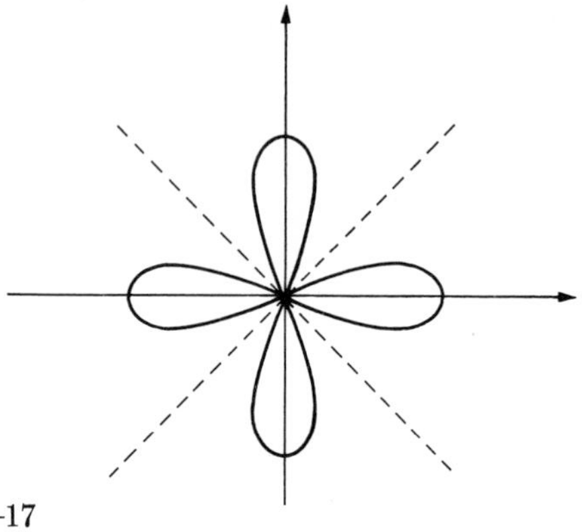

FIGURE 7–17

A technique that is often helpful in making sketches of the loci of polar coordinate equations is to make a preliminary sketch of the locus of the equation in a rectangular (r,θ)-coordinate system. The sketch of (7–23) in such a coordinate system would look like Fig. 7–18.

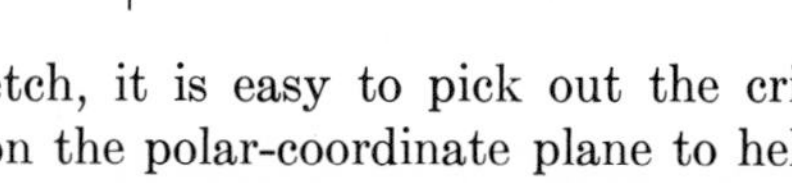

FIGURE 7–18

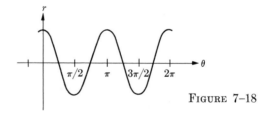

From such a sketch, it is easy to pick out the critical angles which should be marked on the polar-coordinate plane to help with the sketch. These are the values of θ for which $r = 0$ ($\pi/4$, $3\pi/4$, $5\pi/4$, $7\pi/4$ in this case) and values of θ at which r takes on local maximum and minimum values (0, $\pi/2$, π, $3\pi/2$ for the locus discussed here).

The reader is advised to make such a sketch for each of the examples of this section and to see how the rectangular coordinate sketch is related to, and helps to obtain, the polar coordinate sketch.

Example IV. THE 3-LEAFED ROSE

$$r = a \cos 3\theta \qquad (a > 0). \tag{7-24}$$

This equation has a locus as shown in Fig. 7–19. An analysis similar to that above shows that the curve is traced out twice as θ goes from 0 to 2π.

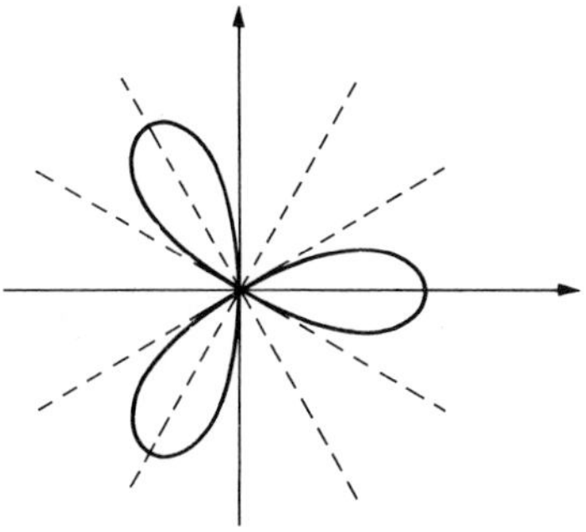

FIGURE 7–19

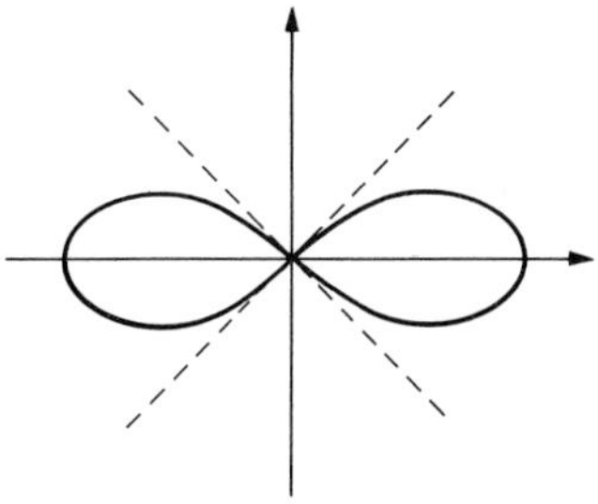

FIGURE 7–20

Example V. THE LEMNISCATE

$$r^2 = a^2 \cos 2\theta. \tag{7-25}$$

The analysis here is similar to that of Example III, except that now the upper and lower leaves cannot appear since $\cos 2\theta$ is negative for $\pi/4 < \theta < 3\pi/4$ and $5\pi/4 < \theta < 7\pi/4$. (See Fig. 7–20.)

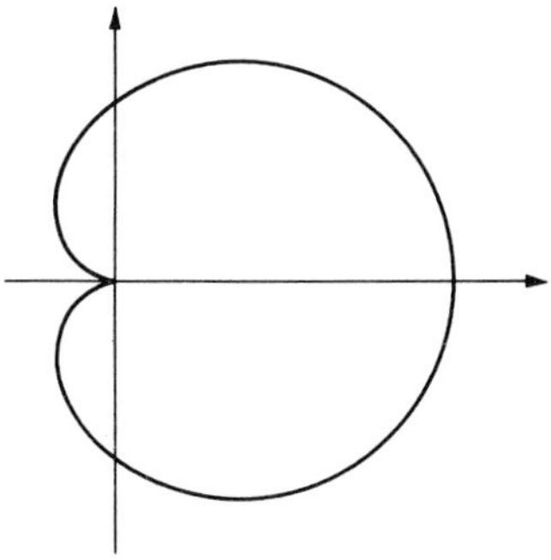

FIGURE 7–21

Example VI. THE CARDIOID

$$r = a(1 - \cos \theta). \tag{7-26}$$

The resulting curve is illustrated in Fig. 7–21. The name, cardioid, comes from the heart shape of the figure. The cardioid finds many uses as examples in calculus courses.

Next we turn to the opposite problem: Given a locus, how do we find its equation? Let us start with a simple one.

Example VII. THE STRAIGHT LINE

$$x = a.$$

Using relations (7–21), we see that every point of this line satisfies

$$r \cos \theta = a,$$

or

$$r = a \sec \theta. \tag{7–27}$$

An analysis such as done above can be made to show that (7–27) is indeed the equation of this single straight line.

As our final example (which we do not label, since it will result in a theorem), let us find the polar form for the equations of the conic sections. To do this, we use the focus-directrix property of the conic sections. Let the distance between the focus and the directrix be p, and let the eccentricity be e. We can assume that the focus is at the origin and let $x = -p$ be the directrix. The equation of the conic section is then

$$|\mathbf{X}| = e|XE|, \tag{7–28}$$

where $|XE|$ is the distance between the point X and the directrix.

There are four possible cases which should be considered: where the point X is to the right or left of the directrix, and where $r = |\mathbf{X}|$ or $-|\mathbf{X}|$. Let us consider only two of these here. The others will be left as exercises. First, suppose X is to the right of $x = -p$, and $r = |\mathbf{X}|$. In this case, the signed distance from X to the y-axis is $\mathbf{X} \cdot \mathbf{e}_1 = |\mathbf{X}| \cos \theta = r \cos \theta$, and hence $|XE| = p + r \cos \theta$. Equation (7–28) then becomes

$$r = e(p + r \cos \theta),$$

which can be solved for r to give

$$r = \frac{pe}{1 - e \cos \theta}\cdot \tag{7–29}$$

Next, suppose that X is to the left of $x = -p$, and that $r = -|\mathbf{X}|$. The signed distance of X from the y-axis in this case is $|X| \cos (\theta + \pi) = -|X| \cos \theta = r \cos \theta$. This number is negative. (This case is illustrated in Fig. 7–22 with the primed coordinates.) Thus

$$|XE| = -r \cos \theta - p,$$

and Eq. (7–28) becomes

$$-r = e(-r \cos \theta - p).$$

Solving for r again results in (7–29).

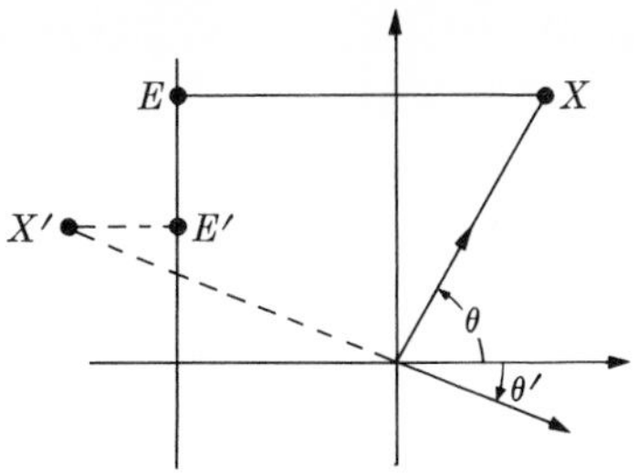

FIGURE 7-22

Without bothering with the other cases, let us turn to Eq. (7-29) and see what the actual locus of it will be. The above discussion shows that every point on the locus of (7-29) will be on the conic, but the question is, will the entire conic be covered?

In the case of an ellipse $0 < e < 1$, and it is easily seen that all the points on the ellipse are obtained. For each θ, (7-29) gives a positive value for r, which is always less than p when $\pi/2 < 0 < 3\pi/2$.

For a parabola, $e = 1$ and r is undefined in (7-29) if $\theta = 0$. All other values of θ between 0 and 2π give positive values of r. Again when $\pi/2 < \theta < 3\pi/2$, r is less than p.

In the case of a hyperbola, $e > 1$, and r is undefined when $\cos\theta = 1/e$. Suppose $\cos\alpha = 1/e$ where α is between 0 and $\pi/2$. Then for $-\alpha < \theta < \alpha$, we see from (7-29) that r is negative. Indeed we can verify that the resulting point is to the left of the directrix. As θ varies within this range, one entire branch of the hyperbola is swept out. When $\alpha < \theta < 2\pi - \alpha$, we see that r is positive in (7-29) and the remaining branch of the hyperbola is produced.

A sketch of the hyperbola that results is shown in Fig. 7-23. Note that the lines determined by $\theta = \pm\alpha$ and $\theta = \pm\alpha + \pi$ are not the asymptotes of the hyperbola. They are parallel to the asymptotes, however, and are shown dashed whereas the asymptotes are represented by solid lines in Fig. 7-23.

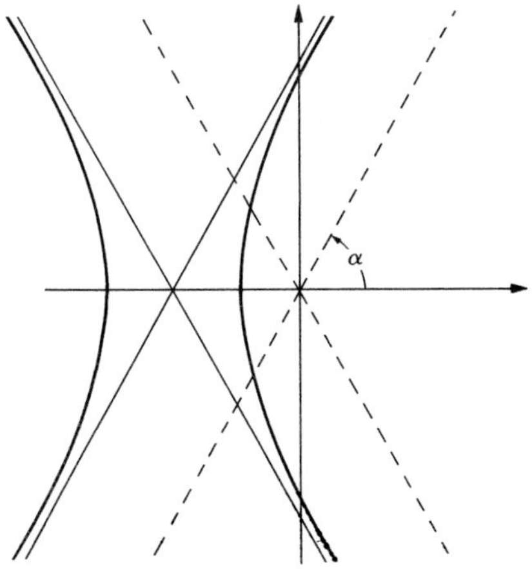

FIGURE 7-23

Putting together the above observations, we find that we have proved the following theorem.

Theorem 7–4. The equation in polar coordinates

$$r = \frac{pe}{1 - e \cos \theta}$$

has as its locus a conic section with eccentricity e, a focus at the origin, and associated directrix $x = -p$.

PROBLEMS

1. If a locus is defined by the equation $r = f(\theta)$ and if $f(\theta)$ is periodic with period 2π, show that the locus has at most two points other than the origin in common with any line through the origin.

2. What are the polar coordinates of the origin?

3. If relations (7–21) are used to transform an equation in cartesian coordinates to one in polar coordinates, will any points of the locus be lost?

4. Sketch the *Spiral of Archimedes*,

$$r = a\theta, \qquad a > 0.$$

What happens if a is negative? Sketch this case also.

5. Find the equation in polar coordinates of the circle

$$(x - a)^2 + (y - b)^2 = R^2.$$

Can you solve for r as a function of θ in the resulting equation? What happens if $R^2 = a^2 + b^2$?

6. If S is the locus of $r = f(\theta)$ and if the plane is rotated about the origin through an angle α, leaving the coordinate system fixed, so that the point set S becomes the point set S', what is the equation of S'?

7. Sketch the loci of the following:

(a) $r = 2a \sin \theta,\ a > 0$
(b) $r = a \sin 2\theta,\ a > 0$
(c) $r = a(1 + \cos \theta),\ a > 0$
(d) $r = a(1 - \sin \theta),\ a > 0$
(e) $r = a \csc \theta,\ a > 0$.

8. Discuss the locus of

$$r = a \cos n\,\theta$$

(a) if n is an even integer; (b) if n is an odd integer.

9. What is the equation in polar coordinates of the line

$$x \cos \alpha + y \sin \alpha = p?$$

10. A locus is said to be symmetric with respect to the origin if whenever X is on the locus then Y is also on the locus where $\mathbf{Y} = -\mathbf{X}$. Prove that if $f(\theta)$ is periodic with period π, then the locus of $r = f(\theta)$ is symmetric with respect to the origin.

11. Prove that if $f(\pi - \theta) = f(\theta)$ for all θ, then the locus of $r = f(\theta)$ is symmetric with respect to the y-axis.

12. Prove that if r is given as a function of θ which involves only $\sin \theta$, then the resulting locus is symmetric with respect to the y-axis.

13. Prove that if $f(-\theta) = f(\theta)$ for all θ, then the locus of $r = f(\theta)$ is symmetric with respect to the x-axis.

14. Prove that if r is given as a function of θ which involves only $\cos \theta$, then the resulting locus is symmetric with respect to the x-axis.

15. If $f(-\theta) = -f(\theta)$ for all θ, what are the symmetry properties of the locus of $r = f(\theta)$? Note that $f(0) = 0$ because of this condition.

16. Let a function $f(\theta)$ be given and suppose that another function $g(\theta)$ is such that $g(\theta) = -f(\theta + \pi)$. Prove that the polar-coordinate equations

$$r = f(\theta)$$

and

$$r = g(\theta)$$

have the same loci.

17. If an equation of a locus in polar coordinates is

$$r = f(\cos \theta),$$

what is the locus of the equation

$$r = -f(-\cos \theta)?$$

18. Use Eq. (7–28) to obtain r as a function of θ for the two cases not discussed in the text. How is the locus of the resulting equation related to the locus of (7–29)?

19. Let $e > 1$, $\cos \alpha = 1/e$, with $0 > \alpha < \pi/2$. Prove that if $-\alpha < \theta < \alpha$, then the point with polar coordinates (r, θ) defined by (7–29) is to the left of the line $x = -p$.

20. What are the loci of the following for $e < 1$? $e = 1$? and $e > 1$?

(a) $r = \dfrac{pe}{1 + e \cos \theta}$ (b) $r = \dfrac{pe}{1 - e \sin \theta}$

(c) $r = \dfrac{pe}{1 + e \sin \theta}$

21. Identify and sketch the loci of

(a) $r = \dfrac{6}{3 + 2\cos\theta}$ (b) $r = \dfrac{4}{5 - 5\sin\theta}$

(c) $r = \dfrac{9}{1 + 3\sin\theta}$ (d) $r = \dfrac{4}{6 - 3\sin\theta}$

22. Sketch the *limaçon*

$$r = a + b\cos\theta$$

(a) if $0 < a < b$;
(b) if $0 < b < a$.

23. Prove that the lemniscate (7–25) is the locus of all points with the property that the product of their distances from the points $(a/\sqrt{2}, 0)$ and $(-a/\sqrt{2}, 0)$ is $a^2/2$. [*Hint:* Use the x-, y-coordinates of the point which are given by the polar coordinates of the point.]

Answers to Selected Problems

Section 1–1

1. $A = D \subset C \subset B = E$; $A = D \subset F$
2. (a) $\{x \mid x^2 < 2\}$ (c) $\{x \mid x = 2k, k \text{ an integer}\}$
   (e) $\{x \mid x > 0 \text{ and } x^2 < 2\}$
3. (a) $\{x \mid 0 < x < 1\}$ (b) $\emptyset$ 4. Yes

Section 1–2

1. Axiom 8 fails 6. All hold.
13. (a) Commutative and associative (c) The number 0 is an identity (on the right). There are right and left hand inverses. $a \circ (-a/2) = 0$, $(-2a) \circ a = 0$.
14. (b) closed under $*$, Δ, and $\circ$.

Section 1–4

2. (a) m is the maximum of A if and only if (*i*) m is the least upper bound of a, and (*ii*) m is in A.
3. (b) $y^2 - 2 = (x^2 - 2)^2/4x^2$

Section 1–5

4. If and only if a and b are both nonnegative or both nonpositive. That is, if and only if $ab > 0$.
7. (a) $-5, 9$ (c) $-2, 3$ (e) $-1, \frac{11}{5}$
8. (a) $x > 8$ and $x < 2$ (c) $x > 1$ and $x < -\frac{1}{2}$

Section 1–6

1. (a) -289 (c) 0 2. (a) -15 (c) 0
3. (a) $-4, -15$ (c) $4, -3, 3$
7. (a) $3\begin{vmatrix} 1 & 2 \\ 6 & -5 \end{vmatrix} + 6\begin{vmatrix} 2 & 5 \\ 6 & -5 \end{vmatrix} - 2\begin{vmatrix} 2 & 5 \\ 1 & 2 \end{vmatrix}$

   (c) $-4\begin{vmatrix} 4 & 6 \\ 5 & 7 \end{vmatrix} + 5\begin{vmatrix} 3 & 5 \\ 5 & 7 \end{vmatrix} - 6\begin{vmatrix} 3 & 5 \\ 4 & 6 \end{vmatrix}$
9. 5

Section 2–1

2. Symmetrically located with respect to: (*i*) the y-axis, (ii) the x-axis, (*iii*) the origin.
3. (a) $4\sqrt{2}$ (c) $2\sqrt{53}$ (e) 14
5. (a) $(x-1)^2+(y-2)^2=16$, $x^2+y^2-2x-4y-9=0$
   (c) $(x+5)^2+(y-3)^2=1$, $x^2+y^2+10x-6y+33=0$
6. (a) $x^2+(y-2)^2=4$, $x^2+y^2-4y=0$
   (c) $(x+2)^2+(y+2)^2=64$, $x^2+y^2+4x+4y-56=0$
7. (a) $(-1, 2)$, 3 (c) No locus
8. (a) $(-1, \frac{3}{2})$, $\frac{3}{2}$ (c) $(-\frac{2}{3}, -3)$, $\frac{8}{3}$
9. The single point (x_0, y_0)
11. (a) $x^2+y^2-7x+11y=0$, $(\frac{7}{2}, -\frac{11}{2})$, $\sqrt{170}/2$
13. $(x-3)^2+(y+7)^2=90$

Section 2–2

2. $x-\dfrac{1}{m}y-c=0$. As m becomes large, the equation tends toward $x-c=0$.
4. (a) $y=2x-11$, $2x-y-11=0$
   (c) $y=5x+10$, $5x-y+10=0$
   (e) $y=-\frac{3}{5}x+\frac{13}{5}$, $3x+5y-13=0$
5. (a) $y=-\frac{1}{2}x-\frac{13}{2}$, $x+2y+13=0$
   (c) $y=-\frac{1}{50}x+\frac{1}{50}$, $x+50y-1=0$
6. (a) $m=2$, $2x-y-5=0$ (c) no slope, $x-4=0$
   (e) $m=0$, $y-5=0$
7. (c) $m=1$, $x-y-12=0$ (e) $m=-94$, $94x+y-690=0$

Section 2–3

1. The line cannot be parallel to the y-axis. If $y=mx+b$ is the equation of the line, then $f(x)=mx+b$.
2. $f(x)=[R^2-x^2]^{1/2}$, domain is $\{x \mid -R \le x \le R\}$, image is $\{y \mid 0 \le y \le R\}$.

Section 2–4

2. (a) Yes, $(x, y) \to (x+h+h', y+k+k')$ (b) Yes
   (c) Yes, if T is given by $(x, y) \to (x+h, y+k)$, then T' is given by $(x, y) \to (x-h, y-k)$.
4. $\{(x, y) \mid |x-2|+|y+4|=1\}$

Section 2–5

2. (a) $\pi/2$ (c) $3\pi/2$ (e) $3\pi/2$ (g) $\pi/2$
   (i) $\pi/4$ (k) $\pi/3$ (m) $7\pi/6$ (o) π
3. (a) $360\,\alpha/2\pi$
4. (a) 90° (c) 270° (e) −90° (g) −270°
   (i) 45° (k) 60° (m) 675° (o) 22860°
7. $\alpha+\beta=\gamma+$ some integral multiple of 2π

Section 2–6

1. (a) $\alpha = k\pi$, k any integer (c) $\alpha = 2k\pi + \pi/2$ (e) $\alpha = 2k\pi - \pi/2$
3. (a) $-\sin(2\pi/5)$ (c) $\sin 0$ (e) $\cos 0$ (g) $-\cot(\pi/6)$
5. (a) $-\sin 23°$ (c) $\sin 5°$ (e) $-\tan 5°$ (g) $-\sec 35°$

Section 2–7

1. (a) $c = 7\sqrt{2}$ (c) $b = 5\cot\alpha$ (e) $a = c\cos\beta$

	a	b	c	$\cos\alpha$	$\cos\beta$	$\cos\gamma$
3. (a)				$\frac{37}{40}$	$\frac{13}{20}$	$-\frac{5}{16}$
(c)				$\frac{43}{48}$	$\frac{29}{36}$	$-\frac{11}{24}$
4. (a)			9	$\frac{5}{9}$	$-\frac{1}{15}$	
(c)		5		$\frac{37}{40}$		$\frac{13}{20}$
5. (a) Impossible						
(c)		3	$\frac{7}{9}$			$\frac{1}{3}$
(e_1)			5		$-\frac{1}{15}$	$\frac{5}{9}$
(e_2)			$\frac{27}{5}$		$\frac{1}{15}$	$\frac{11}{25}$
6. (a)	4	2			$\frac{7}{12}$	
(c) Impossible						

Section 3–1

1. (a) 7 (c) $\sqrt{94}$
2. The only point is (1, 1, 2)
3. (a) $x^2 + y^2 + z^2 - 6x - 2y + 4z - 11 = 0$
4. It is a sphere if $B^2 + C^2 + D^2 > 4AE$. The center is at $(-B/2A, -C/2A, -D/2A)$. The radius is $[(B^2 + C^2 + D^2 - 4AE)/4A^2]^{1/2}$.
5. (a) $(3, -1, -2)$, 3 (c) $(\frac{5}{6}, -1, 2)$, $\sqrt{301}/6$
6. $x^2 + y^2 + z^2 - 6x + 2z - 15 = 0$, center $(3, 0, -1)$, radius 5

Section 3–2

1. (a) $(\frac{2}{7}, \frac{6}{7}, \frac{3}{7})$, (c) $(-\sqrt{3}/9, -\sqrt{3}/9, 5\sqrt{3}/9)$
2. (a) $(-5, 4, -4)$, $\sqrt{57}$, $(-5/\sqrt{57}, 4/\sqrt{57}, -4/\sqrt{57})$
   (c) $(1, -1, 0)$, $\sqrt{2}$, $(1/\sqrt{2}, -1/\sqrt{2}, 0)$
6. (a) $(\frac{1}{2}, 3, 5)$, $(\frac{4}{3}, \frac{7}{3}, \frac{17}{3})$, $(-\frac{1}{3}, \frac{11}{3}, \frac{13}{3})$
   (c) $(\frac{1}{2}, \frac{1}{2}, 1)$, $(\frac{1}{3}, \frac{2}{3}, 1)$, $(\frac{2}{3}, \frac{1}{3}, 1)$

Section 3–3

1. $P = (a_1 + b_1, a_2 + b_2, a_3 + b_3)$
2. $100\cos\beta$, where β is the angle between the string and the vertical.

Section 3–4

4. (a) 7, 3, −4 (c) 0, 0, 0
5. 5, 0, −2 (c) 0, 0, 0
7. (a) 1, 1, −1
8. (a) $[\frac{3}{7}, -\frac{6}{7}, \frac{2}{7}]$ (c) $[\frac{12}{13}, 0, -\frac{5}{13}]$
9. (b) All but $P8$

Section 3–5

2. (a) $[\frac{16}{49}, \frac{48}{49}, \frac{24}{49}]$ (d) $[\frac{434}{59}, \frac{62}{59}, -\frac{186}{59}]$
3. (a) $[-\frac{14}{29}, \frac{28}{29}, -\frac{21}{29}]$ (c) $[0, 0, 0]$ (e) $[\frac{40}{29}, -\frac{80}{29}, \frac{60}{29}]$
4. $a_1\mathbf{e}_1$, $a_2\mathbf{e}_2$, $a_3\mathbf{e}_3$ 5. (a) $-\frac{34}{63}$ (c) $\frac{10}{91}$
7. $[-2, 1, 0]$

Section 3–6

3. $$\left(\sum_{i=1}^{n} a_i b_i\right)^2 \leq \left(\sum_{i=1}^{n} a_i^2\right)\left(\sum_{i=1}^{n} b_i^2\right)$$

7. This reduces to the triangle inequality for scalars.

Section 4–1

1. (a) $x + 2y + 7z + 7 = 0$ (c) $z = 0$
3. (a) $5x + y + z - 10 = 0$, $(0, 0, 10)$
   (c) $x + y + 2z = 0$, $(0, 0, 0)$
4. (a) $(0, 0, -5)$, $[3, -1, 1]$ (c) $(0, 0, 0)$, $[2, 1, 4]$
5. $2x - y + z - 4 = 0$. One of the three quantities a, b, or c must be nonzero. If $a \neq 0$, say, then there are really only three unknowns: b/a, c/a, and d/a.

Section 4–2

1. (a) $[-5, 8, -19]$ (c) $[-4, -8, -4]$

5.

$\times$	$\mathbf{e}_1$	$\mathbf{e}_2$	$\mathbf{e}_3$
$\mathbf{e}_1$	0	$\mathbf{e}_3$	$-\mathbf{e}_2$
$\mathbf{e}_2$	$-\mathbf{e}_3$	0	$\mathbf{e}_1$
$\mathbf{e}_3$	$\mathbf{e}_2$	$-\mathbf{e}_1$	0

7. (a) $3x + y - z + 4 = 0$ (c) $x - z + 1 = 0$
9. $[2, -7, -1]$

Section 4–3

1. (a) $22/\sqrt{83}$ (c) 1
2. If the sign is positive, the vector from the plane to the point is parallel to the given normal vector. If the sign is negative, this same vector is collinear with, but not parallel to, the given normal.

4. (a) $$\left[1 - \frac{66}{\sqrt{83}}, 3 - \frac{154}{\sqrt{83}}, 1 + \frac{110}{\sqrt{83}}\right]$$ (c) $[-2, 1, -4]$,

6. (a) $-\frac{1}{14}$, (c) $-\frac{1}{2}$ (e) 0
9. Plane: $2x + 2y - z + 5 = 0$, distance 6

Section 4–4

1. (a) $\mathbf{X} = [1, 2, 7] + t[4, 1, 6]$
   (c) $\mathbf{X} = [11, 12, 13] + t[9, 11, 14]$
   (e) $\mathbf{X} = [0, 1, 2] + t[0, 0, 1]$
2. (a) $\mathbf{X} = [1, -1, 0] + t[-1, 5, 13]$
   (c) $\mathbf{X} = t[1, 1, -1]$
   (e) $\mathbf{X} = [-\frac{9}{14}, 1, -\frac{27}{28}] + t[44, -28, -4]$
3. The value of t depends on the particular equation, but the point is:
   (1a) $(0, \frac{7}{4}, \frac{11}{2})$, $(-7, 0, -5)$, $(-\frac{11}{3}, \frac{5}{6}, 0)$
   (1c) $(0, -\frac{13}{9}, -\frac{37}{9})$, $(\frac{13}{11}, 0, -\frac{25}{11})$, $(\frac{37}{14}, \frac{25}{14}, 0)$, (1e) —, —, $(0, 1, 0)$
   (2a) $(0, 4, 13)$, $(\frac{4}{5}, 0, \frac{13}{5})$, $(1, -1, 0)$, (2c) $(0, 0, 0)$
   (2e) $(0, \frac{364}{616}, -\frac{630}{616})$, $(\frac{26}{28}, 0, -\frac{31}{28})$, $(-\frac{315}{112}, \frac{31}{4}, 0)$
7. (a) $t = -3$, $(-2, 9, -11)$ (c) $t = -2$, $(3, 8, -15)$
9. $\mathbf{X} = [1, -1, 2] + t[3, -2, 1]$
11. (a) $(5, 7, -10)$ (c) $(7, 0, -3)$
12. (a) $X = [5, 7, -10] + t[16, 31, 9]$
13. (a) $\sqrt{143}/7$ (c) $\sqrt{61}/\sqrt{65}$

Section 5–1

4. (a) $[-16, -82, 36]$
6. (a) $\sqrt{899}$ (c) $\sqrt{276}$
7. 2
8. (a) $\sqrt{66}$
12. $$V = \begin{vmatrix} a_1 & a_2 & a_3 \\ b_1 & b_2 & b_2 \\ c_1 & c_2 & c_3 \end{vmatrix}$$
14. $\mathbf{X} = \mathbf{U} \times \mathbf{B}$ where $\mathbf{U}$ is any vector such that $\mathbf{A} \cdot \mathbf{U} = -1$, hence the complete solution is $\mathbf{X} = \mathbf{B} \times \mathbf{A}/|\mathbf{A}|^2 + c\mathbf{A}$, for any c.
16. (a) $(\mathbf{A} \cdot \mathbf{B})\mathbf{A} - (\mathbf{A} \cdot \mathbf{A})\mathbf{B}$ (d) $(\mathbf{A} \cdot \mathbf{A})^2(\mathbf{A} \times \mathbf{B})$
    (e) $(\mathbf{A} \cdot \mathbf{A})^2(\mathbf{A} \cdot \mathbf{B})\mathbf{A} - (\mathbf{A} \cdot \mathbf{A})^3\mathbf{B}$

Section 5–2

7. $$x = \frac{\mathbf{D} \cdot \mathbf{B} \times \mathbf{C}}{\mathbf{A} \cdot \mathbf{B} \times \mathbf{C}}, \; y = \frac{\mathbf{A} \cdot \mathbf{D} \times \mathbf{C}}{\mathbf{A} \cdot \mathbf{B} \times \mathbf{C}}, \; z = \frac{\mathbf{A} \cdot \mathbf{B} \times \mathbf{D}}{\mathbf{A} \cdot \mathbf{B} \times \mathbf{C}}.$$
   A solution exists if $\mathbf{D} = \mathbf{0}$, or if $\mathbf{D} \neq \mathbf{0}$ and $\mathbf{A}$, $\mathbf{B}$, and $\mathbf{C}$ are not coplanar (are linearly independent).
11. (a) $\mathbf{C} = 4\mathbf{A} - \mathbf{B}$ (c) $\mathbf{C} = -5\mathbf{A} + 6\mathbf{B}$
12. (a) $\mathbf{D} = 2\mathbf{A} + 4\mathbf{B} - \mathbf{C}$ (c) $\mathbf{D} = 10\mathbf{A} + 2\mathbf{B} - 2\mathbf{C}$

Section 5–3

1. (a) $\frac{1}{\sqrt{10}}[1, 3, 0]$, $\frac{1}{\sqrt{10}}[-3, 1, 0]$, $[0, 0, 1]$
   (c) $\frac{1}{\sqrt{14}}[2, 1, -3]$, $\frac{1}{\sqrt{826}}[24, -9, 13]$, $\frac{1}{\sqrt{59}}[-1, -7, -3]$

2. $B = a_1u_1 + a_2u_2 + a_3u_3$, where a_1, a_2, and a_3 are:

(a) $\dfrac{4\sqrt{10}}{5}, \quad \dfrac{2\sqrt{10}}{5}, 2$ (c) $0, \dfrac{56}{\sqrt{826}}, \quad \dfrac{22}{\sqrt{59}}$

6. (a) $x' = \dfrac{1}{\sqrt{10}}x + \dfrac{3}{\sqrt{10}}y,\ y' = \dfrac{-3}{\sqrt{10}}x + \dfrac{1}{\sqrt{10}}y,\ z' = z$

(c) $x' = \dfrac{2}{\sqrt{14}}x + \dfrac{1}{\sqrt{14}}y - \dfrac{3}{\sqrt{14}}z,\ y' = \dfrac{24}{\sqrt{826}}x - \dfrac{9}{\sqrt{826}}y + \dfrac{13}{\sqrt{826}}z,$

$z' = \dfrac{-1}{\sqrt{59}}x - \dfrac{7}{\sqrt{59}}y - \dfrac{3}{\sqrt{59}}z$

7. (a) $x' = \frac{3}{5}y + \frac{4}{5}z,\ y' = \frac{12}{13}x - \frac{4}{13}y + \frac{3}{13}z,$
$z' = \frac{25}{65}x + \frac{48}{65}y - \frac{36}{65}z,$
$\mathbf{A} = -\frac{2}{5}\mathbf{u}_1 + \frac{71}{13}\mathbf{u}_2 - \frac{7}{65}\mathbf{u}_3.$
9. (a) $[-\frac{33}{65}, -\frac{27}{65}, -\frac{21}{65}]$ (c) $[\frac{7}{15}, -\frac{3}{15}, \frac{1}{15}]$
10. (a) $[1, -1, 0]$, $[0, 1, -1]$, $[0, 0, 1]$ (c) $[\frac{3}{14}, \frac{1}{14}, -1]$, $[\frac{8}{14}, -\frac{2}{14}, -1]$,
$[-\frac{5}{14}, \frac{3}{14}, 1]$

Section 5–4

1. (a) $[1, 2, 0]$ (c) $\frac{1}{59}[162, -105, 211]$
2. (a) $\frac{1}{10}[3, -1, 10]$ (c) $\frac{1}{14}[54, 6, 38]$
4. (a) $P_1\colon \sqrt{11/2}$, $P_3\colon \sqrt{1782/83}$ (b) $L_2\colon 20/\sqrt{59}$, $L_4\colon 2/\sqrt{6}$

Section 6–1

1. (a) $3x^2 - (y - 1)^2 - (z - 1)^2 = 0$ (c) $y^2 - x(z - 1) = 0$
2. (a) $3x^2 - y^2 + 2y - 2 = 0$, hyperbola (c) $x + y^2 = 0$, parabola
5. (a) $(b_1^2 - \lambda^2)x^2 + 2b_1b_2xy + (b_2^2 - \lambda^2)y^2 = 0$
(c) $\mathbf{B} = [0, \sqrt{2}/2, \sqrt{2}/2]$, $\lambda = \sqrt{2}/2$, for example, give $x^2 = 0$.

Section 6–3

1. (a) $b^2 = a^2(1 - e^2)$, $c = ae$, $d = a/e$
(c) $b^2 = a^2 - c^2$, $d = a^2/c$, $e = c/a$
(e) $a^2 = b^2 + c^2$, $d = (b^2 + c^2)/c$, $e = c/[b^2 + c^2]^{1/2}$
(g) $a = c/e$, $b^2 = c^2(1 - e^2)/e^2$, $d = c/e^2$
(i) $a = de$, $b^2 = d^2e^2(1 - e^2)$, $c = de^2$
2. (a) $d^2e^4 - d^2e^2 + b^2 = 0$
4. (a) $F = (0, 3), (0, -3)$, $PV = (0, 5), (0, -5)$, $CV = (4, 0)$, $(-4, 0)$, $e = \frac{3}{5}$, dir: $y = \frac{25}{3}$, $y = -\frac{25}{3}$.
(c) $F = (\sqrt{65}, 0), (-\sqrt{65}, 0)$, $PV = (9, 0), (-9, 0)$, $CV = (0, 4)$, $(0, -4)$, $e = \sqrt{65}/9$, dir: $x = 81/\sqrt{65}$, $x = -81/\sqrt{65}$.
(e) $F = (\pm 1, 0)$, $PV = (\pm\sqrt{5}, 0)$, $CV = (0, \pm 2)$, $e = 1/\sqrt{5}$, dir: $x = \pm 5$
(g) $F = (\pm\sqrt{6}, 0)$, $PV = (\pm\sqrt{10}, 0)$, $CV = (0, \pm 2)$, $e = \sqrt{15}/5$, dir: $x = \pm 5\sqrt{6}/3$

5. (a) $\frac{x^2}{9} + \frac{y^2}{8} = 1$ (c) $24x^2 + 25y^2 = 216$

(e) $24x^2 + 40y^2 = 960$ (g) $9x^2 + 25y^2 = 144$

6. (a) $F = (\pm 1, 0)$, $PV = (\pm 3, 0)$, $CV = (0, \pm 2\sqrt{2})$, $e = \frac{1}{3}$, dir: $x = \pm 9$

(c) $F = (\pm\frac{3}{5}, 0)$, $PV = (\pm 3, 0)$, $CV = (0, \pm 6\sqrt{6}/5)$, $e = \frac{1}{5}$, dir: $x = \pm 15$

(e) $F = (\pm 4, 0)$, $PV = (\pm\sqrt{40}, 0)$, $CV = (0, \pm\sqrt{24})$, $e = \sqrt{10}/5$, dir: $x = \pm 10$

(g) $F = (\pm\frac{16}{5}, 0)$, $PV = (\pm 4, 0)$, $CV = (0, \pm\frac{12}{5})$, $e = \frac{4}{5}$, dir: $x = \pm 5$

Section 6–4

2. (a) $pd = 8$, $cd = 6$, $V = (\pm 8, 0)$, $F = (\pm 10, 0)$, $e = \frac{5}{4}$, dir: $x = \pm\frac{32}{5}$, asym: $y = \pm 3x/4$

(c) $pd = 3$, $cd = 2$, $V = (0, \pm 3)$, $F = (0, \pm\sqrt{13})$, $e = \sqrt{13}/3$, dir: $y = \pm 9/\sqrt{13}$, asym.: $y = \pm 3x/2$

(e) $pd = 3$, $cd = 4$, $V = (\pm 3, 0)$, $F = (\pm 5, 0)$, $e = \frac{5}{3}$, dir: $x = \pm\frac{9}{5}$, asym: $y = \pm\frac{4}{3}$

(g) $pd = 6$, $cd = 2$, $V = (\pm 6, 0)$, $F = (\pm 2\sqrt{10}, 0)$, $e = \sqrt{10}/3$, dir: $x = \pm 18/\sqrt{10}$, $y = \pm 2x/6$

3. (a) $\frac{x^2}{25} - \frac{y^2}{75} = 1$, (c) $\frac{25x^2}{64} - \frac{25y^2}{336} = 1$, (e) $\frac{x^2}{16} - \frac{y^2}{64} = -1$,

4. The equation is

$$\frac{x^2}{a^2} - \frac{y^2}{b^2} = -1.$$

The two hyperbolas have the same asymptotes.

9. Any pair determine a unique hyperbola:

(a, b) $c^2 = a^2 + b^2$, $d^2 = a^4/(a^2 + b^2)$, $e^2 = (a^2 + b^2)/a^2$

(a, d) $b^2 = a^2(a^2 - d^2)/d^2$, $c = a^2/d$, $e = a/d$

(b, e) $a^2 = b^2/(e^2 - 1)$, $c^2 = b^2e^2/(e^2 - 1)$, $d^2 = b^2/e^2(e^2 - 1)$

If b and d are given, then e must satisfy the equation

$$e^4 - e^2 - b^2/d^2 = 0.$$

This equation is quadratic in e^2. One of the two possible solutions is negative. Hence there is only one e which can satisfy this equation.

Section 6–5

1.

	axis	directrix	focus
(a)	$x = 0$,	$y = -4$,	$(0, 4)$
(c)	$x = 0$	$y = \frac{1}{2}$,	$(0, -\frac{1}{2})$
(e)	$x = 0$,	$y = \frac{5}{16}$,	$(0, -\frac{5}{16})$
(g)	$x = 0$	$y = -\frac{1}{16}$,	$(0, \frac{1}{16})$

2. (a) $y^2 = 8x$ (c) $y^2 = 2x$ (e) $x^2 = -4y/3$ (g) $y^2 = 2x$
(i) $x^2 = -12y/5$
4. (a) $9x^2 - 400x + 16y^2 - 300y - 24xy = 0$
(c) $x^2 - 4x + y^2 - 12y - 2xy + 20 = 0$

Section 6–6

1. (a) hyperbola, $C = (1, 3)$, $F = (1, 8), (1, -2)$, $V = (1, 7), (1, -1)$, pr axis: $x = 1$, conj axis: $y = 3$, dir: $y = \frac{31}{5}$, $y = -\frac{1}{5}$, asym: $4x - 3y + 5 = 0$, $4x + 3y - 13 = 0$, $e = \frac{5}{4}$
(c) ellipse, $C = (-1, 7)$, $F = (-1, 11), (-1, 3)$, $PV = (-1, 12), (-1, 2)$, $CV = (2, 7), (-4, 7)$, pr axis: $x = -1$, conj axis: $y = 7$, dir: $y = \frac{53}{4}$, $y = \frac{3}{4}$, $e = \frac{4}{5}$
(e) ellipse, $C = (3, -1)$, $F = (6, -1), (-2, -1)$, $PV = (8, -1), (-2, -1)$, $CV = (3, 3), (3, -5)$, pr axis: $y = -1$, conj axis: $x = 3$, dir: $x = \frac{34}{3}$, $x = -\frac{16}{3}$, $e = \frac{3}{5}$
(g) parabola, $V = (\frac{1}{2}, 2)$, $F = (2, 2)$, axis: $y = 2$, dir: $x = -1$
(i) circle, center $(3, -\frac{1}{3})$, radius $\frac{4}{3}$

3. (a) $\dfrac{(x-3)^2}{9} + \dfrac{(y-2)^2}{25} = 1$ (c) $(x-7)^2 = 4(y-5)$,

(e) $\dfrac{(x-3)^2}{1/4} - \dfrac{(y+1)^2}{4} = -1.$

4. $y^2 = -(1-e^2)x^2 + 2(1+e)x$; as $e \to 0$, equation becomes $(x-1)^2 + y^2 = 1$, which is the equation of a circle of radius 1 with center $(1, 0)$; as $e \to 1$, the equation becomes $y^2 = 4x$, which is the equation of a parabola.

Section 7–1

2. $x = x' \cos\theta - y' \sin\theta$, $y = x' \sin\theta + y' \cos\theta$

4. $y = \dfrac{a^2b^2 - (b^2 - a^2)x^2}{2abx}$. 5. $160x^2 - 24xy + 153y^2 = 24{,}336.$

Section 7–2

3. (a) parabola, $\sin\theta = \frac{4}{5}$, $\cos\theta = \frac{3}{5}$,

$$25x'^2 + 28x' - 104y + 100 = 0$$

(c) hyperbola, $\theta = \pi/6$,

$$2x'^2 - 2y'^2 = -1$$

4. Maximum when $\phi = \theta$, minimum when $\phi = \theta + \pi/2$

Section 7–3

2. The planes are made up of the asymptotes of the hyperbolas.
4. (a) elliptic cone (c) ellipsoid (e) hyperbolic paraboloid
(g) parabolic cylinder

5. (a) hyperboloid of one sheet (c) two planes (e) circular cone
   (g) prolate spheroid
6. (a) A hyperboloid of two sheets centered at (—3, 0, 1). Vertices at (—3, 1, 1) and (—3, —1, 1).
   (c) An ellipsoid with center at (2, —2, 2).
   (e) Hyperboloid of two sheets with center at the origin and vertices at (0, 4, 0) and (0, —4, 0).
   (g) A hyperbolic cylinder with axis $x = -3$, $z = 0$.

Section 7–4

2. $r = 0$ and any θ
6. $r = f(\theta - \alpha)$.
9. $r = p \sec(\theta - \alpha)$
17. It is the same
21. (a) Ellipse (b) parabola (c) hyperbola (d) ellipse

Index

ABCDE698765